THE 'MONOTYPE'
CASTING MACHINE MANUAL

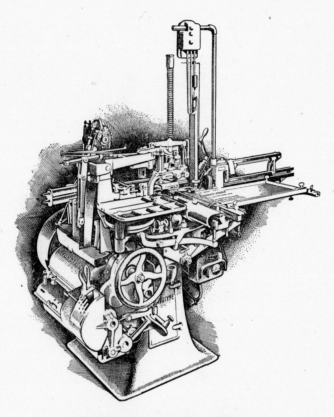

A COMPOSITION CASTER FITTED WITH
DISPLAY TYPE AND LEAD AND RULE
ATTACHMENTS

THE 'MONOTYPE' CASTING MACHINE MANUAL

Published by
THE NATIONAL COMMITTEE OF MONOTYPE USERS' ASSOCIATIONS
11 BEDFORD ROW LONDON WC1
IN ASSOCIATION WITH THE MONOTYPE CORPORATION LIMITED

Published 1952

Printed by
SIMSON SHAND LTD, THE SHENVAL PRESS
LONDON AND HERTFORD

CONTENTS

FOREWORD

THIS MANUAL is not by any means meant to cover every possible instruction concerning the running of a 'Monotype' caster, but it will be found that, if the instructions given herein are closely followed, there will be little left which could be learnt by other means than practical experience.

The best training is actual daily contact with the machine, but the attendant will add to his efficiency by consulting this manual on details of adjustment and other problems which are not clear to him.

The manual will be found useful for reference, enabling the attendant to refresh his memory on adjustments and practices designed to maintain the efficiency of the machine. A thorough understanding and careful application of the instructions given will establish his reputation as an intelligent and painstaking attendant. It will also serve to remind him that there are many things which should be strictly avoided.

An attendant's duties are in the first place directed to the changing of the matrices, moulds and normal wedges, and to seeing that the quality of type produced is satisfactory. In doing this he should satisfy himself that all adjustments in connection with changing a fount are scrupulously exact to the standard laid down in this manual; that his metal is kept clean, of standard quality, and maintained at the correct temperature; that his pump connections are working correctly; that the metal channels are clean; and that the type is cast and delivered to the galley without hitch of any kind. Beyond this, he has to keep his machine clean and oiled, and to see that no screws or nuts work loose.

The attendant should draw a line between calling on the Monotype Corporation's inspectors for advice regarding trivial details, and the obstinate attempt to do for himself work (whether repairs or adjustments) which he must know he is not qualified to undertake.

This manual is issued with the idea of giving an attendant an opportunity of studying every motion on the machine, tracing such motions from their starting points (the driving cams), and guiding him as to how such parts should be adjusted. Although it explains the methods of detaching various parts it does not follow that any group or part should be frequently or even occasionally disconnected without a reasonable purpose.

Acknowledgment is due to Messrs Fry's Metal Foundries Ltd., for kindly supplying the material for the headings 'Metal Hints' on pages 109 to 113 and 'Metals for use on Monotype Machines' on pages 196 to 212.

INSTALLATION

A 'MONOTYPE' CASTER should be installed in a room or section of a room that is light and free from dirt or dust. A strong bench should be provided, as well as a suitable cupboard for storing accessories and spare parts.

Sufficient space should be allowed around the machine to permit free access by the operator to any part of the mechanism.

When installing a first 'Monotype' caster the possibility of increasing the plant should not be overlooked. Advice as to installation layout can always be obtained from The Monotype Corporation Ltd.

PLUMBING

CERTAIN PLUMBING is necessary for water inlet and drainage, compressed air supply, and gas or electric heating for melting the metal.

A compressed air installation must be provided, with an air storage tank combined with water-cooling equipment for extracting moisture from the air. The fitting of an air-filter will ensure clean air to the keyboards and casters.

TOOLS

THE CASTER ATTENDANT should maintain his tools in good condition. A bad habit is to use screwdrivers for stirring the metal or for testing it to see if it has commenced to melt. This softens the point of a screwdriver, causing it when used on hardened screws to become blunted and burred. The point of a screwdriver should be kept correctly tempered, and should be so ground that it has no tendency to slip out of the screw slot. In tightening or loosening a screw the driver should be held firmly down in the slot of the screw head, as frequent slipping out will ruin the edges of the screw slot, rendering it impossible to thoroughly tighten the screw, or to loosen it when required. The handles should never be battered upon with a hammer.

The pump body and nozzle should always be drilled when cold, otherwise the drill will become softened and useless.

The attendant should be provided with the following tools:

TOOLS PROVIDED WITH MACHINE

Screwdrivers: 5CT1, 5CT2, 5CT3, 5CT5, 5CT6, 5CT7, 5CT8; Wrenches: 2 each of 6CT1, 6CT4, 6CT6, 6CT14; 1 each of 6CT2, 6CT5, 6CT3, 6CT10, 6CT9, 6CT11, 6CT12, 6CT13, 6CT7, a6CT16, 6CT20, 6CT21; Nozzle Squaring Post 8CT6; Nozzle Gauge 8CT3; Piston Cleaning Tool xa29CT; Pump Cleaning Tool xb21CT; Pump Body Bearing Cleaning Tool 4CT4; Ingot Mould 2CT1; Iron Ladle 3CT1; Skimming Spoon 3CT2; Well Arm Drill 4CT1; Dowel Punch—long 7CT1; Dowel Punch—short 7CT2; 2 Oil Cans 14CT1; Jaw Tongs Spring Box Grease Gun 42CT1.

The following parts are supplied with new installations only unless specially ordered:—

1″ Micrometer 8CT1; Type Alignment Gauge a8CT2; Eye Glass 9CT1; Tweezers 10CT1; Centring Pin Gauge 8CT4; Matrix Assembling Fixture x56A or xa56A.

It is necessary to have a spare wrench, $\frac{5}{16}″ \times \frac{9}{32}″$ 6CT6, so that two of these may be used in tightening the nuts at the end of the transfer rods, otherwise the lock-nuts cannot be tightened without twisting the transfer rods.

EXTRA MATERIAL WHICH SHOULD BE PURCHASED

A good hammer, about $1\frac{1}{2}$ lb. in weight. Storage boxes for loose matrices. Cupboard for tools. About 6 feet of rubber hose, to fit an air pipe nozzle. Two oil cans (one for machine oil and one for mould oil). A strong vice, with 3″ or $3\frac{1}{2}″$ jaws. A suitable bench. Hand brace. One set of galley 'point' measure gauges 8CT7. Nozzle drills: $\frac{1}{8}″$ 4CT2, for drilling nozzle from the lower end; $\frac{1}{16}″$ 4CT3, for drilling the point of nozzle.

NOZZLE DRILLING

One $\frac{1}{16}″$ drill should be reserved specially for clearing the nozzle point when required, without removing nozzle from the machine. All other drills and taps should only be used on nozzles or pump body when cold. *On no account should drills or screwdrivers be dipped in molten metal, as this softens them and renders them unfit for general use.*

TYPE METAL

A reasonable reserve of type metal must be provided, in order to avoid too frequent smelting. This metal is an alloy of tin, antimony and lead. A good all-round standard mixture is 9% tin, 19% antimony, and 72% lead; another is 10% tin, 16% antimony, and 74% lead. (See further p. 196 onwards.)

RE-MELTING FURNACE

A suitable re-melting furnace should be provided and the metal cast into ingots of suitable size. In re-melting, an efficient non-corrosive cleansing flux should be used in moderation, and an excessive temperature should be avoided. (See p. 209.)

OIL

Only good machine oil should be used for lubricating the caster mechanism, and special heat-resisting oil for type moulds. If strip material is to be cast, the strip moulds should be lubricated with commercial castor oil.

LITERATURE

Caster attendants should be provided with duplicates of all matrix-case layouts used by the keyboard operators; also with card of type sizes, alignment charts, and any other useful information. It is further recommended that each attendant should possess a Monotype Book of Information.

PRINCIPAL FEATURES

THE PRINCIPAL FEATURES of a 'Monotype' caster are the matrices, the mould, and the pump. These are in contact with each other at the most important point of operation of the machine—that at which the type is cast.

All other parts of the machine function (1) to bring the required matrix directly over the casting aperture in the mould, (2) to adjust the mould so that any type cast will be of the required width, and (3) to eject the type from the mould and convey it to the type channel.

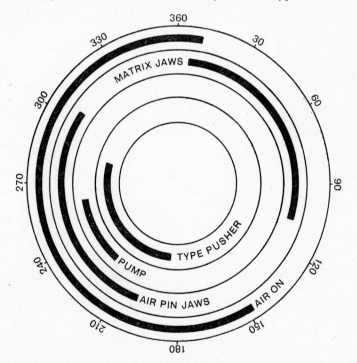

This chart shows commencement of certain functions which take place after compressed air has passed through perforations in ribbon, which can here be assumed to be for the letter 'a'.

Compressed air comes on at 148°, and pin jaws start closing at 200°, matrix jaws start closing at 5°, and finish at 107°, having taken matrix-case and normal wedge to position.

During the next revolution of caster, after next perforations have received compressed air, the foregoing 'a' will be cast at 220°.

Note that from the time the air is passed through the perforations it will be at 185° during the *third* revolution later that the 'a' will start being pushed to the type channel, as it is obvious from the chart that during any casting it must be the type previously cast that is being pushed to the type channel.

It will be understood that, although all operations of selecting a matrix, sizing the mould, casting a type and conveying a type to the type channel, are performed during every revolution of the machine, it takes part of three revolutions between the presentation of the per-forations at the air tower and the placing of the finished type in the type channel. See Timing of Cams, pp. 9 and 195.

THE MATRIX-CASE

This contains the matrices of the different characters. They are prisms of special brass, each containing at the lower end the recessed impres-sion of a character, and at the upper end a conical hole by means of which the matrix can be aligned correctly over the mould.

The matrices are held in the matrix-case by wires and each row is located between spacing bars.

THE MOULD

This in the main consists of a base, a sliding blade, blade side blocks, jet ejector blade, and crossblock. The blade and side blocks rest on an intermediate plate fixed to the base, the blade being free to move between the two side blocks; the crossblock moves at right angles to the blade, forming a metal-tight joint against the faces of the blade side blocks. The blade and blade side blocks correspond in height to that of type from foot to shoulder; the thickness of the blade corresponds to the body size of the type; the set (width) of the type is determined by the distance between the blade and the face of the crossblock at the time the type is cast. A jet blade is contained in the crossblock; this ejects the tang cast on the 'foot' of the type body. The jet blade is operated by a cam fastened to the mould base.

VARIOUS PATTERNS OF MOULD

COMPOSITION MOULD.—For composing in sizes up to 12 point inclusive.

COMPOSITION MOULD (bevelled on top).—For composing 13 point and 14 point from .2″ × .2″ matrices.

LARGE TYPE COMPOSITION MOULD.—For composing type from 12 point to 24 point from .4″×.2″ and .4″×.4″ matrices. Mould Body supplied with interchangeable insets for various point sizes.

DISPLAY TYPE MOULD.—Mould body supplied with interchangeable insets for various point sizes, from 14 point to 36 point, similar to Large Type Composition Mould, but with the nick on the opposite side of the mould blade.

MOULD BLADE ABUTMENT

This carries an adjustable screw c14c1 against which the mould blade is drawn and by which the width of type is approximately adjusted.

MOULD BLADE SIZING WEDGES

These are five in number: normal wedge, type transfer wedge, space transfer wedge, and two justification wedges.

TYPE TRANSFER WEDGE

The type transfer wedge operates between the normal wedge and a fixed abutment.

SPACE TRANSFER WEDGE

The space transfer wedge is located above the type transfer wedge and operates between the normal wedge and the two justification wedges.

JUSTIFICATION WEDGES

These rest on a shelf and are only brought into action when the space transfer wedge is in operation.

THE PUMP

The pump operates in the same manner as an ordinary typecasting machine pump. It consists of a plunger and pump body, fitted with a nozzle for seating into a coned hole on the under side of the mould, through which the metal is forced in casting the type.

IMPORTANCE OF ACCURATE TIMING OF ADJUSTMENTS

Some adjustments are so close to those of other sections that there is risk of overlapping of functions if the timings are not accurately made.

For example: normal wedge locking pin clears wedge teeth at 2°, matrix jaws start closing at 5°, locking bars reach base of stop rack teeth at 5°.

Another group of close adjustments is:

Centring pin reaches base of cone holes 208°.

Matrix seats on mould 210°.

Mould blade finishes sizing 12 points 210°.

MECHANISM OF THE CASTER

For general illustrations of parts refer to BOOK OF PARTS OF 'MONOTYPE'
CASTING MACHINES

DRIVING

THE CASTER IS DRIVEN by a pulley keyed to the front camshaft, and the speed should be varied by means of a coned pulley or other speed-varying gear, from 145 revolutions per minute for 12-point type up to 180 revolutions per minute for 6-point type.

The belt travels through a shifter eye, for the purpose of bringing it, when required, on to a 'loose' pulley running by the side of the 'fixed' pulley. The pulley runs clockwise, and the shifter eye should encircle and lead the belt as the latter approaches the pulley. A jointless driving belt should be used, but where this is not available *care should be taken that the belt joint or fastener does not hit the shifter eye*, as in that event the shifter is likely to be broken. The belt should be $1\frac{1}{4}''$ wide when used on standard machine, and $1''$ wide on machine fitted with display attachment, and should be kept fairly taut in running, otherwise the machine will run irregularly.

BELT GUARD

Factory regulations insist that all belts should be protected by a reasonable guard, and the pattern supplied by The Monotype Corporation Ltd., complies with the official regulations.

This guard is a neat fixture, resting on guide rails, so that it can easily and quickly be withdrawn for inspection of the pulleys or belt.

SPEED OF RUNNING

Basically this depends on the efficient workable temperature of the mould, which in turn depends on the cubic content of metal injected into the mould per minute, and the temperature of the alloy. Small type sizes may consequently be cast faster than large type, and 'solid' composition faster than 'open'.

A moderate speed produces type of better density than a high speed, especially in the case of large display type, owing chiefly to the longer pause on the piston before the piston starts its return stroke.

For average composition and standard type metal the following speed *limits* can be recommended, but should not be exceeded:

5, 6, 7 point, 180 r.p.m.; 8, 9, 10 point, 160 r.p.m.; 11, 12 point, 150 r.p.m.; 14 point, 100 r.p.m.; 18 point, 60 to 80 r.p.m.; 24 point, 50 to 60 r.p.m.

As to speeds when casting large type composition (.4″ matrices), see pp. 134, 135 and 190.

OPERATING LEVER AND BELT SHIFTER

The belt shifter eye 4E is adjusted by a set screw on the belt shifter arm 2E fixed to the belt shifter ring a5E by a clamp and screw bolt. This arm can be adjusted to any position around the ring casting, to suit the angle of the driving belt. The ring carries a guide pin a5E2, and when the belt is on the loose pulley this pin, by coming in contact with a latch on the side of the type pusher cam, prevents the machine being reversed.

The belt shifter ring rod 6E, screwed in and clamped to the ring, runs along the back of the machine, and carries the belt shifter arm 2E. This projects upward to meet the operating lever spring box 37F communicating with the operating lever a32F. The belt shifter ring rod is encircled by a coil spring, which maintains a tendency to pull the belt shifter eye over the loose pulley. The operating lever spring box 37F between the belt shifter arm and operating lever is bored to receive a spring plunger to act as a buffer to the operating lever when starting the machine by hand. The end of this spring box is slotted to receive the end of the operating lever. The operating lever is attached to the galley mechanism bracket by a bolt and nut, and one end of the lever has a step which engages a latch on the automatic stopping gear.

LUBRICATING THE LOOSE PULLEY BEARINGS

The introduction of the speed gear for the display type attachment made it essential to introduce an improved method for oiling the loose pulley. Operators will find a hole for this purpose drilled through the boss of the driving pulley a64E which is continued at an angle through the driving cam shaft. This pulley should be oiled daily.

DRIVE ADJUSTMENTS

STROKE OF BELT SHIFTER

When handle of lever a32F is pushed to left and the right arm engaged by latch a33F, the belt must be moved completely from loose pulley xc65E to driving pulley a64E; and when latch a33F is released (by hand or automatically) the spring 6E2 must move the belt from driving pulley a64E to loose pulley xc65E.

Push handle of lever a32F to right, against the galley pan shelf. Move the spring box 37F forward until plunger 37F1 touches the left arm of lever a32F.

Move the rod 6E forward until washer 6E1 is brought against the camshaft stand c12EE by ring a5E. If arm 2E is too far forward to permit this, the screw 2E1 must be loosened and arm 2E shifted to the rear.

With the parts in this position, loosen the screw 2E1 and move arm 2E along the rod 6E until it stands $\frac{1}{64}''$ behind spring box 37F. Tighten the screw 2E1.

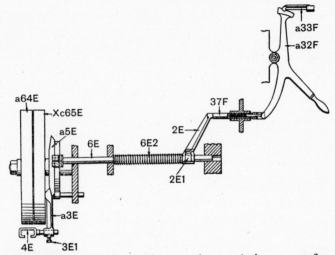

Loosen the set screw 3E1 and move the eye 4E in, or out from, the arm a3E so that when lever a32F is moved to left and engaged by its latch, the belt will have moved completely off loose pulley xc65E on to driving pulley a64E, and when the lever a32F is released the belt will be moved completely off driving pulley a64E on to loose pulley xc65E.

Tighten the set screw 3E1.

With handle of lever a32F pushed to right as far as possible, the washer 6E1 and ring a5E against stand c12EE, the spring box 37F against left arm of lever a32F, the arm 2E should clear rear end of spring box 37F by $\frac{1}{64}''$.

Adjust the eye 4E to make the belt shift completely from loose pulley to fixed pulley when starting the machine; and to be completely off the fixed pulley when the machine is stopped.

BELT SHIFTER RING GUIDE PIN a5E2

The position of the guide pin must be controlled to give maximum engagement for type pusher cam latch b75E2 and also to give sufficient clearance for type pusher cam lever during its movement.

This is obtained when the belt shifter mechanism is in its inoperative position by loosening the nut 5E4 and turning the guide pin by means of the tommy-pin hole provided until a clearance of approximately $\frac{1}{32}''$ is made between the front end of guide pin and side of type pusher cam lever. Tighten the locking nut firmly when the correct setting is obtained.

CAMS

THE MACHINE POSSESSES two sets of main cams, which actuate levers to impart the desired movement upon the various mechanisms employed.

The cams are eight in number per set, and each set is keyed to a shaft carrying on its end a toothed wheel, the whole being supported by a bracket screwed to the machine base. The action of the cams is positive, because where any cam is convex its counter cam is concave.

The two shafts are geared by an intermediate wheel, to cause both sets of cams to rotate in the same direction.

The locking bars are operated by means of a separate single cam positioned on the left-hand camshaft between the centring pin cam and the jaw tongs cam, and the lever roller is kept to the face of this cam by the action of the spring c33E7 on the locking bar operating rod. *Be sure that this roller revolves as the cam rotates, otherwise it may wear a flat upon its periphery, and upset the locking bar release adjustment.*

DISTINCTIVE MARKINGS

For ease of reference the cams are lettered A, B, C, D, I, E, F, G, H, starting from the handwheel. The type carrier cams are A, pump cams B, transfer wedge cams C, centring pin cams D, jaw tongs cams E, paper tower cams F, mould blade cams G, type pusher cams H, and the locking bar cam I.

The cams on the right-hand camshaft (driving) have the letters A, B, C, etc., cast on them in a circular recess; the left-hand cams (driven) have the letters cast in a square recess.

TIMING THE CAMS

The two groups of cams are geared by an intermediate wheel, and for the purpose of easily finding the correct meshing the gear wheel 11E3 on the end of the left-hand camshaft is marked '0', while the counter gear 10E5 at 340° is marked '1'. The intermediate gear 80E1 is correspondingly marked '0' and '1'. At a certain period of the machine's revolution the figures '0–0' and '1–1' synchronize.

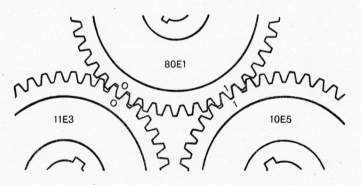

The gear wheel attached to the right-hand camshaft is marked around its circumference with the degrees of a circle, twenty by twenty,

B

fractions of twenty being ascertainable by means of a vernier scale attached to the gear cover. Nearly all adjustments of the machine are timed from these scales. As to Timing of Cams, see further p. 195.

CAMSHAFT BEARINGS

These should be periodically lubricated through the small oil cups located in the camshaft stand just above the bearings, as oil cannot reach them from any other source. The cams run partly submerged in an oil bath, and if kept clean require little attention.

REMOVING AND REPLACING A CAMSHAFT

Detaching the cams in the event of an obstruction is an operation that should be undertaken only by a skilled attendant. Usually in such cases it is necessary to lower only the set of cams nearest the cause of obstruction, which is done by removing the oil pan group and the camshaft bearing caps beneath the ends of the camshafts. If the machine has been wedged in such a position that it may be necessary, when replacing the cams, to turn it forward to make the correct gearing, care must be taken to keep all lever rollers on the faces of the set of cams which have not been removed. This may be done by pressing the levers against the cams by hand, turning the machine inch by inch by the hand driving wheel until the figures '0' and '1' synchronize; then tighten the bearing caps, and the gearing will be correct. Should any difficulty be experienced in getting the gear teeth to mesh correctly, it may be necessary to slacken slightly the bearing caps of one set of cams so as to give more freedom of entry to the intermediate gear wheel. The bearing caps should be tightened again immediately the gearing is correct.

During the foregoing operation care should be bestowed upon the type pusher lever and type carrier lever, to see that the lever rollers follow the cams of the undetached camshaft; *any anxiety concerning these may be avoided if the type carrier and type pusher are first removed.*

MACHINE JAMMED THROUGH OBSTRUCTION TO TYPE CARRIER

Sometimes the machine may become jammed through the type carrier becoming wedged. To decide if this is the cause, remove the type pusher and the pin connecting the type carrier to the type carrier lever, and then try gently to turn the machine a little by hand. If the machine thus becomes free it will be necessary to remove only the obstruction to the type carrier.

In the event of the machine becoming jammed no undue force should be exerted to turn it. On no account should the cams be interfered with unless it is positively known that they are obstructed by some foreign object, and all efforts to remove such obstruction have failed.

CAM LEVERS

To ENSURE the cam lever rollers and cams are adequately lubricated, the oil in the bath should be maintained at the correct level; this is clearly seen by the gauge on left-hand side of oil bath.

HOW ATTACHED

The first three cam levers A, B and C are fulcrumed on a shaft in the camshaft stand casting towards the front of the machine; the fourth and fifth, D and E, in an extension bracket screwed on to the main stand; the sixth, seventh and eighth, F, G and H, on a shaft at the rear end of camshaft stand; and the locking bar cam lever c34EE rocks on a pin in a boss on the camshaft stand.

CAM LEVER ROLLERS

Each lever carries a roller on its lower end, which requires no attention beyond being kept clean and lubricated by immersion in the oil bath. *No attempt should be made to detach the rollers from the levers,* owing to their special form of construction, but it should be seen that they are always revolving freely.

CAUSE OF BROKEN TYPE CARRIER LEVER

Sometimes the type carrier cam lever becomes broken after having replaced a type carrier, through neglecting to replace the connecting rod spring abutment 21B10 in the slot provided for it. *This breakage would not occur if, after replacing a type carrier, the precaution is taken of gently turning the machine by hand to note if any obstruction prevents the machine from being easily turned.*

REMOVING CAM LEVERS

In the event of the type carrier lever being broken, it will be necessary to remove the gear cover c19E and the camshaft stand cap a12E8. Then remove the handwheel and take off the front bearer cap 12E4, and drive the shaft from rear to front. When doing this the lower end of jaw tongs cam lever should be to the right (machine at 120°) so as fully to expose the end of shaft. In replacing the handwheel, see that the figure '0' on worm shaft worm 80E6, comes between the two figures '0' on the galley cam shaft worm wheel 15F3. It is also necessary to get the figures '0' and '1' on the cam gear wheels to correspond with '0' and '1' on the intermediate gear wheel. To get the teeth to mesh easily it may be necessary partly to lower one set of cams—those at the left for preference—by loosening the camshaft bearer screws and immediately tightening them when the gears have been correctly meshed. The B and C cam levers are also removed in the foregoing manner.

To remove the F, G or H cam levers, take out split pin and washer at front end of corresponding shaft, also the screw on top of bearer between F and G cams, and withdraw shaft to rear.

To remove the jaw tongs cam lever, remove transfer wedge rod link mechanism, withdraw the fulcrum pin to the front. *Do not attempt to turn the machine with the fulcrum pin partly withdrawn, but, having removed the lever, immediately replace and secure the fulcrum pin.*

To remove locking bar cam lever, unhook the lever from the locking bar operating rod b33E, remove the fulcrum stud a35E, and then disengage the handwheel and turn camshaft to most convenient position.

TYPE CARRIER
(FOR PLATE SEE PP. 227, 228)

THE TYPE CARRIER xd20B is operated by the A cam lever 72EE, and, as its name implies, has for its object the carrying of type from mould to type channel prior to the complete line being transferred to the galley. At one end the carrier is connected to the mould crossblock; at the other to the cam lever by an adjustable rod, with a left-hand and right-hand screw thread. The type is ejected from the mould into an opening in the type carrier, where it becomes held by the type clamp d26B, supported by a spiral spring a26B2. To prevent the type turning sideways a flat type support spring b31B is provided. When machine is in casting position the opening in the type carrier is brought opposite the type channel, so that the type previously cast can be ejected from the carrier by the type pusher, the type support spring having previously been withdrawn clear of the type. The type support spring is operated by a rock lever d20B3 coming in contact with the overhanging section of the type carrier shoe b23BB, and when pulled to the left a clear passage is given to the type and type pusher. After the type has been cast, a slight movement of the carrier to the left causes the tang cast at the foot of the type body to be sheared off.

On the type carrier connecting rod is a coil spring 21B9 which acts as a buffer at the end of the right-hand stroke, and during casting keeps the cam lever roller firmly against the driving cam. The extension rod below the connecting rod is fitted with a coil spring 22B4 to act in similar manner at the end of the left-hand stroke. On the lower edge of the carrier, where it connects with the mould, is a small flat shield a20B5, which acts as a shield to protect the type from particles of metal that might otherwise reach it during the period of ejection from the mould.

TYPE CARRIER CAM LEVER EXTENSION a72E4

The cam lever extension a72E4 and eye a21B5 of connecting rod are each provided with various connecting pin holes for different purposes.

Here are the various connections of type carrier forked eye a21B5 to type carrier cam lever extension.

    1 and A—Composition.

    2 and B—14- to 36-point display.

    3 and B—14- to 24-point large type composition; use mould cross-block coupling hook 56B1.

    3 and B—14- to 18-point display type; use type channel block xh51F, and mould crossblock coupling hook 56B1.

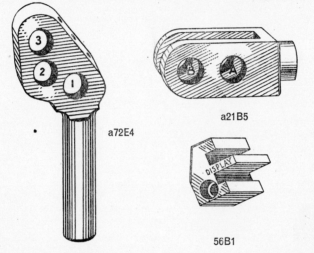

a72E4

a21B5

56B1

REMOVING TYPE CARRIER

Turn machine to 20°, disconnect and remove the mould crossblock; disconnect the connecting rod forked eye a21B5 from cam lever; remove short type carrier shoe b24B with plate a24B2 and long shoe b23BB; carefully lift out the carrier.

REPLACING TYPE CARRIER

Before replacing a type carrier observe that all parts are thoroughly clean. The type clamp must not have any play, and its face must be parallel with the corresponding face of the type carrier; it must also be not more than .002″ below the face of the type carrier (*i.e.* the side which comes against the pin block) and must slide perfectly freely.

See that there is no burr on the type support spring bar f31B1B, where it abuts against its stop inside the carrier. Particular care should be taken to see that every part affecting the type carrier works freely, but without side play, otherwise thin spaces or characters may not become properly clamped after ejection from the mould.

Before connecting the type carrier to its cam lever *place the upper spring abutment* 21B10, *through which the connecting rod passes, in the slot provided for it,* as neglect to do this will result in a broken type carrier cam lever.

The connecting pin 21B7 should be inserted with the head at the rear side of the cam lever. This ensures that should the carrier become wedged in the right-hand position the pin may easily be withdrawn.

To guard against breakages, cultivate the habit of turning the machine carefully and slowly by hand after replacing a type carrier or any other part.

Care should be taken that no particles of metal or dirt adhere to the two shoes before they are screwed down. In fixing the shoe b23BB the short screw must be placed at the left-hand end.

ADJUSTMENTS

TYPE CARRIER EXTENSION a22B

This must be adjusted so that there is a measurement of 4 inches from end of carrier to face of sleeve a22B2, against which the spring abuts.

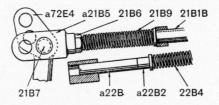

a72E4   a21B5   21B6   21B9   21B1B

21B7   a22B   a22B2   22B4

TRAVERSE OF TYPE CARRIER

Remove mould and see that pin 21B7 is in right-hand hole of type carrier forked eye a21B5, and in lower hole of cam lever extension a72E4, with head of pin facing rear of machine.

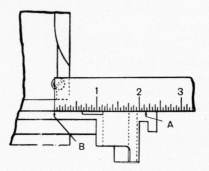

Distance between 'A' and 'B' must be $2\frac{5}{32}''$. To obtain this, raise or lower cam lever extension a72E4.

Turn machine to 220°, in which position the wall in type carrier opening against which the type is clamped must be in line with face of fixed type channel block a51FF. Adjust by screwing connecting rod 21B in or out as required, and fasten nuts 21B2 and 21B6.

Turn machine to 80° and see that the face 'C' in type carrier opening against which the type is clamped is $1\frac{1}{2}''$ from end face of 'B' air pin block. If incorrect, turn machine to 220° and raise or lower the cam lever

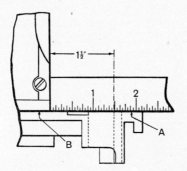

extension a72E4, and reset according to instructions in last preceding paragraph; then turn machine to 80° and test again the measurement from end face of 'B' air pin block.

TYPE CLAMP d26B

See that this slides freely, and that its face does not stand beyond the face of the carrier, thereby creating unnecessary friction. If it does not

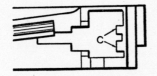

work freely type-turning will result, and the type clamp or type support spring b31B may become damaged.

TYPE SUPPORT SPRING b31B

The end of this spring passes through the type clamp d26B. When the spring is at its extreme forward position its right-hand end should not touch the type carrier body or rub against the sides of the type clamp.

PUMP

(FOR PLATE SEE PP. 229–238)

THE PUMP MECHANISM is actuated by driving cam 66E.

Levers lift the pump body so that the nozzle makes contact with the mould base, and the piston then forces metal into the mould against the face of the matrix, thus forming a type. The nozzle is then moved away from the mould, so that it shall not become cooled by too long contact with the mould.

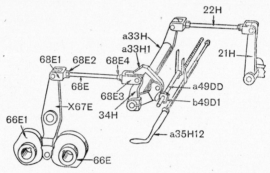

The cam lever connecting rod 68E operates the pump operating lever 34H; this is clamped to a shaft 33H7. Loose upon this shaft is the pump rocker arm a33H, which has two levers, one near the pump operating lever 34H and one at the rear end of the main stand. This latter lever is connected to the pump bell crank 21H located in the pump bracket. One end of this bell crank is forked to engage the piston operating rod lower cross head 19H1 attached to the vertical piston operating rod 19H, the reciprocation of which operates the mechanism for raising and lowering the pump body and piston. This piston operating rod 19H must reciprocate only when a casting is required; for this reason the pump rocker arm a33H is free on its shaft. The pump operating lever 34H has a square end, and the pump rocker arm near it carries a latch a33H1 for locking the two levers. When these two levers are locked together motion is given to the piston operating rod 19H, but when disengaged the pump operating lever 34H will reciprocate without carrying with it the pump rocker arm, and the pump will remain at rest.

PUMP HAND TRIP

To disengage the pump rocker arm latch a33H1, such as whilst the justification wedges are being positioned at the end of a line, or when the pump is disconnected by hand, the pump trip tube a49DD is provided, on which a collar is so adjusted that when the trip tube is in its normal position the collar b49D1 rests near the side of the latch, but when the trip tube is drawn forward the collar becomes positioned in the path of the latch and disengages it from the pump operating lever 34H. A spring automatically returns the pump trip tube, carrying the collar clear of the latch when the machine is required to cast.

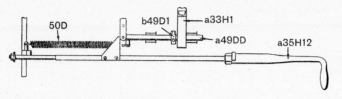

MELTING POT AND PUMP BODY

The melting pot is attached to a swing frame and is raised or lowered by a screw, up to or away from its working position. Immersed in the melting pot is the pump body xg23H. At one end of the pump body is a piston m17HH which, when depressed, forces the metal into the mould. By the action of the pump mechanism the pump body first rises, so that the nozzle 14H becomes seated in the mould base, forming a metal-tight joint whilst casting takes place; immediately after the type has been cast the pump body recedes to prevent chilling of metal at the nozzle point.

The action of the pump mechanism is as follows: As the pump bell crank 21H rises, taking with it the piston operating rod 19H, the crosshead 19H1 compresses the pump body spring a31H, causing the spring rod 31H1 to rise by the spring acting against a shoulder at the upper end of the rod. Crossheads a19H3 and 31H2 are attached to the upper ends of these two rods. Two levers are connected to the crossheads, the pump body lever xc24H terminating in the pump body and the piston lever xc18H engaging the piston. At a given distance in the rise of the rods 19H and 31H1 the latter is checked in its upward motion by the nuts 31H13 coming in contact with the swing frame post.

By this time the pump body will have risen, causing the nozzle to become seated in the mould base. Although the progress of the spring rod 31H1 has been arrested, the pump operating rod 19H continues its upward motion, with the result that the piston lever is rocked by the spring causing the piston to descend. The piston lever is connected by a link a32H to the pump body lever xc24H; therefore the upward motion of the spring rod in raising the end of the piston lever is resisted by the pump body lever. The piston in descending is therefore opposed by the pump body trying to rise; in short, the pump body and piston are working against each other. Were it not for this balanced action the nozzle would be forced away from the mould in the event of a piston becoming seized in the pump body, because the nozzle-lifting spring a27H would not be strong enough to withstand the resistance of the piston. When the mould has received sufficient metal to form the body of the letter to be cast the piston operating rod 19H will not have completed its stroke; its surplus motion will be absorbed by compression of the piston spring.

The pump body rises in a perfectly vertical direction through being supported at each end on separate levers c25HH and b26HH. These levers are operated by the pump body lifting spring a27H and the pump body operating lever 29H. When the pump body spring rod 31H1

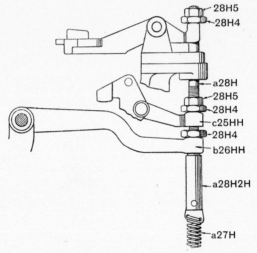

descends, the end of the piston lever xc18H depresses the pump body operating rod lever 29H, causing the pump body to recede from the mould. ·

ADJUSTMENTS

PUMP CAM LEVER CONNECTING ROD 68E

To ensure that the pump rocker arm latch a33H1 will engage the pump operating lever 34H when the pump trip tube collar b49D1 is moved free of the pump rocker arm latch, release the pump hand trip, and see that the trip tube collar has moved clear of the rocker arm latch a33H1.

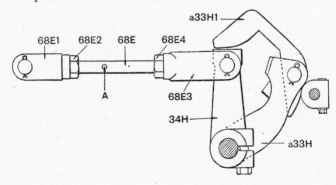

Then adjust the length of the rod 68E so that, when the machine is turned until the pump operating lever 34H has pushed the arm a33H as far to the right as possible, and the plunger a33H4 is in contact (without compression) against the main stand, the latch a33H1 will drop over the upper end of the pump operating lever 34H, and the adjustment is correct.

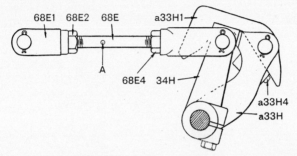

To shorten or lengthen the pump cam lever connecting rod 68E loosen the lock nuts 68E2 and 68E4, and turn the rod in or out of the eyes 68E1 and 68E3, as required, using a pin wrench in hole 'A'; then tighten the lock nuts.

PUMP ROCKER ARM PLUNGER a33H4

Turn machine to about 100° (pump cam lever in extreme right-hand position) and adjust connecting rod 68E so that the pump body operating lever 34H contacts firmly on the pump rocker arm a33H without compressing buffer spring a33H6.

PUMP BELL CRANK CONNECTING ROD 22H

Adjust the pump bell crank connecting rod 22H so that the measurement between the centres of the two connecting eye pins 22H5 is $10\frac{3}{4}''$. This ensures that at each end of the stroke of the pump bell crank 21H there is equal clearance from the swing frame post and the main stand bw36EE.

For convenience of turning the connecting rod 22H a hole is provided in the centre of the rod, so that a pin wrench may be applied after loosening the right-hand and left-hand nuts 22H2 and 22H4. Always tighten these nuts after making an adjustment.

PUMP TRIP TUBE COLLAR b49D1

The pump trip tube collar b49D1 must be moved to behind the pump rocker arm latch a33H1 when the justification wedges are being positioned or when the pump hand trip is latched.

Release the pump hand trip handle a35H12 and see that the pump trip spring 50D has moved the tube a49DD completely to the rear.

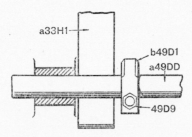

Turn machine to 150° to bring pump rocker arm latch a33H1 to its extreme right-hand position. Loosen the clamp screw 49D9 and position the collar on the tube $\frac{1}{32}$" from the side of the latch. Tighten the clamp screw. Test the adjustment by pushing the collar by hand against the latch, when a slight movement will be observed. Then insert a justification wedge lever arm rod 15D3 in centring pin lever, turn machine one revolution, and note that the collar has been taken to behind the latch, disengaging the latch from the pump operating lever 34H.

REMOVING PUMP TRIP TUBE AND COLLAR a49DD AND b49D1

First take pump rocker arm latch away from tube collar by turning machine to 210° with pump rocker arm latch engaged. Remove spring 50D, disengage rock lever b9D1 to allow operating lever a48DD to swing back, then slacken clamp screw 49D9 in collar b49D1. The rod may now be withdrawn from pulley side of machine, the collar dropping off.

A sign that the collar has slipped in the direction of the pulley side of machine is the casting of letters at the end of each line whilst the justification wedges are being positioned. If the collar is set too far towards the galley side of machine the pump will not operate, as the pump rocker arm latch will remain disengaged.

SQUARING NOZZLE TO MACHINE BASE

The nozzle must rise perpendicularly to the mould and seat a metal-tight fit in the mould base.

Remove matrix-case, bridge, mould and piston from machine; screw on the nozzle gauge 8CT3; raise melting pot to casting position; release pump hand trip and turn machine to 220°. In this position fill the gap between the pump body lifting lever b26HH and stand b37H with an equal thickness of type. Lower the melting pot and remove nozzle from pump body, also remove nozzle gauge 8CT3. Raise melting pot to casting position, making sure the packing beneath pump body lifting lever is still in position and machine is at 220° position. Screw in position the nozzle squaring post 8CT6, making sure the shoulder is screwed against the pump body.

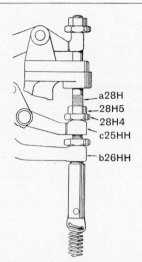

Loosen the lock nut 28H5 and move the nut 28H4 (above pump body lifting lever c25HH) up or down until nozzle squaring post 8CT6 is square with top of main stand. This is most important. Test the squaring post

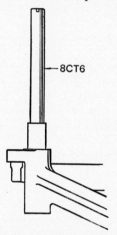

to right and left with a square resting on top surface of main stand. Tighten the lock nut 28H5 and test again with the square, to see that the adjustment holds. The post will stand square, front and rear, unless the pump body or its lifting lever c25HH are badly worn, in which case they should be renewed.

Remove nozzle squaring post 8CT6 and the packing beneath end of pump body lifting lever b26HH.

NOTE.—*If the nozzle does not rise perfectly vertical into the mould base, the nozzle will quickly become severely worn at its point.*

TO CENTRE THE NOZZLE TO ITS SEAT IN MOULD

It is most essential that the nozzle 14H enters its seat in mould base without any side movement.

Remove piston and mould.

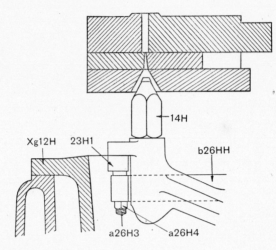

The object is to ensure that when the nozzle is seated in its bearing in the mould, the pump body lifting lever pin a26H3 is central in its pump body bearing 23H1.

It is assumed the pump body operating rod nut 28H4 (above the pump body lifting lever b26HH) has not been altered after squaring the nozzle to mould.

Screw on the nozzle gauge in the mould position.

Screw the nozzle to pump body.

Loosen the two melting pot stud nuts a12H10, but not the melting pot casing screw 12H8.

Loosen the three adjusting screws a37H9 and a37H10.

Raise melting pot to casting position, release pump hand trip, and turn machine to 220°. In this position the nozzle should seat snugly in its bearing in the nozzle gauge.

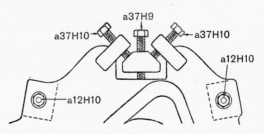

Prise up the end of pump body lifting lever b26HH and insert sufficient types beneath it to take the nozzle about $\frac{1}{8}''$ away from its seating; then by hand slide the pump body slowly backward and forward and from left to right, and note that the nozzle point can be moved freely all around the centre of its seating. If so, tighten the stud nuts a12H10 and the adjusting screws a37H9 and a37H10.

Remove the packing beneath pump body lifting lever, and turn machine by hand to see if nozzle still enters its seating freely in the centre.

PUMP BODY MOVEMENT

(For machines prior to number 22,000 and not converted)

Assuming the pump connecting rods 68E and 22H, and the pump trip tube collar b49D1, have been correctly adjusted, the adjustments of pump to mould are as follows:

With mould and matrix-case in position, insert piston in pump body, and raise melting pot to casting position. Loosen the nuts at lower end of pump body spring rod 31H1, so that they are well clear of the casting; release hand trip and turn machine to 220°, to bring nozzle in contact with mould. Adjust the crosshead stop 31H8 so that connecting pin 32H1 is free in hole in piston lever. Rotate the upper nut 31H13 at lower end of pump body spring rod 31H1 until it contacts with the casting.

Adjust the nut 28H4 at top end of pump body operating rod, so that the operating rod lever 29H is about $\frac{1}{16}''$ clear of the machined recess in lower edge of piston lever xb18H; tighten lock nut 28H5. Turn machine and tighten the lock nut 31H13.

PISTON

The loose end d17H10 on piston should have $\frac{1}{32}''$ movement (one half turn of the adjusting screw). It is adjusted to regulate the metal supply by loosening the nut a17H13 and moving the screw n17H11 as required. As the piston descends, the lower face of the nut a17H13 makes a metal-tight joint with the loose end of piston; as the piston rises, the loose end comes away from the nut, permitting the metal to flow down the inside of the piston end and along the grooves in the piston stem end screw.

Keep the piston clean with a suitable brush. Never use a file or emery cloth on the piston. The presence of grease, paste or oil on the piston quickly carbonizes under the heat of the metal, and the residue adheres to the interior wall of the pump body channel and nozzle, and in the pump body under the nozzle. If allowed to accumulate unduly this carbonized matter becomes difficult to drill.

PISTON SPRING

Assuming all other pump adjustments are in order, the compression of the piston spring must be adjusted to exert sufficient pressure in

forcing the metal into the mould to ensure that the type will be perfectly cast.

Screw down the nut 20H5 on the pump spring rod 20H1 to increase
the pressure of the spring 20H.

This additional spring pressure, applied as the piston wears, com-
pensates for the loss of metal which leaks past the piston. For casting
composition when the piston is not worn, the pump spring rod 20H1
usually extends above the nut about $\frac{1}{4}''$; for casting small display type,
or when a piston is worn, the rod may extend above the nut an inch or
more. For casting large display type a stronger spring a20H should be
used in conjunction with the auxiliary centring pin spring xb36A.

DUPLEX PISTON SPRING xb20H

The duplex piston spring is specially designed for use on composition
moulds fitted with solid gib plate adjustment of the crossblock. Where
a mould with spring supported gib plate is in use, the piston spring
pressure should be adjusted accordingly.

A flanged washer centralizes the springs. When the lock nuts are
assembled and are level with the top of piston rod, the combined
strength of both springs is approximately 75 lb. The piston rod nut for
composition can be screwed down to give a maximum pressure of
approximately 160 lb. A shoulder on the rod limits the travel of the
adjusting nut. Pressure applied advances at the rate of 80 lb. per inch.

The piston rod for composition machines fitted with lead and rule
and/or display type attachment is graduated in inches and the adjusting
nut can be screwed down to give a pressure of approximately 490 lb.

The most suitable position of the piston spring rod adjusting nut
can only be decided by the machine operator, as much depends on the
condition of mould, pump body, piston, quality of metal and heating
equipment.

NOTE.—*Special attention must be given to the correct spring tension
when changing from lead and rule or display type casting to composition.*

PUMP BODY VALVE b23H6

The object of this valve, when the old style solid piston was in use,
was to delay the metal in the pump body returning to the level of the
metal in the pot, thereby limiting the air gap between top of metal in
the pump body and upper end of mould blade, and consequently
reducing the length of piston stroke.

If on the return stroke of the pump piston the metal remained too near
the top of nozzle, the metal chilled in the nozzle point, producing 'stop
casting'. On the other hand, if the metal receded too far from the
nozzle point, type was cast hollow. As the solid piston returned, the
small hole in the valve caused a slight suction on the metal in the pump

body, causing the metal to recede slightly from the nozzle point. Where the loose piston end is in use there is very little 'pull' on the column of metal in the pump body on the return stroke of the piston, as the incoming metal enters past the piston valve, thereby supplying the vacuum.

CLEANING THE PUMP BODY AND NOZZLE

Remove nozzle from pump body before removing pump body from melting pot.

The pump body should be drilled periodically. Unscrew the end plug 23H4 immediately the pump body has been removed from the metal pot, before any metal around the thread has time to congeal. Then drill up the channel in the pump body until the end of the long drill becomes visible at the nozzle end. Then drill down below the nozzle seating.

Clean off any dross adhering to the pump body valve b23H6, and wipe.

Wipe the piston bearing clean.

Drill the main nozzle hole with a $\frac{1}{8}''$ drill, and the point of nozzle with a $\frac{1}{16}''$ drill. The nozzle should be cooled off before drilling, otherwise the drills will become softened.

Replace pump body valve and plug. To do this it may be necessary to place the pump body in the molten metal for a minute or two, in order to melt any metal in the threads, and then at once tighten the plug.

Replace nozzle.

If too much pressure is exerted in trying to remove the pump body plug when the pump body has become chilled, the base of the plug may be broken.

NOTE ON DRILLING

The pump body and nozzle body should always be drilled when cold, in order not to soften the drills and thereby render them useless. A special $\frac{1}{16}''$ drill should be reserved for drilling down the nozzle point when it becomes choked during casting, as the drill will become useless for any other purpose.

In drilling down the nozzle point never let the chuck of the hand brace touch the nozzle point.

If the thread on the nozzle in the pump body becomes clogged, clear the thread with a $\frac{1}{2}''$ tap, 13 threads per inch. *On no account use this tap in a hot pump body, as this will soften the tap and render it useless.*

PUMP ADJUSTMENTS FOR MACHINES NUMBERED 22,000 AND OVER
AND FOR MACHINES CONVERTED TO THIS PATTERN

With the pump hand trip disengaged, turn machine to 80°. Loosen the right-hand nut 22H2 and left-hand nut 22H4. Adjust the pump bell

C

crank connecting rod 22H to give $\frac{1}{64}''$ clearance between crosshead 'Tufnol' collar 31H16 and swing frame post d38H. Lock the nuts 22H2 and 22H4 firmly in position. Turn machine one complete revolution and check that the adjustment holds.

Loosen the lock nuts 31H13 on lower end of pump body spring rod 31H1 so that they are well clear of swing frame post. Turn machine to 220° and loosen the pump body spring rod crosshead stop nut 31H9; then turn the crosshead stop 31H8 in a clockwise direction until the pump lever connecting link pin 32H1 is quite free. Next turn the crosshead stop anti-clockwise until the connecting link pin commences to contact the piston lever. In this position turn the crosshead stop clockwise a further half turn and lock in position with the nut 31H9. Turn machine to 80° and if necessary readjust the pump bell crank connecting rod to give $\frac{1}{64}''$ clearance between crosshead 'Tufnol' collar and swing frame post. Lock the nuts 22H2 and 22H4 firmly in position. Turn machine one complete revolution and check that adjustment still holds.

Rotate the upper nut 31H13 at lower end of rod 31H1 until it contacts with the casting. Turn the machine and lock the nut 31H13 in position.

PISTON LEVER XC18H AND PUMP LEVER CONNECTING LINK a32H

Note the piston lever centre hole is now slotted and a longer spring has been applied to the pump lever connecting link plunger a32H3.

TRANSFER WEDGES
(FOR PLATE SEE PP. 239–244)

THE SECRET OF JUSTIFICATION of lines of type is wrapped up in the transfer wedges. The various thicknesses of character bodies depend on the position to which the mould blade is pulled back, and this is governed by the position of the normal wedge. The various thicknesses of word spaces depend on the positions of two justification wedges. When

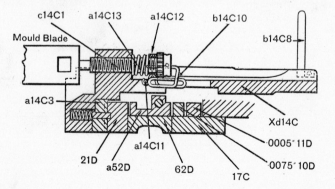

characters are being cast, the justification wedges are not in use; but when word spaces are being cast, the justification wedges are in operation. The normal wedge is usually in the 6-unit position when word spaces are cast, but may be in any other unit position provided necessary provision has been made at the keyboard.

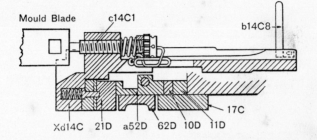

The justification wedges are put in or out of operation by means of two transfer wedges, placed one on the other, each being half the height of the normal wedge. The lower transfer wedge is brought into

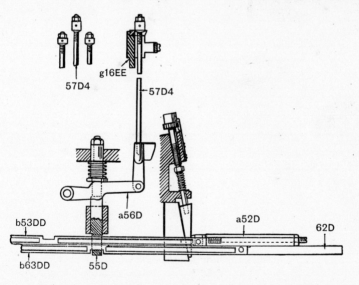

operation each time a *character* is required; the upper wedge then rests idly forward. The mould blade is pulled against an abutment block in front of the normal wedge, and this is drawn against the section of the normal wedge selected by the raised unit pin. The normal wedge is drawn against the lower transfer wedge, and this wedge against an abutment on the rear air pin block. When a *space* is to be cast the lower transfer wedge operating rod is held forward, the upper rod recedes,

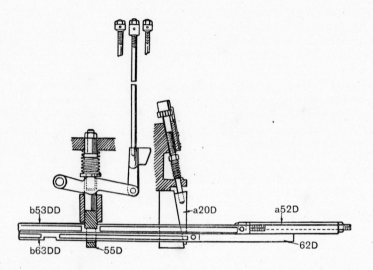

and the mould blade is pulled against its abutment, this against the normal wedge, the normal wedge against the upper transfer wedge, the upper transfer wedge against the two justification wedges, and these against an abutment on the rear air pin block. The positions of the two justification wedges depend on the thickness of space required.

The space transfer wedge is adjusted in its relation to the character transfer wedge so that when the .0075″ justification wedge is in No. 3 front air pin block position, and the .0005″ justification wedge is in No. 8 front air pin block position, any type cast when the upper transfer wedge is in operation will be of exactly the same thickness as when cast with the lower transfer wedge in operation.

The space transfer wedge is fitted with an adjustable screw which (when the space transfer wedge is in its operative position) comes in contact with the micrometer wedge. By means of this adjusting screw 52D1 the correct relation between the two transfer wedges is obtained. A complete turn of the transfer wedge adjusting screw makes a difference to the mould blade opening of approximately .0003″.

Before the casting of any line commences, the justification wedges are brought to positions indicated by perforations in the control ribbon, and remain in these positions during the casting of the line (or section of a line in tabular composition). The positioning of the justification wedges occupies two revolutions of the caster.

Immediately a type has been cast, the tension of the mould blade sizing spring is released, and the transfer wedge is moved to the right to permit the normal wedge (or justification wedge) to be freely moved to a new position.

TRANSFER WEDGE OPERATING RODS

These are operated by cam 'C'. Connected to the cam lever, which is provided with an adjustable post 59D1 for regulating its throw, is an ingenious link mechanism for reciprocating either transfer wedge operating rod. When the space transfer wedge operating rod b53DD is locked to the right by transfer wedge shifter 55D the lower operating rod b63DD is pulled to the left. This action is repeated every time a character has to be cast, but when a justifying space is required, the lower transfer wedge operating rod becomes latched to the right, and the upper operating rod b53DD is pulled to the left. The spring box x60D provides a yielding abutment at the end of each cam lever stroke.

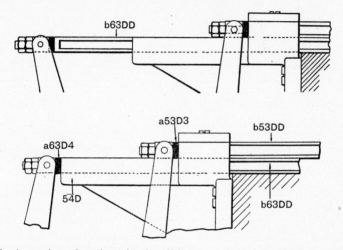

The 'space' perforations in the ribbon consist of two holes—one for raising the 6-unit air pin on the front air pin block; the other for bringing into operation the transfer wedge shifter lever arm rod 57D4, the head of which then engages the centring pin lever. The lower end of this rod is attached to the transfer wedge shifter lever a56D, which

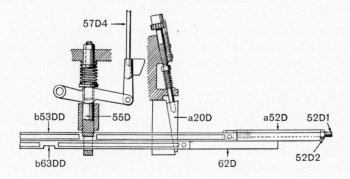

is held down by spring pressure. The transfer wedge shifter lever operates the transfer wedge shifter 55D. The two transfer wedge rods pass through a slot in the transfer wedge shifter, which permits only one transfer wedge rod to reciprocate. The upper transfer wedge rod has a recess on its upper side. When the shifter lever arm rod 57D4 is not raised the lower transfer wedge rod reciprocates; when the shifter lever arm rod has been engaged in the centring pin lever the upper transfer wedge rod reciprocates.

The transfer wedges are attached loosely to the ends of the transfer wedge rods, and the one in operation is drawn against a vertical micrometer wedge a20D. This wedge is adjusted by a finely threaded screw, and is used for very fine type body adjustments.

The upper transfer wedge is fitted with an adjusting screw for obtaining correct relation between the upper and lower transfer wedges. With the justification wedges in 3/8 positions the space transfer wedge in operation should produce types to exactly similar measurements as when the type transfer wedge is in operation. When once correctly adjusted this screw should not be altered.

REMOVING SPACE TRANSFER WEDGE OPERATING ROD b53DD

Insert transfer wedge shifter lever arm rod 57D4 in centring pin lever, and turn machine until upper transfer wedge rod has nearly reached its left-hand limit of travel. Remove nuts and washer a53D3 at rear end of space transfer wedge rod and then from metal pot side of machine pull out wedge and rod.

REMOVING TYPE TRANSFER WEDGE OPERATING ROD b63DD

See that the transfer wedge shifter lever arm rod 57D4 is not engaged in centring pin lever.

Turn machine until lower transfer wedge rod has nearly reached its left-hand limit of travel, remove nuts and washer a63D4 at rear end of type transfer wedge rod, and pull out transfer wedge and rod from metal pot side of machine.

REPLACING TYPE TRANSFER WEDGE OPERATING ROD b63DD

From metal pot side of machine pass the type transfer wedge operating rod b63DD—the longer rod—through eye in transfer wedge shifter 55D, keeping the recess in the rod downward. Before pushing rod home, place on the type transfer wedge 62D. Pass rod through the guide 54D at rear of machine, and insert washer a63D4 on rod *before* inserting end of rod in transfer link (short rear link). Fix nuts on end of rod, but in tightening the nuts see that the transfer rod does not become turned sideways or it will not function freely.

REPLACING SPACE TRANSFER WEDGE OPERATING ROD b53DD

Insert transfer wedge shifter rod 57D4 in centring pin lever and turn machine to 60°; push type transfer wedge operating rod b63DD to right, so that shifter 55D enters the recess in type transfer wedge operating rod. Pass the rod through eye in transfer wedge shifter 55D, on top of the type transfer wedge operating rod, keeping the recess facing upward. Attach the space transfer wedge, and pass rod through guide at rear of machine. Insert washer and then attach rod to transfer link—long one. Fix nuts on end of rod, taking care that the rod is not turned sideways or it will not be located freely. Turn machine to 180°, push the rod to right by hand, and feel if it springs back freely to seating position. Both transfer rods should be tested in this manner, as it is essential for perfect justification of lines that these rods work freely. To test the space transfer wedge operating rod, the transfer wedge shifter lever arm rod must be engaged in centring pin lever. When the machine is working, look occasionally to see if the nuts have worked loose on end of transfer rods.

ADJUSTMENTS

TRANSFER WEDGE SPRING BOX ROD 60D6D

See that there is no end-to-end looseness on spring box rod 60D6D, which will be the case if the adjusting nut 60D8 is not up to the abutment 60D11, or screwed too much against it; after adjusting, tighten by the lock nut 60D9.

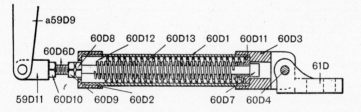

With the two transfer wedge operating rods b53DD and b63DD connected up, and free in the guide 54D, adjust the rod 60D6D in the eye 59D11 until the compression on the spring, with machine at 180°, is equal to that shown when the machine is at 65°.

TRANSFER TONGS CAM LEVER EXTENSION 59D1

When a transfer wedge operating rod is at end of its left-hand stroke (at 180°) the compression on the spring in spring box should be about $\frac{1}{8}''$, and when at end of its right-hand stroke (65°) the compression should also be about $\frac{1}{8}''$.

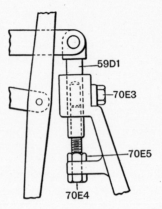

To obtain this movement (assuming the transfer wedge spring box rod 60D6D has been correctly adjusted) loosen the clamp bolt 70E3 and the lock nut 70E5, and raise or lower the post 59D1 by turning the adjusting bolt 70E4, and tightening the lock nut 70E5 and clamp bolt 70E3.

TRANSFER WEDGE SHIFTER LEVER ARM ROD 57D4

Engage transfer wedge shifter lever arm rod in centring pin lever and turn machine to 60°. Loosen the nuts a57D1 and 57D2. Raise transfer wedge shifter lever a56D with the right hand until shifter 55D contacts top of slot in type transfer wedge operating rod b63DD. In this position screw down the adjusting nut a57D1 until contact is made with centring pin lever plate c16E6. Lock firmly in position by means of nut 57D2.

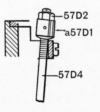

JUSTIFICATION WEDGE LEVER ARM ROD 15D3

The justification wedge lever arm rods raise the justification wedges so that the matrix jaws may move them to the required positions. At the same time they actuate mechanism for placing the pump out of action and for causing the galley cam to take the completed line to the galley.

The lower surface of the nuts a15D1 and a57D1 are spherical in shape for ease of action.

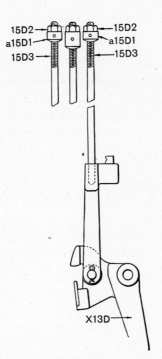

The points to observe in adjusting these rods are:

The justification wedges must be raised so that their teeth are lifted above the fixed tooth; the projection at the end of each wedge must be sufficiently high for the matrix jaws correctly to engage it; the wedges must not be raised so high that they are forced against the underside of the locking bar e13B.

See that the rods are screwed tightly into the lever, and unscrew the nuts a15D1 and 15D2 toward the top of the rods.

Engage the rods and turn machine so that the centring pin lever is at the top of its stroke, the matrix jaws are fully open, and the justification wedges are suspended in their 1–1 positions. Adjust the nuts a15D1 and 15D2 so that the top of the projection on each wedge is level with the top of the matrix jaw. Move the wedges so that the tooth which is nearest the projection is directly under the locking bar, and (with the pump hand trip unlatched) test that the nuts on each rod will clear the centring pin lever plate c16E6 when pressure is applied to the lower end of the corresponding justification wedge lever. If necessary, loosen the nuts and lock firmly in position. This is a most important adjustment. If the centring pin lever at the end of its upper stroke strains the rod 15D3 it will quickly break.

BELL CRANKS 4D, 5D, 6D ON JUSTIFICATION AIR PIN BLOCK

The bell cranks 4D, 5D, 6D are adjusted in similar manner to 5D shown in illustration.

The transfer wedge shifter lever arm bell crank 4D should be adjusted first. With the air on, and using the 'S' perforation, turn machine to 240°. The transfer wedge shifter lever arm rod 57D4 is thus engaged with centring pin lever plate c16E6, and air pin a2D is against its abutment a3D1 (air pin block cover plate). Adjust the bell crank 4D by means of abutment screw 4D1 so that the transfer wedge shifter lever arm rod 57D4 clears front of slot in centring pin lever plate c16E6 by $\frac{1}{64}$". Using the .0005" and .0075" perforations, adjust the justification wedge lever arm bell cranks 5D and 6D in same way as bell crank 4D, using abutment screw 5D1 and 6D1 and air pins 1D.

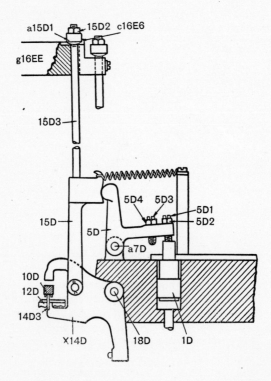

Adjust each bell crank 4D, 5D and 6D by means of stop screw near the fulcrum, so that each lever arm rod, as it disengages from centring pin lever, will fall into a position just clear of the centring pin lever plate 16E2 when centring pin lever is in its highest position.

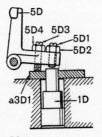

SPACE TRANSFER WEDGE a52D

Place justification wedge 11D in No. 8 position and justification wedge 10D in No. 3 position. Cast some type (from 18-unit position for preference) with the type transfer wedge in operation, and a similar number from the same unit position with the space transfer wedge in operation. If the screw 52D1 in the space transfer wedge is correctly adjusted, the two castings will be exactly the same in width measurement. It is useful to remember that one complete turn of the screw will alter the size of product approximately .0003".

COMPOSITION IN SET SIZES OVER 12 SET

All justifying scales for sets above 12 set are based on a 5-unit minimum space, and on the keyboard the keybars and stopbars are arranged accordingly. This avoids any alteration of the transfer wedge adjustment for sets above 12 set.

TRANSFER WEDGE OPERATING ROD END NUTS

Occasionally examine these to see that they are not loose, or incorrect line justification may develop.

BRIDGE
(FOR PLATE SEE PP. 263–266)

THE 'BRIDGE' on a 'Monotype' casting machine carries the matrix-case above the mould.

A compound slide permits any matrix to be located at its required position over the mould.

A lever on the bridge lowers and raises the matrix-case to and from the mould.

The 'centring pin' on the bridge aligns the matrix accurately over the mould and holds it firmly in position whilst a casting is made.

A cam attached to the centring pin lever actuates the low-space mechanism when special 'low-space' matrices are positioned beneath the centring pin.

The centring pin also operates the normal wedge locking pin b14BB, raises the justification wedge lever arm rods 15D3, and raises the transfer wedge shifter lever arm rod 57D4.

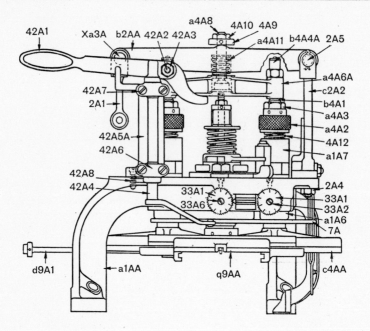

REMOVING BRIDGE

The bridge is taken off with the matrix jaws fully opened and matrix-centring pin lever on top throw. Make sure that the machine is in a suitable position (about 360°) before the bridge link pin is removed from bridge lever. If this is not attended to, there is a risk of breaking or straining the lower spring abutment of centring pin.

Should the machine become jammed so that the bridge cannot be taken off on account of the matrix jaws not being fully opened, disconnect the draw rod from the sliding frame q9AA; the bridge can then easily be removed, and the type carrier also, if desired.

TESTING ALIGNMENT AFTER REPLACING BRIDGE

After replacing the bridge, always test the alignment of the type to ensure that it is correct to standard.

CENTRING PIN GAUGE

The point of matrix-centring pin should periodically be examined and tested with a matrix-centring pin gauge, and any burr that may have appeared on the point should be removed.

NOTE

Never leave any screws or nuts loose on the bridge.

CENTRING PIN
(FOR PLATE SEE P. 263)

THE CENTRING PIN CAMS control the centring pin lever, which in turn operates the bridge mechanism for carrying the matrix-case, operates the centring pin and normal wedge locking pin, as well as the mechanism for controlling the casting of high or low spaces.

The centring pin lever also switches the two transfer wedges in or out of action, and cuts out the pump stroke whilst the justification wedges are being positioned.

The matrix-case is supported in the bridge, clear of the mould, in a sliding frame which permits the matrix-case to be moved in two directions at right angles to each other: in one direction to be stopped at the required position in relation to the front air pin block, and in the other direction to be stopped at the required position in relation to the rear air pin block.

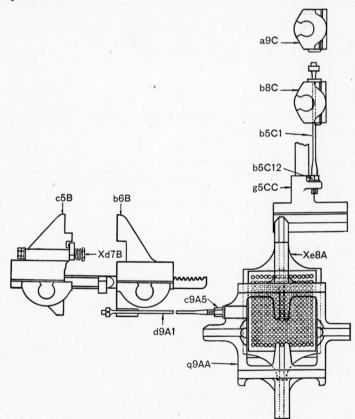

As soon as the matrix-case has been taken to the required position by the matrix jaws, the operating end of the centring pin lever descends, taking the bridge lever with it. The bridge lever depresses a cross-beam, which is checked by two stops to prevent the matrices being hammered against the mould surface; the continued movement of the centring pin then clamps the required matrix firmly to the mould ready for the casting. In the meantime the normal wedge locking pin enters the corresponding tooth of the normal wedge, so that the mould blade can be sized according to the position of this wedge.

LOW SPACES CAUSED BY NON-CONED MATRIX BLANKS

For casting low spaces the mould blade is built in two sections, one over the other. Both sections are moved in unison when type or high spaces are needed, but when low spaces are required the upper section is held forward, so that the incoming metal cannot contact the matrices, and shortened spaces are cast.

The upper section of the mould blade is operated by one of two levers; one for causing the upper blade to work in unison with the lower blade, the other for causing the upper blade to remain closed.

For casting different thicknesses of low spaces, the matrix-case is equipped with special non-cone matrix bodies. When these are positioned over the mould the downward movement of the centring pin is limited, and this restriction of movement causes a small selecting lever to be rocked, which in turn causes another lever to push the mould blade forward.

ADJUSTMENTS

BRIDGE LEVER FULCRUM ROD

The distance from the upper surface of the bridge casting to the centre of the bridge lever fulcrum pin 2A5 is $4\frac{15}{16}''$. After tightening the rod firmly in position, see that the end of the bridge lever b2AA enters freely in the fork of the bridge lever connecting link 2A1. On post-war casters the bridge lever fulcrum rod c2A2 is in one piece with the yoke 2A3, and when the lower nut is tightened the height of the fulcrum pin centre is correct. After tightening the nut see that the other end of bridge lever freely enters the connecting link 2A1.

CENTRING PIN BUSHING

Before placing the bridge on machine, adjust the sleeve a6A6 at the top end of bushing, and the nut a6A22 at the lower end, so that the centring pin will slide freely without the slightest shake.

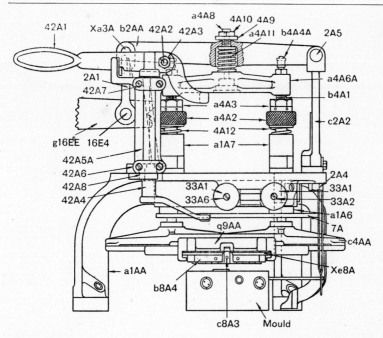

DRAW RODS

Turn machine slowly until centring pin is about to contact a low space matrix and adjust the draw rods so that the centring pin is central over the matrix. Then position a character matrix over the mould, and see that the centring pin enters the coned hole without moving the matrix-case. If there is the slightest movement in either direction re-adjust the indicated draw rod and firmly tighten it in position. Carefully check this adjustment each time a fount is changed.

DESCENT OF MATRIX-CASE

With the matrix-case in the central position, and machine at about 350°, remove the link pin xa3A, uncouple the matrix-case from the cross slide, loosen the two carrying frame stop nuts a4A2, and insert two thicknesses of spool paper between the mould and matrix-case.

Depress the bridge lever b2AA to ensure that the full pressure of the crosshead spring a4A11 is being exerted, and bring down one stop nut a4A2 until the paper can be moved without tearing if lightly pulled or causing any movement of the matrix-case. Continue to depress the bridge lever and bring down the other stop nut a4A2 until the paper is free, then very slightly unscrew this nut until the paper can again just be moved without tearing. Lock both nuts firmly in position and if adjustment is correct, three thicknesses of paper will cause the matrix-case to move.

Both stop nuts a4a2 should contact the stops. On post-war machines the stops are tubes, enclosing the raising springs 4a12, making the contact of nuts to stops visible.

ASCENT OF MATRIX-CASE

Insert link pin xa3a and loosen the cross beam lock nut 4a10.

Place matrix-case in central position and turn machine to casting position (220°).

Place one thickness of spool paper between the nut 4a9 and bridge lever b2aa, and bring down the nut until it just contacts with the paper. Lock the nuts firmly together and check setting. It is of much importance that this adjustment should be carefully made; failure to do so will result in excessive wear on the matrices and on the mould where the matrices make contact.

The object of having the least possible compression on the crossbeam stud spring a4a11 is to delay as long as possible the seating of the matrix on the mould, thereby giving the matrix-case the maximum time possible to settle after being brought to casting position and to ensure the mould blade is sized before the matrix is seated on the mould.

Imperfect draw rod adjustment and imperfect bridge adjustments are main causes of mould surface wear. Before the centring pin becomes seated in a matrix, the matrix-case must be stationary, with the axis of matrix perfectly central with axis of the centring pin. Mould surface wear is caused mainly by the matrices being drawn to position after contacting the mould.

CENTRING PIN TIMING

With link pin xa3a inserted and matrix-case still in central position, with a character matrix in central position of matrix-case, turn machine slowly until one thickness of spool paper can just be withdrawn from between matrix-case and mould. Loosen the centring pin lock nut a5a2, and rotate the adjusting nut 5a1 to give .018″ clearance between underside of adjusting nut 5a1 and top of centring pin spring abutment (upper) d5a5. Lock nut and check setting.

NORMAL WEDGE LOCKING PIN

The normal wedge locking pin descends between two teeth in the normal wedge, so that the wedge is firmly held in position in order that the mould blade may be accurately withdrawn to the required set measurement.

Adjust the nut 14b5 so that the locking pin slides freely in its bearings without the slightest shake.

If, during adjusting, the locking pin becomes too tight in its bearing, turn back the nut and tap it lightly on the top with a piece of wood or lead, and then tighten up again to within a short distance of its previous position. Never leave the nut off its seating.

NORMAL WEDGE LOCKING PIN LIFT

To obtain the correct lift, turn machine until centring pin lever is at its highest position and partly insert a normal wedge so that its plain part comes under the locking pin. Unscrew the nuts at top end of locking pin until locking pin rests on the normal wedge. Advance the lower nut to contact with the abutment piece 14B10 and then make exactly one-and-a-half turns more. This will raise the locking pin $\frac{1}{16}''$ clear of

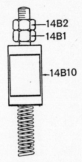

normal wedge. Lock the nuts firmly together and remove, or properly insert, the normal wedge. When locking or unlocking the nuts at top of locking pin, always use two spanners; failure to do so may cause the threaded portion of locking pin to become loose in the lower end, or the end of bushing guide screw b14B6 may become broken. If correctly adjusted, the spring abutment 14B10 should begin to leave the nut 14B1 at 178°.

JAW TONGS SPRING BOX
(FOR PLATE SEE PP. 245–248)

THE CONSTRUCTION of the jaw tongs spring box and tong mechanism is very ingenious, and so seldom thoroughly understood, that a detailed technical description of it is worthy of a little concentrated study.

The underlying principle of the matrix-case positioning mechanism is the provision of two groups of tongs to move the matrix-case direct from one casting position to the next, without first returning the matrix-case to a zero starting point and then going to the next desired position. Therefore, for example, when a letter has to be cast twice, the matrix-case remains in a stationary location during the period of two casts.

Both pairs of tongs (upper and lower) of each group are driven from the same stud on the corresponding jaw tongs bell crank, and one tong

D

of each pair is linked to its own fulcrum post. Therefore the slightest movement of the bell crank causes one pair of tongs to move in one direction and the associated pair to move in the opposite direction.

The jaw tongs cam lever has a positive backward and forward movement, and is connected to a spring box frame by means of a ball and socket joint. This provides for the vertical radial movement of the cam lever and the horizontal radial movement of the connecting rods attached to the jaw tongs bell crank. In other words, it is a universal movement joint.

There are two matrix jaw tongs bell cranks; one for the front air pin block tongs and one for the rear air pin block tongs, and for economy of space both bell cranks are fulcrumed on the same post.

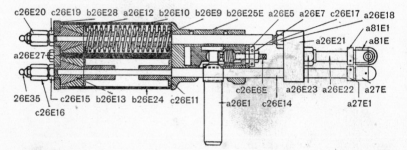

Each jaw tongs bell crank is connected by a ball and socket joint to a driving rod passing through the spring box tube cap b26E25E. The mechanism is similar for both bell cranks.

The left-hand section of the two connecting rods is reduced in diameter to carry abutments to support powerful springs confined in two suitable tubes. Nuts on the end of the connecting rods pull the shoulder on the rods up to the spring abutments c26E11, so that there is no end shake on the rods. Therefore, as the cam lever moves the spring box frame in either direction, the frame pulls or pushes the jaw tongs bell cranks, and these in turn reciprocate the tongs to move the matrix-case to position and to meet a raised air pin for the next matrix-case position.

When the upper end of the cam lever moves to the left, the matrix jaws close. When the jaws meet, the movement of the spring rods is checked, and any continued movement on the spring box tube cap advances the right-hand spring abutments c26E11 and compresses the springs.

When the upper end of the cam lever moves to the right, the pin jaws close. When these jaws meet, the movement of the spring rods is checked, and any further movement on the spring box tube cap causes the tube plate b26E28 to overcome the left-hand spring abutments c26E11 and thereby compress the springs.

The springs act as buffers to absorb the overthrow momentum of the matrix-case, and also act as a safety device against any obstruction to the movement of the jaws. When any pair of jaws meet, the other pair connected to the same bell crank reach the limit of opening.

ADJUSTMENTS

BEFORE PUTTING SPRING BOX on machine, adjust the two ball sockets a81E and a27E on jaw tongs bell cranks so the ball ends are quite free without shake, then tighten nuts a81E1 and a27E1. Adjust the ball plug c26E6E so that ball extension is also free without shake and centralize ball extension a26E1 in the opening in spring box tube cap b26E25E by means of plug button a26E5. Tighten the nut a26E7 and check that ball extension is still just free.

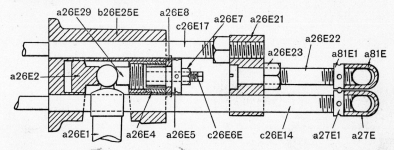

Make sure that the shoulders on rods c26E17 and c26E14 are in contact with spring abutments c26E11, then rotate nuts c26E15 and c26E19 so they lightly contact on brake covers at end of spring box, and in this position firmly lock the nuts.

Attach spring box and bell cranks to machine and set adjusting screw a24E7 in cam lever so that a gap of $\frac{1}{8}''$ exists between top of cam lever and underside of square portion of ball extension. Make sure that hole in ball extension is parallel with rod c26E14 which passes through it, then tighten the two bolts 24E2 on cam lever.

Place matrix jaw tongs in position on machine; the shorter pair over rear pin block, and longer pair over front pin block. Secure by lock slides b38E15. Apply the pin jaw tongs keeping the spring post 55E13 to the left on front tongs and post 56E17 to the rear on rear tongs. Attach pin jaw tongs spring and links, the long link 60E is connected to the left tong on front tongs, the short link to rear tong on rear tongs.

The matrix jaws should meet firmly at 105°. This result is obtained by turning the plug button a26E5 to right or left, as required without disturbing adjustment of ball plug c26E6E. When testing this adjustment, the ball plug lock nut a26E7 should be tightened.

(Machines supplied between 1923 and 1943 were fitted with E4 jaw tongs cams and on these machines the closing of matrix jaw tongs should be adjusted to meet firmly at 108°.)

The front and rear matrix jaws should be adjusted to close simultaneously by releasing the nut a26E18 and turning the rod c26E17 to right or left as required. Tighten the nut a26E18 and check setting. Turn machine until matrix jaws are fully opened and see that they are approximately $\frac{1}{16}''$ clear of their respective buffers.

Perforate a piece of spool paper to raise the H air pin on rear pin block and number 1 pin on front pin block. Turn machine to 320° and adjust studs a55E15 and 56E3 until each pair of pin jaws lightly grip one piece of spool paper when nuts on pin jaw studs are tightened.

After these adjustments are completed it should be observed that a clearance of at least $\frac{5}{32}''$ is obtained between the striking edge of each pin jaw and the first air pin, when pin jaws are fully opened.

The following points are worth remembering in connection with the spring box mechanism and its adjustments:

The ball sockets must be adjusted so that there is no evidence of shake between ball and socket when the lock nut is secured, and yet the socket should move freely, otherwise a breakage might occur quickly.

There must be no lost motion on the spring box rods, which will happen if the nuts at the end of the rods are screwed too far on the rods or not far enough. If too far on, the springs will be compressed within the limit of their abutments; if not far enough the rods will be loose. In these circumstances the looseness of the rods or spring assembly will cause a time lag or loss of movement on the jaw tongs.

Closing the matrix jaws earlier increases the compression on the connecting rod springs and delays the opening of the jaws till the extra spring compression has been returned.

Apart from a worn cam lever roller, the stroke of the cam lever can only be altered by raising or lowering the ball head. This increases or reduces the movement on the jaw tongs bell cranks in both forward and backward directions.

Loss of motion on the tongs, apart from wear on the connections, can only be obtained by the nuts at end of spring box connecting rods being too far forward or not far enough, thereby leaving the springs or rods loose in the tubes.

The left-hand spring abutments are supported by wooden brakes to check overthrow of the matrix-case, especially when being taken from zero position to the first two or three air pin positions. In these instances, as the cam lever slows down near the end of its stroke, the matrix-case is shuttled against the right-hand matrix jaw, causing the left-hand jaw to abut the stop rack head; the overthrow on the right-hand jaw then puts a strain on the jaw tongs bell crank driving stud 21E2 pulling it to the right, causing the spring box rod c26E17 to overcome the resistance of the spring brake a26E12; this compresses the springs, and puts a sharp closing movement on the pin jaws.

Although the compressed air valve on the air tower is closed at 10°, any raised air pin held by the right-hand pin jaw (by tension of the equalizing spring) cannot be released until the left-hand pin jaw contacts its rear abutment. Therefore when the matrix-case has to be moved from the extreme left-hand position to the extreme right-hand position, the contacted right-hand air pin cannot be released before the matrix jaws are nearly closed and have started to slow down. It is at this period that the matrix-case is overthrown against the right-hand jaw with sufficient force and leverage to cause the corresponding spring box rod to overcome its driving spring and thus slightly reverse the pin jaw tongs. If this happens before the released air pin has had time to become seated, the pin jaw will reverse violently against the descending air pin and probably chip it. This can only happen to the first two or three air pins.

JAW TONGS SPRING BOX LUBRICATION

To provide for the more efficient lubrication of the wooden brakes, the spring rods now have their ends drilled to permit the use of a grease gun for forcing grease around the brakes and corresponding cones.

Fill the grease gun with suitable grease and replenish each tube of spring box with a few strokes from the gun each week.

As an excess of grease would impose a strain upon the spring box mechanism, care must be exercised in the application of the grease gun.

PIN JAW TONGS (Front)

To overcome the possibility of air pins becoming chipped by the occasional sudden temporary reversal of the pin jaw tongs as the matrix-case is moved from extreme left to extreme right, the right-hand blade of the front pin jaw tongs is made in two pieces, one piece being spring supported against the other. If the concussion happens to occur just as the right-hand pin jaws begin to leave the air pin, the pressure of the free section of the tong prevents the air pin from partially descending, thereby presenting full resistance to the reversal of the air pin jaw.

In adjusting the closure of the air pin jaws make certain there is (at about 340°) a clearance of two thicknesses of spool paper between the two jaws, to permit the tong spring to function if needed. If the jaws are adjusted firmly together there is a possibility of the rear section of the tong breaking due to frequent strain.

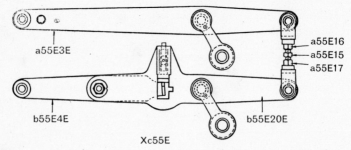

a55E3E

a55E16
a55E15
a55E17

b55E4E

b55E20E

Xc55E

NOTE

Do not think that any imperfection in jaw tongs adjustment can be made good by altering the position of the nuts on the spring rods at the rear end of the spring tubes. There is only one adjustment for these nuts, and that is to take the shoulder of the rods up to the spring abutments, no more and no less, otherwise there will be a loss of spring box motion.

STOP RACKS AND LOCKING BARS
(FOR PLATE SEE PP. 249, 250)

Two LOCKING BARS accurately locate and fix the two stop racks after they have been positioned by the pin jaws meeting against a raised air pin.

Immediately the pin jaws have closed, the locking bars enter the stop rack teeth and hold the racks firmly in position until the matrix jaws have brought the matrix-case draw rod heads to the position of the stop

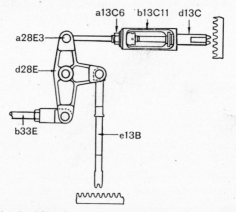

a13C6　b13C11　d13C

a28E3

d28E

b33E

e13B

rack heads. The locking bars are withdrawn clear of the stop racks whilst the air pin jaws proceed to close, taking the stop racks to the next raised air pin position.

The rear locking bar d13c is adjustable for length; the front locking bar e13b is not adjustable.

ADJUSTMENTS

SAFEGUARD

To provide against the possibility of jamming the rear locking bar (such as by turning the machine a revolution before the locking bar adjustment is completed) loosen the nut a13c6 and turn it away from yoke b13c11.

LENGTH OF REAR LOCKING BAR d13c

With the locking bar off the machine, see that there is a measurement of $7\frac{9}{16}''$ from centre of bell crank pin a28e3 to end of teeth of locking bar d13c. Before starting to readjust the length of the locking bar loosen the nut a13c6, and tighten it immediately after making the adjustment.

SEATING THE LOCKING BARS IN TEETH OF STOP RACKS

There must be equal spring compression on both locking bars when seated in the stop racks.

Turn machine so that locking bar operating rod b33e is at left end of its stroke, and note that each locking bar is seated between two teeth of its stop rack.

Loosen the nut a13c6 and turn the adjusting nut a13c5 as required; tighten the nut a13c6, and note that there is not more than $\frac{1}{32}''$ clear-

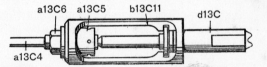

ance between head of locking bar d13c and yoke b13c11. Whilst tightening the nut a13c6, have the locking bar d13c seated in the stop rack and hold the nut a13c5 with a pin wrench.

The eye of a13c4 should seat squarely in slot at end of bell crank.

LOCKING BARS TO CLEAR STOP RACKS

Turn machine until locking bar operating rod b33e is at right end of its stroke. In this position the end of teeth in front locking bar e13b should clear the teeth of the stop rack by $\frac{3}{32}''$. If necessary alter the length of the rod b33e to obtain this result, loosening the nuts a33e6

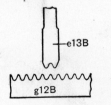

and a33E2 and turning the rod b33E into or out from its end connections a33E5 and c33E1, using a pin wrench inserted in hole of rod b33E located about $1\frac{1}{2}''$ from the right end of rod. *Note that rod* b33E *has right and left screw threads.*

Tighten the nuts a33E6 and a33E2 and see that the adjustment holds.

EFFECT OF PIN JAW WEAR ON STOP RACK POSITIONING

Should a stop rack or locking bar become broken examine the corresponding front pin jaw to see that it is not worn where it contacts the air pins. Excessive wear upon the pin jaw or upon the upper end of the air pins causes the stop rack to be carried too far in the direction of the zero air pin position, and as the locking bar enters the teeth of stop rack, the head of the latter will be forced back against the pin jaw. The frequency of this strain in time may break either the stop rack or the locking bar. When the pin jaws are closed (340°) the head of the stop rack should not touch either pin jaw; this would indicate that as the locking bar enters the stop rack no strain is placed upon either the teeth of the locking bar and stop rack or upon the stop rack projection.

AIR TOWER
(FOR PLATE SEE PP. 256–262)

THIS IS A BOX containing pipes (thirty-one in number) which communicate between the perforations in the ribbon and the air pins in the three pin blocks. A line of thirty-one holes in a crossgirt at the top of the air tower leads to the pipes, and the ribbon passes over this line of holes, being fed by spur wheels engaging the side perforations in the ribbon. Hinged at the top of the tower is a clamp, called an air bar a2GG, faced with a narrow leather pad, which covers the row of holes.

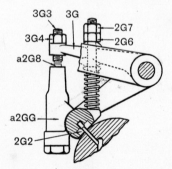

A pipe at the side of the tower conducts air to the hollow end of the air bar shaft, and then down the left air bar arm, to beneath a small valve. When the air bar is clamped to the crossgirt and the air valve is depressed, the air is conducted to a groove in the leather pad, and through any perforation in the ribbon. The 'F' cams operate the feeding of the ribbon over the crossgirt, and the clamping of the air bar is also operated by the 'F' cams.

As the ribbon is passed over the crossgirt it is rewound on a spool. The spool is attached at one end to a short shaft carrying a ratchet 23G. A finger 23G3, screwed to top of paper feed operating rod, lifts a pawl 23G1 on the upward stroke, and this pawl, by means of a tension spring 24G, advances the ratchet on the downward stroke of connecting rod, thus keeping the ribbon taut.

PAPER FEED LOCKING LEVER 12G

The paper feed may be arrested by disconnecting the hook 4G1 and turning down the paper feed locking lever 12G. To restart the paper feed first release the locking lever 12G and then connect the hook 4G1. The reverse of this order will result in the paper marginal holes becoming ripped.

ADJUSTMENTS

THE MEASUREMENT BETWEEN upper end of slot in link 4G3 and lower edge of slot in hook 4G1 to be adjusted to $4\frac{5}{16}''$.

Adjust the valve screw 3G3 so that it protrudes $\frac{5}{32}''$ below lower face of air bar clamping lever 3G.

Adjust the two lower nuts 2G6 to give a measurement of $\frac{27}{32}''$ between top face of guide plate 18G6 and top face of air bar spring stud washer 2G5. Tighten the two lock nuts 2G7.

Turn down the sleeve a4G7 until there is a clearance of about $\frac{1}{8}''$ between the two nuts a4G8 and 4G4, to prevent jamming of stud a19G1 against upper end of slot in link 4G3 when machine is turned.

Adjust the length of air tower operating rod 54E to a measurement of $14\frac{7}{8}''$ between the centres of the two eyes 54E1 and a54E3.

Release hook 4G1 from stud 3G1.

Raise lever 12G.

Adjust the spring rod nut a17G7, at top end of spring box, so that rod is not loose in box.

STROKE OF PAPER FEED PAWL RING a14G

Adjust right-hand screw 1G20 so that when contacted by the lug on paper feed pawl ring a14G, the spurs on the pin wheels which feed the paper are in line with air holes in the crossgirt, and the upper pawl

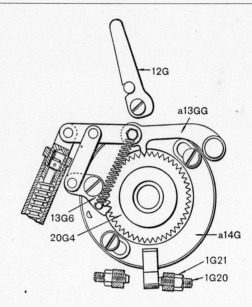

a13GG is in a position to enter centrally between two teeth of ratchet 20G4.

Adjust left-hand screw 1G20 so that when contacted by the lug on paper feed pawl ring a14G the lower pawl 13G6 points centrally between

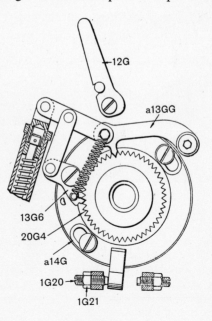

two teeth of ratchet 20G4. Turn machine slowly by hand, and note if the pawl enters teeth of ratchet 20G4 without moving the ratchet and putting a drag on upper pawl a13GG.

The lock nuts 1G21 should be tightened when testing these two adjustments.

AIR TOWER OPERATING ROD 54E

With locking lever 12G raised, adjust the air tower operating rod 54E to give one-third upward compression and two-thirds downward compression of the spring in paper feed spring box.

Place four thicknesses of spool paper between leather packing and crossgirt, and, with the hook disconnected from stud 3G1, turn machine slowly until one thickness of spool paper is just gripped lightly between

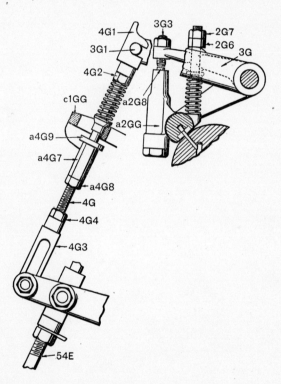

the projection on paper feed pawl ring and right-hand stop screw 1G20. Unscrew the adjusting sleeve a4G7 on air bar connecting rod 4G; engage the hook and adjust the connecting rod 4G so that the paper over the crossgirt can just be withdrawn. Tighten nuts 4G2 and 4G4 and check the setting.

With the four thicknesses of paper still over crossgirt, engage hook and turn machine so that the air tower lever stud a19G1 is approximately central in the slot of connecting link 4G3; then adjust the sleeve a4G7 so that the paper can just be withdrawn without undue resistance from under leather packing. Lock the sleeve firmly in position.

It is important that the lug on paper feed pawl ring a14G reaches the stop screw 1G20 before the leather pad is clamped to the ribbon, otherwise the paper marginal holes will be ripped.

AIR VALVE OPERATING SCREW 3G3

Disengage the hook and remove paper to allow the leather packing to contact on the crossgirt, then adjust the air valve operating screw 3G3 so that one thickness of spool paper can just be withdrawn from between the screw and valve. The following points should be checked:

When the operating rod 54E is at the top of its stroke, it must be possible to depress the hook 4G1 about $\frac{1}{16}''$, to indicate that the stud a19G1 is not jamming against upper end of slot in link 4G3.

The air valve a2G8 should have a movement of about $\frac{1}{16}''$ when depressed by the air bar lever 3G.

When the operating rod 54E is at the bottom of its stroke, the spring 4G5 must not be compressed solid, and the finger 23G3, which operates the winding spool driving ratchet pawl, must be clear of the casting which carries the ratchet.

PAPER WINDING SPOOL X21G

Remove shaft 21G5G and adjust the driving disc 21G7G so that when the button 25G2 is in its seating, and the shaft is held in position with the disc in contact with the driving shaft 22G1, there is $\frac{1}{64}''$ clearance between end of button and shaft.

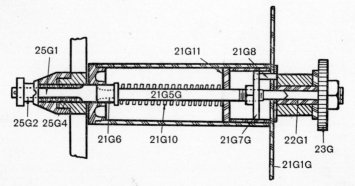

With the spool removed, and button 25G2 engaged in its operating slot, measure the distance that the winding spool spring box plunger 25G1 projects from the side of its bearing. With shaft 21G5G pressed

inward by the amount of this projection, adjust the shaft driving disc
21G7G so that driving disc pin 21G8 projects $\frac{3}{32}$".

MOULD BLADE OPERATING MECHANISM
(FOR PLATE SEE PP. 251–253)

THE MOULD BLADE cam lever moves a connecting rod in one direction
to pull the mould blade back prior to the casting of a type, and in the
opposite direction after casting to eject the type from the mould into
the type carrier. Excess of lever motion during sizing of the mould blade

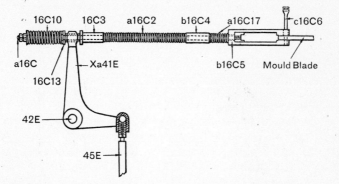

is absorbed by spring 16c10, and during ejection of type from mould
by the combination of springs a16c2 and a16c17.

Special care should be taken in regard to the timing of the sizing
stroke of the mould blade bell crank xa41E, otherwise it may happen
that the mould blade may not be completely sized before the matrix is
seated on the mould, causing undue wear on matrix and upper mould
blade surface.

The centring pin reaches the base of matrix cone hole at 208°, and the
matrix seats on mould at 210°; therefore when on 12-point type, and
casting an 18-unit character, the mould blade should be completely
sized not later than 206°.

Immediately the mould blade is completely sized, the sizing spring
abutment 16c13 begins to move away from the distance sleeve a16c1.

The mould blade is connected to the rod a16c by a fork b16c5, which
operates along an extension on the C pin block. When mould blade
sizing takes place, the fork b16c5 pulls the mould blade against an
adjusting screw in the abutment slide xd14c. This screw is for adjusting
the mould blade till the correct size of type is obtained, acting as an
abutment for the mould blade each time it is pulled back. The rod a16c
carries two springs, used for ejecting the type from the mould. Behind
the bell crank lever is the mould blade sizing spring 16c10.

ADJUSTMENTS

MOULD BLADE CONNECTING ROD BALL SOCKETS 46E AND 47E

These are to be adjusted so that they can be moved freely without looseness. If unduly tight the connecting rod will certainly break, owing to intermittent side strain. The ball sockets should be adjusted with the connecting rod 45E removed.

Loosen the nuts 46E1 and 47E1 with a spanner wrench and turn the plugs 46E2 and 47E2 in the ball sockets until the sockets are free without looseness when the nuts 46E1 and 47E1 are tightened. When tightening the two nuts 46E1 and 47E1, hold the plugs 46E2 and 47E2 with a pin wrench.

REPLACING AND ADJUSTING CONNECTING ROD 45E

Enter the rod 45E in ends of both ball socket plugs at the same time, noting that one end of the rod has a left-hand thread for plug 47E2.

With a mould in position on machine, and the mould blade coupled to fork b16c5, adjust the rod 45E so that when machine is at 92° there is a compression of $\frac{1}{8}''$ between abutment 16c3 and sleeve a16c1. Tighten the connecting rod nuts 45E1 and 45E2, and see if the adjustment remains correct.

The final observation should be to see that when the largest point size of mould in use is on machine, and its normal wedge in 18-unit position, the mould blade is completely sized before the matrix is seated on the mould.

MOULD BLADE CAM LEVER EXTENSION 44E1

This attachment is applied to obtain an increased mould blade movement for moulds larger than 18 units $12\frac{1}{2}$ set (.1729''). When the

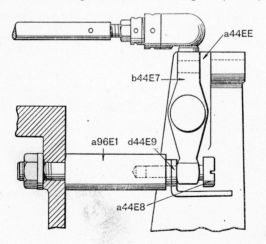

screw a44e8 is connected to the upper end of lever b44e7, the cam lever a44ee functions for all sizes from 12 point and under.

When the screw a44e8 is connected to the lower end of lever b44e7, the cam lever functions for sizes above 18 units 12½ set.

To change from 12 point and under, remove the screw a44e8 and distance piece d44e9.

Place the distance piece d44e9 between lower end of lever b44e7 and abutment a96e1, with tongue of distance piece towards abutment a96e1, and insert and tighten the screw a44e8.

MOULD BLADE OPERATING ROD NUT 16c9

Tighten the nut 16c9 at end of mould blade operating rod a16c, and then unscrew it one-half turn. Lock firmly in this position.

MOULD BLADE OPERATING ROD a16c

With a 12-set normal wedge in the 18-unit position, and the mould blade fully open to approximately 12 points, adjust the mould blade connecting rod 45e so that there is $\frac{1}{8}''$ compression on the sizing spring 16c10. Turn machine till mould blade is in its maximum forward position, and check that there is approximately $\frac{1}{8}''$ clearance between the ejecting spring abutment 16c3 and the distance sleeve a16c1.

Be very particular with this adjustment in relation to the seating of centring pin. The mould blade must be completely sized before the matrix is seated on the mould.

TYPE PUSHER
(FOR PLATE SEE PP. 254, 255)

THE TYPE PUSHER ejects the types from the type carrier, pushing them into a channel until the line is complete, when it is taken to the galley.

ADJUSTMENT

TYPE PUSHER CONNECTING ROD 77e

The only adjustment in connection with the type pusher is that it should push the type $\frac{1}{32}''$ beyond the spring latches a50f2 and a51f3 in the channel blocks. Adjust the nuts at the end of the type pusher connecting rod 77e to obtain this condition.

LOW QUAD MECHANISM
(FOR PLATE SEE P. 279)

THE MOULD BLADE is made in two pieces. Normally the blade works as one piece, but when low quads or low spaces are required, the upper section of the blade is moved and held forward underneath the matrix, so that a type body of reduced height is cast. The low quad mechanism is brought into action by matrices having no cone holes. These cause the centring pin to take a shorter stroke, and this actuates a lever which holds the upper section of the mould blade forward.

Space matrices *with* cone holes produce high spaces, *i.e.* type height less depth of matrix punching. Space matrices *without* cone holes produce low spaces, *i.e.* type height less depth of matrix punching and depth of upper mould blade.

When coned matrices are presented to the mould, the centring pin in descending operates the character lever d29A4A for opening the upper mould blade, so that either type or high spaces may be cast.

The absence of a cone hole causes the centring pin to take a shortened stroke, thereby rocking a selecting lever a16E20E and causing it, as the centring pin lever descends, to operate the space lever d29A9A for closing the upper mould blade.

ADJUSTMENTS

CENTRING PIN SPRING ABUTMENT CAM PLATE 5A7

Place a normal wedge, of largest set size likely to be used, in 18-unit position, and see that the mould adjusting screw c14c1 is set to give correct mould opening. Turn machine to 200° with centring pin in the coned hole of a character matrix. Loosen the cam plate bolt nut 5A9 so that the cam plate is out of action, and loosen the lock nut 16E19 on the actuating lever adjusting screw 16E18, and screw it down until it just touches the centring pin lever g16EE, and then screw back one-quarter turn. Lock the nut, and check that the adjustment still holds, and that the upper mould blade is fully open.

LOW QUAD SELECTING LEVER a16E20E

Turn machine so that the centring pin lever is in its highest position, and adjust the spring abutment cam plate 5A7 horizontally so that it nearly contacts with selecting lever a16E20E. This can be checked by watching the end of selecting lever, and making the adjustment so that lever just breaks contact with side of slot in which it operates, then slightly moving the cam out of contact with lever.

Without moving the spring abutment cam plate from its horizontal position, move it vertically till it just causes the selecting lever to break contact with the side of slot in which it operates. Lock the spring abutment cam plate firmly in this position.

Turn machine to the quad position (on low space matrix), and see that the end of selecting lever clears the top of character lever as it passes from character lever to low quad lever. Should it not do so, slightly raise the cam. Also see that selecting lever, when over the low quad lever, is just clear of side of slot in actuating lever.

When adjusting the centring pin for alignment, it may be necessary to alter slightly the horizontal position of the spring abutment cam plate 5A7. Moving the centring pin in the direction of the selecting lever without readjusting the spring abutment cam plate, will cause increased pressure on the centring pin. As a final check on the adjustment, place machine in casting position with centring pin in coned hole of a character matrix. If the mechanism has been correctly adjusted it should be possible, with the fingers exerting about 15-lb. pressure, to lift the centring pin well clear of the mould.

LOW QUAD SELECTING LEVER CAM LEVER a16E26E

Remove bridge and loosen the selecting lever fulcrum bolt nut 16E24. Move the selecting lever cam lever a16E26E so that it positions the selecting lever a16E20E over the space lever d29A9A, and carefully adjust the eccentric bolt a16E23 to give .003″ clearance between selecting lever and side of slot in which it operates. Lock the bolt firmly in position and check that the adjustment still holds.

Replace the bridge and turn machine to 40°, and adjust the actuating lever adjusting screw 16E18 so that the cam face of the lever a16E26E is just clear of the selecting lever. Firmly tighten the adjusting screw nut 16E19.

The centring pin can be adjusted for alignment without interfering with the setting of this mechanism.

Turn machine to 18-unit position (on low space matrix), and note that end of selecting lever clears top of character lever as it passes across from character lever to low space lever. Should it not do so, slightly raise the cam. Also see that selecting lever, when over the low space lever, is just clear of side of slot in actuating lever.

If the mechanism has been correctly adjusted it should be possible, with the fingers exerting about 15-lb. pressure, to lift the centring pin well clear of the mould.

IMPROVED LOW QUAD OPERATING MECHANISM

Remove bridge and loosen the selecting lever fulcrum bolt nut 16E24. Move the cam lever a16E26E so that it positions the selecting lever a16E20E over the space lever d29A9A, and carefully adjust the eccentric bolt a16E23 to give .003″ clearance between selecting lever and side of slot in which it operates. Lock the bolt firmly in position and check that the adjustment still holds.

Replace bridge, and turn machine to 40° and adjust the actuating lever adjusting screw 16E18 so that cam face of lever a16E26E is just clear of selecting lever. Firmly tighten the nut 16E19.

E

Place a normal wedge of the largest set size that is likely to be used in the 18-unit position and see that mould blade abutment slide adjusting screw is set to give correct mould operating. Turn machine to 204° with the centring pin in coned hole of matrix. Adjust actuating lever adjusting screw 16E18 so that one thickness of spool paper can just be withdrawn from under the head of screw when lock nut is tightened. Return the machine to 40° and adjust cam lever eccentric 16E30 so that cam face of lever just contacts with selecting lever. Lock the cam lever locking screw.

The centring pin can be adjusted for alignment without interfering with the setting of this improved mechanism.

LINE SHIFTING AND GALLEY MECHANISM
(FOR PLATE SEE PP. 272–278)

AT THE COMPLETION of every line two operations are required—the passing of the completed line to the galley and the adjustment of the two justification wedges so that every space in the line next to be cast will be of the required thickness to make the line correct in length. These two operations take place simultaneously.

POSITIONING THE JUSTIFICATION WEDGES

At the end of each line the ribbon receives two sets of two perforations. One perforation in each set permits air to be conducted to D pin block and the other to B pin block. The air directed to D pin block

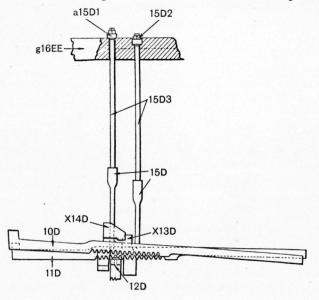

raises one of two pistons, which causes a corresponding headed rod
15D3 to enter a slot in the side of the centring pin lever when at the end
of its down stroke. As the centring pin lever rises it lifts the headed rod.
These two rods are connected to levers x13D and x14D, which project
under the justification wedges, and consequently these are also lifted.
A projection on the end of each justification wedge becomes placed in
the track of the matrix jaws, and these in closing carry the wedge to a
position relative to the raised air pin.

RANGE OF JUSTIFICATION WEDGE ADJUSTMENT

As there are fifteen air pin positions on the B pin block, each justification wedge can assume fifteen positions. One justification wedge has
a gradient of .0075″ per shift, and the other a gradient of .0005″ per
shift. The smallest space obtainable is that cast when both wedges are
in the extreme right-hand (1–1) position, and this can be gradually
increased by moving the finely tapered wedge tooth by tooth to the
fifteenth position. This wedge can then be returned to the first position,
and the coarse wedge shifted to the second position, when .0075″ will
have been added. By repeating these movements until every tooth
position of the .0075″ wedge has been used in combination with every
tooth position of the .0005″ wedge, a range of 225 different justifying
space thicknesses is obtained. (For Justification Tables, see pp. 218 and
219.)

PUMP CUT OUT AT END OF EACH LINE

The positioning of the two justification wedges occupies two revolutions of the machine after the completion of the preceding line, and

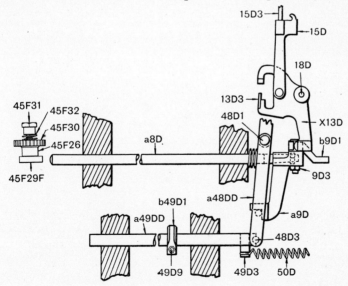

whilst they are being positioned no casting must take place. The completed line then starts to be removed to make room for the line to follow, and the pump mechanism is put out of action. These requirements are fulfilled simultaneously by mechanism operated by the justification wedge levers. Each time the wedge levers x13D and x14D are rocked by the centring pin lever, they press against a rock lever b9D1 connected to a rod a8D which leads to the galley trip lever d45FF. Screwed to this rod is an arm a9D, the end of which operates a tube a49DD carrying the pump trip tube collar b49D1. Therefore, when the wedge levers x13D and x14D lift the justification wedges they also push the galley trip rod a8D to start the galley mechanism and the pump trip tube a49DD to stop the pump. When the wedge lever arm rods 15D3 become disconnected from the matrix-centring pin lever the justification wedges become seated on the fixed tooth 12D; the rod a8D and tube a49DD are then returned by the spring 50D attached to the pump trip rod.

DOUBLE JUSTIFICATION

Each time rock lever b9D1 is operated by wedge lever x13D or x14D the galley trip rod a8D moves forward $\frac{3}{16}''$, but when both wedge levers are lifted simultaneously the galley trip rod moves forward double that distance. *The galley trip lever* d45FF *may be adjusted so that when the galley trip rod* a8D *goes forward only* $\frac{3}{16}''$ *it will not start the galley mechanism;* in this case both justification rods 15D3 must be lifted simultaneously to start the galley mechanism. This adjustment is necessary when tabular matter with many columns is being cast, each column having to be justified as a separate line but not taken to the galley till the last column has been cast; then the double justification perforations (.0075″ *and* .0005″), being acted upon simultaneously, cause the galley trip rod to operate.

DIRECTION OF RIBBON FEED

In studying casting machine problems always remember that the ribbon is advanced step by step in a reverse direction to that in which it was advanced on the keyboard. For example: if a ribbon has a 'double justification' of 3/8–8, the casting machine will accept the '8–8' perforations first, and then the '3'. Both justification wedges will first be taken to No. 8 air pin position, and then the .0075″ wedge will be taken to No. 3 air pin position.

LINE SHIFTING

Each line of type is accumulated in a channel at the side of the galley. One side of the channel is a fixed wall, whilst the opposite side is adjustable, being held forward by a spring, and so set that the channel is slightly less in width than the body of the type to be cast. The type is thus supported by pressure between the channel walls. Each wall carries a spring latch to prevent the type falling back as the type pusher recedes. Upon completion a 'line hook' xa19F draws the line to the galley. When the line has reached a position opposite the galley a rule rises, and the line is pushed into the galley. The rule then descends, and the line hook returns to a position of rest, ready for withdrawing the next line.

LONG LINE AND SHORT LINE AUTOMATIC STOP

At one side of galley entrance is an adjustable stop slide a44FF, which includes a lever a44F9F for operating the starting lever latch a33F. As the line of accumulated type is being drawn to the galley, its forward end rests against a line support xh30F. This line support has a keyway at one end to correspond with a ward on the stop slide a44FF. Should the line be shorter than the galley entrance, the line support will foul the ward on the stop slide, and will push it, thereby disengaging the starting lever, causing the driving belt to be drawn over the loose pulley. Should the line be too long, the end type or quad will push the stop slide a44FF, thereby causing the machine to stop.

VARIOUS LINE SUPPORTS

There are several patterns of line support for different purposes. See Index of Book of Parts of 'Monotype' Casting Machines under Groups 29F and 30F.

GALLEY MECHANISM

A vertical shaft 15FF, worked by a worm upon the handwheel shaft, constantly revolves, carrying with it the ratchet 15F2. A horizontal cam b14FF, through the centre of which the vertical shaft 15FF passes, remains idle, latched to a trip lever d45FF by a pawl 14F1F. When the trip lever releases the pawl, as at the end of a line, the pawl engages the ratchet 15F2, and the galley cam b14FF is thereby revolved with the shaft 15FF. The cam operates a lever 25FF which connects to a slide bar a21F carrying the line hook xa19F, and this engages the line of type and draws it to the galley. A cam surface on the underside of the galley cam operates the rule lever xa40F to raise the rule e39FF, and a cam surface around the galley cam operates a lever 5F to push the line into the galley. Upon completion of the revolution, the cam is again latched to trip lever d45FF, and remains idle till the next line is ready for transference to the galley. One revolution of the galley cam occupies seven revolutions of the machine, during which other types are being cast. The shortest justified line which can be cast must contain at least six type bodies.

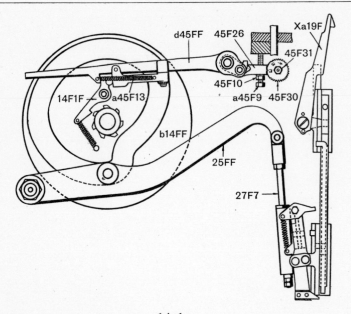

GALLEY CAM DRIVING PAWL 14F1F

The galley cam is correctly timed if the tooth marked '0' on the worm 80E6 engages between the two teeth marked '0–0' on the worm wheel 15F3. This may be tested by engaging the two justification wedge lever arm rods in the centring pin lever and turning machine slowly till the galley trip lever has released the galley cam driving pawl 14F1F. The pawl should then contact on the ratchet 15F2 about one-tenth of an inch past the engaging edge of a tooth so that the ratchet revolves nearly the distance between one tooth and another before engaging the pawl.

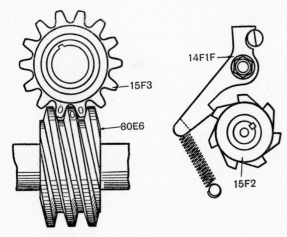

LUBRICATING THE GALLEY CAM SHAFT 15FF

The galley cam carries a sleeve 14F8 through which the vertical shaft 15FF runs. It is most important that this shaft should occasionally be lubricated through the hole in the upper centre of the shaft; also through the hole in cam near the ratchet teeth.

TRIP LEVER d45FF

Place reversible plate a45F15F out of action, and adjust the trip lever stop screw a45F9 so that there is $\frac{1}{32}''$ gap between pawl 14F1F and bottom of trip lever hook.

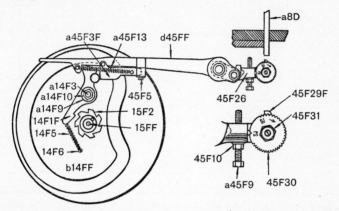

Release pump trip handle, engage both justification wedge lifting rods, and turn machine until centring pin lever is in its highest position. Adjust the screw 45F1 so that the projecting part of trip lever clears the pawl by $\frac{1}{32}''$.

ADJUSTMENTS

GALLEY TRIP LEVER—IMPROVED DESIGN—ADJUSTMENT

Release pump trip handle. Engage the 11D justification wedge lifting rod and turn machine until centring pin lever is in its highest position. Set the cam adjuster 45F30 to 'SJ' position. With the cam 45F29F on end of adjuster in contact with the galley trip rod a8D, partly disengage the trip lever until a gap of $\frac{9}{32}''$ is obtained between the top of galley cam driving pawl 14F1F and the trip lever. Tighten the bolt 45F27 and see that gap is still correct and the cam still in contact with galley trip rod.

Engage the 10D justification wedge lifting rod and turn machine one complete revolution to release lifting rods and disengage rock lever from rock lever stop.

Adjust the stop screw a45F9 to contact main galley stand until a gap of $\frac{1}{32}''$ is obtained between top of galley cam driving pawl 14F1F and the trip lever.

For single justification set trip lever adjuster to 'SJ' position.

For double justification set cam adjuster to 'DJ' position for slow running speeds of machine. Should the speed of machine be increased, the movement of galley trip rod will also increase due to overthrow. In this case slacken the adjuster lock nut 45F31 and set cam adjuster in an anti-clockwise direction to allow for overthrow. Lock the nut 45F31.

COLUMN PUSHER XC1F

Adjust the fulcrum screws 4F1 and a4F3 so that column pusher moves freely, has no side shake, and clears fixed type channel block by the thickness of a piece of spool paper.

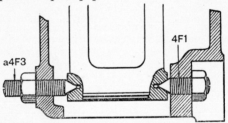

COLUMN PUSHER SPRING BOX 8F

Release the galley cam driving pawl 14F1F so that galley cam is set in motion, and turn machine until column pusher is completely forward to the right. Engage the belt shifter and adjust the spring box so that there is .010″ gap between the projections on the thick line support xh30F and the stop slide a44FF. This should leave the column pusher approximately $\frac{1}{32}''$ in advance of column rule e39FF.

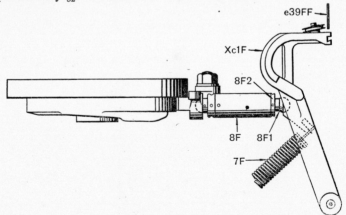

COLUMN PUSHER ADJUSTING CAM DISC a2F1

With column pusher adjusting cam disc a2F1 in the 12-point position and column pusher at rest, the face of column pusher should be .008″ behind a line of 12-point type in the type channel. Adjust the stud nuts 3F3 to obtain this condition.

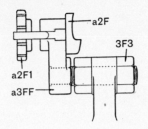

COLUMN RULE e39FF

The rule lifting rod nuts 39F4 and 39F5 should be so adjusted that, when the column pusher has just started to move back, there is a $\frac{1}{64}″$ clearance between top of pusher or repeater line-support and under edge of rule.

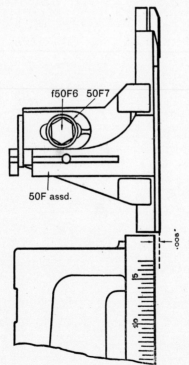

LINE SUPPORT PUSHER SPRING BOX—ADJUSTMENT

Release abutment screw 211F14. Remove chain anchor pin 211F4. With line support engaged against its stop c1F6, place chain anti-clockwise around sheave and spring box drum. Rotate drum clockwise to give one quarter turn tension on spring and secure chain to drum by means of the anchor pin. See that the spring box is correctly positioned to bring chain in line with its sheave.

Withdraw line support until it just disengages from front end of column pusher and then rotate abutment 211F12 anti-clockwise on the support 211F7F to make contact with stop pin on rear of spring box drum.

The correct adjustment of these parts obviates any possibility of too much tension being applied to the spring box spring.

TRAVERSE OF LINE TO GALLEY ENTRANCE

Adjust line hook operating bar stop screw b22F1 at end of galley stand so that line hook xa19F brings the far side of the last letter cast in a line just clear of the end of fixed type channel block a51FF.

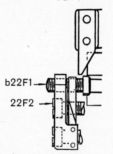

LINE HOOK OPERATING SLIDE SPRING BOX a27F

With galley cam at end of its revolution, bring adjusting nut 27F8 lightly against spring abutment 27F5. Lock firmly in position with lock nut 27F9. Adjust the spring box rod 27F7 in spring box rod eye 27F10 to give equal compression on spring 27F4 at both ends of the stroke.

PUMP TRIP ROD

TO TURN MACHINE without casting type, the pump trip handle a35H12 must be latched to the post stop a31F7. The handle is connected by a spring box to a rod b35H1H carrying a plate 35H4 with a cranked upper end. When pulled to the front, this plate pushes the trip tube a49DD, causing the collar b49D1 to disconnect the pump latch from pump operating lever. The trip spring 50D returns the pump trip rod b35H1H and trip tube a49DD when the pump trip handle a35H12 is released.

REMOVING PUMP TRIP ROD b35H1H

Disconnect pump trip handle a35H12 by loosening the nut a35H8, and removing nut, washer and spring at front end of the rod, also nut at rear end of rod. Then remove connecting pin 22H5 from pump bell crank connecting rod 22H (the one near the cam side of machine). Push pump trip rod b35H1H towards galley side of machine so that the end clears the casting, and then draw rod out from rear side of machine.

INSERTING ROCK LEVER b9D1

Should the rock lever b9D1 become disengaged, take the pump latch a33H1 away from collar b49D1 by turning machine to about 210° with pump rocker arm latch engaged, then remove pump trip spring 50D, and latch the pump hand trip a35H12 to stud a31F7 on main galley stand. The rock lever may then be easily replaced. Should the rock lever become disengaged the lines will not be taken to the galley.

GALLEY TRIP ROD ARM ROCK LEVER STOP

THIS IS FOR automatically cutting out the pump action in cases where the keyboard operator has made an error and has repeated the composition of such line.

The attachment consists of an extension to the galley trip rod arm rock lever b9D1 of the casting machine, and a stop piece a9D4 which is held in position by the justification air pin block screw nut 40E1.

Should the keyboard operator wish to prevent a line being cast he may do so (at any position of the line which he may be operating) by depressing one of the lower justification keys.

As the ribbon passes (in reverse direction) through the casting machine this perforation will cause the rock lever b9D1 to be held forward, thereby holding the pump out of action during the rest of the

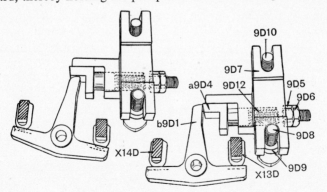

line, until the appearance of the .0075″ perforation causes the justification wedge lever x14D to be pushed forward, thus releasing the extension on b9D1 from stop a9D4.

The casting machine galley trip lever should be kept adjusted for
double justification, so that when the .0005″ perforation occurs alone
it will not cause the galley to be tripped into action.

Keyboard operators should not be encouraged to become careless
in operating the keyboard and resort too frequently to the use of the
line canceller, especially when on wide measures, as the cessation of the
pump action causes the mould to become cooler, resulting in the first
line cast after the pause to be slightly long.

GALLEY TRIP ROD ARM ROCK LEVER STOP—MODIFIED DESIGN—
     ADJUSTMENT

Release pump trip handle, engage 11D justification wedge lifting rod
and turn machine until pump trip tube collár b49D1 has $\frac{1}{4}$″ engagement
with pump rocker arm latch a33H1.

Push rock lever stop group towards front of machine until the stop
a9D4 contacts tail of rock lever b9D1. Securely fasten by means of the
two screws 9D8 and 9D10.

Turn machine one complete revolution, engage both 10D and 11D
justification wedge lifting rods and adjust position of rock lever stop
a9D4 to clear right-hand side of rock lever as it returns to its inoperative
position. Lock the two nuts 9D5 and 9D6.

AIR COMPRESSOR

THE AIR COMPRESSOR should be cleaned regularly and lubrication
attended to daily. The lubricators should be so adjusted that the oil
neither runs away so quickly as to over-lubricate nor so slowly as to
render the pistons liable to seize. The minimum speed should be such
as to ensure a slight escape of air at the exhaust valve on air tank when
the full plant of keyboards and casters is working. (For Air Compressor
and Power Tables, see pp. 214–215.)

The compressor should be tested periodically to see that the crank
is not loose in its bearing. If any difficulty is experienced in getting full
pressure when starting, the valves should be cleaned, as dirt between
valves and their seatings allows the air to return to the cylinders as the
pistons recede. The valves may be examined by removing the end nut
with square key provided.

The oil box on top of compressor must be kept full of oil, and if the
lubricating wick is disturbed at any time the side cover should at once
be removed to see if the licker is failing to touch the wick; if so, readjust
to touch. The wick should be washed in paraffin at least once every six
months.

The wicks leading from oil box to connecting rod should wipe the licker, which is fitted on to the large end of the connecting rod, and it should be carefully noted that this action is correct according to the direction of running. If this adjustment is incorrect the oil will be thrown away from the crank..

Used oil should be drained off the compressor by the tap at the base at least once a week while the compressor is stopped.

Belts should not be too tight, as this does not permit smooth running of the compressor and tends to wear the side bushes.

The pressure regulating valve should be fixed between the compressor and the tank, so that hot air instead of cold is blown off when the supply exceeds the demand.

If at any time the valves stick they should be cleaned.

The speed of the compressor should be carefully attended to. It should not be run with an extravagant excess of air blowing off when all machines are in operation.

AIR COMPRESSOR—5 CUBIC FEET

This compressor delivers 5 cubic feet of free air at a speed of 325 r.p.m. It is of the two-cylinder horizontally-opposed type fitted with a single double-ended piston, actuated by an eccentric-driven connecting rod. The driving shaft runs in a double-row ball bearing at one end, and a roller bearing at the other, whilst the 'big-end' bearing of the connecting rod is also fitted with roller bearing. The air is taken into the compressor through a felt and gauze filter pack, which cleans it and prevents abrasive particles being drawn into the working parts.

The filter pack may be removed and washed in trichlorethylene when necessary. A spare filter is supplied to enable the fouled filter to be thoroughly cleansed while the compressor is kept in operation.

The inlet and delivery valves which are situated in the cylinder head are spring loaded and are automatic in operation.

The main shaft is constructed so as to allow it to be withdrawn complete with its bearings, without disturbing the bearings in any way. The cylinders and body are cast in one piece to ensure true alignment and avoid distortion. The cylinders are fitted with detachable heads.

The connecting rod 'big-end' bearing is fitted with steel rollers which are assembled in a special bronze cage. The end bearing is of the standard plain bronze bush type.

The oiling system is fully automatic and is operated by a mechanically driven pump which draws oil from a sump in the compressor base and supplies a distributing chamber, which, in turn feeds the cylinder walls and gudgeon pin bearing. The flow of oil can be regulated as required by the adjustment of a knurled nut. The pump is provided with a by-pass which is so arranged as to supply a continual flow of oil through the shaft bearings, any excess of oil being drained back to the sump.

This forms a complete circulating system.

The pump consists of a small piston working in a cylinder operated by an eccentric which is affixed to and driven by the main shaft. It operates by drawing a quantity of oil up from the sump past a ball non-return valve on the outward stroke and on the return stroke forces the same quantity of oil upwards, past a second non-return valve through the feed spout into a glass-covered distributing chamber. The distributing chamber is drilled to lead the oil to both cylinders and through the piston to the gudgeon pin. A hand-operated needle valve is fitted on the delivery side of the pump so that the supply of oil can be regulated as required, and the excess oil which accumulates when the valve is set at minimum is returned through a by-pass valve to the shaft bearing housing. This ensures continual lubrication of the bearings.

For normal running the needle valve should be set so that two drops of oil pass from the feed spout into the distributing chamber every minute. It will be noted when the compressor is started up cold a little time will pass before oil commences to flow. A small tray is situated in the sump which collects the returning oil from the cylinders. This tray is placed so as to allow the 'big-end' of the connecting rod to dip into the oil for lubrication.

The sump is provided with a drain plug filler cap and strainer and the oil level should be maintained to within $\frac{1}{2}''$ of top of the filler cap.

A $\frac{3}{4}$ H.P. motor is required to drive the compressor to maintain a gauge pressure of 20 lb. per square inch.

POINTS TO BE TAKEN CARE OF IN EVENT OF FAILURE

Failure to obtain sufficient air pressure.—Make sure that both inlet and delivery valves are seating correctly.

Ascertain safety valve working efficiently.

Remove air filter pack at frequent intervals and wash thoroughly in trichlorethylene so as to allow free ingress of air.

Failure of oil supply.—Check level of oil in sump.

Unscrew regulating valve full out for a few minutes whilst compressor is running to clear any air locks which may be present.

Dismantle pump by removing plugs a1CK177, a1CK179, 1CK182, and 1CK160, examine ball valve seatings and clear all passages, reassemble pump, taking care to see that all parts are clean.

Run compressor and prime pump by removing adjusting valve 1CK158.

AIR TANK

This requires daily attention. See that no water is allowed to accumulate in the tank, but blow it off two or three times per day by the cock provided. Check occasionally during the day that the water in the outside tank is not warm; if it is, allow more cold water to circulate. Carelessness on this point may be very detrimental to the keyboards, because unless the moisture is extracted from the air by being condensed in the tank tubing (and thence blown out), it will be precipitated in the cold interior of the keyboards, and the resultant rust will not only clog the movement of the parts rusted but the dry dust flaking will be blown through the air channels to such an extent that the keyboard will sooner or later become unworkable. The pressure should be maintained at 15 lb., and the exhaust valve and its seating occasionally cleaned to keep the valve working freely. The pipes leading from the air tank to the keyboards should not be too small in diameter, or the speed of the air passing through them will be impeded. For three keyboards a pipe of $\frac{3}{4}''$ inside diameter will be sufficient; for more than three keyboards $1''$ inside diameter is recommended.

Always keep the tap on condenser very slightly open, as this allows moisture to escape before it can accumulate.

CONDENSATION

In certain atmospheric conditions there is a probability of an undesirable amount of condensation accumulating in pipes and cylinder through which compressed air passes. This condensation can become a source of concern where the compressed air is used for operating delicate mechanism.

The condensation is due to excessive lowering of temperature of metallic parts against which compressed air expands when released, so that the moisture in the air settles on the cold metal surfaces. Pipes heated by compressed air during the day may accumulate condensation during a cold night.

Certain precautions can be taken to reduce the condensation, such as by extracting moisture from the air before using it as a source of energy, by passing it through water-cooled pipes.

In regard to the plumbing there should be a gradual decline in the pipes from the compressor to a couple of feet beyond the last point of use (usually the last of a row of keyboards) so that a blow-off cock may be opened before starting each morning and any condensation blown away. The blow-off cock should always be opened at finishing time.

WATER CONSUMPTION

The maximum water consumption on each caster is 3 gallons per hour; on each compressor ($\frac{3}{4}''$) $6\frac{1}{2}$ gallons per hour.

AIR CONSUMPTION

At 15-lb. pressure per square inch the air consumption per keyboard, producing about 8,000 ens per hour, is approximately 1.15 cubic feet per hour.

The air consumption per caster, at 150 r.p.m., is approximately 1.29 cubic feet per hour.

ELECTRIC CURRENT

The caster is usually driven direct by an electric motor and when used on a supply of A.C. single phase a $\frac{3}{4}$ H.P. constant speed motor is used and the speed range is obtained by the interchanging of different diameter pulleys.

With all other electric supplies a $\frac{1}{2}$ H.P. variable speed motor is used.

When the machine is equipped with electrically heated metal pot, the current consumed is approximately 2 units per hour.

DISMANTLING A 'MONOTYPE' CASTER*

TURN MACHINE APPROXIMATELY to zero position (between 360° and 10°). In this position the matrix jaws are just beginning to close and the centring pin lever is at its uppermost position.

Disconnect the air bar clamping lever connecting rod connecting hook 4G1. Cut off water from mould, and run down metal pot, making sure that the metal is completely molten, and swing it clear of mould.

REMOVE MOULD OILER

If screwed pattern lubricating cups are in use, they cannot be removed until the mould is taken off.

Disconnect the crossblock oiler from its anchor and swing clear of the mould.

MATRIX-CASE

Remove bridge lever link pin xa3A, withdraw fibre stop 7A, and disconnect rear end of matrix-case from the cross slide g5CC. Slightly depress the bridge lever b2AA, keep matrix-case towards the centre of carrying frame c4AA, and withdraw the matrix-case. The cross-beam lifting lever 42A1 enables matrix-case to be removed for inspection or any other purpose without removing bridge lever link pin.

BRIDGE

Take out the two screws a1A1, and lift bridge off, taking care not to bend the sliding frame draw rod d9A1.

MOULD

Remove the mould blade operating rod fork pin c16c6, and link connecting the mould crossblock to type carrier. Remove the three screws from mould base, then the two mould clamps a48E and a49E.

---

* These instructions apply to a standard composition caster without optional attachments.

Lift mould off carefully. Remove the two lubricating cups (if screwed pattern) from mould, also the equalizing gear fulcrum block if mould below 20,000 is in use. Thoroughly clean mould, blow water out of the water course, oil the mould and store away in proper box.

NORMAL WEDGE

Press forward the matrix jaw latch c7BB and turn latch upward so that it will rest on top of the matrix jaw. Hold mould blade abutment slide forward by pressing the mould blade abutment slide spring post b14c8 towards mould, and withdraw normal wedge from left of machine.

BUFFERS

Remove front buffer mechanism.

TONGS AND JAWS

First remove connecting link 60E, and then the opposite connecting link 61E. Remove pin jaw tongs spring. Remove nut and washer from pin jaw tongs bell crank stud and remove bell crank. Remove pin jaw tongs by carefully lifting up, without undue strain on any particular point. To remove the matrix jaw tongs first slide back the retaining latches from the matrix jaws.

When removing the matrix jaw tongs, have the tongs nearly parallel at centre of pin blocks. For this turn the machine to about 240°, in which position the stop racks may be moved to any desired position.

FRONT PIN JAWS 16BB AND 17BB

Remove matrix jaw shoe packing block screw a9B3, and matrix jaw shoe packing block shoe a9B4. Loosen the pin jaw guide rod expansion screw b18B1 at end of guide rod, and remove screw a9B7. Remove pin jaw guide rod and pin jaws.

FRONT MATRIX JAWS c5B AND b6B

Take off packing block shoe a9B4, packing block cover 11B2, and then remove the hexagon-headed bolt 11B1 beneath it. Take out two screws 8B1 at *top* of matrix jaw shoe, and screw 8B2 at side of matrix jaw shoe near rear of machine. Lift off matrix jaw shoe 8B, and packing blocks at each end of matrix jaw race.

TYPE PUSHER b29BB

With machine at 360°, take off rear buffer mechanism, then take out split cotter pin at end of type pusher connecting pin a29B6, remove connecting pin, and draw pusher back. Press pusher to the left to clear its bell crank, and draw it back *over* mould blade bell crank. If necessary, pull back the type pusher bell crank by hand when removing type pusher.

F

TRANSFER RODS AND TRANSFER WEDGES

First remove upper transfer wedge and rod. To do this, insert transfer wedge shifter lever arm rod 57D4 in matrix centring pin lever, and turn machine until upper transfer rod has nearly reached its backward limit of travel. Remove nuts at rear end of upper transfer rod and then from metal pot side of machine pull the upper transfer wedge forward, and with it the transfer rod.

When removing the lower transfer wedge and rod do *not* have the transfer wedge shifter lever arm rod engaged in centring pin lever. Turn machine until lower transfer rod has nearly reached its backward limit of travel, remove nuts at rear end of transfer rod, and pull transfer wedge and rod forward from metal pot side of machine. In removing the transfer rods be careful not to lose the tufnol washers a53D3 and a63D4 at end of transfer rods.

JUSTIFICATION WEDGES 10D AND 11D

Remove justification wedge stop block 19D. Engage justification wedge lever arm rods 15D3 in centring pin lever, turn machine until centring pin lever is at its upper position, and withdraw justification wedges from cam side of machine.

JAW TONGS SPRING BOX AND BELL CRANK

Remove nut 22E2 and washer from top of bell crank. Loosen the two clamp bolts 24E2 on top of cam lever. Turn machine till air tower lever a19G is at its highest position (60°). Lift the bell crank lever and spring box up together, and draw towards metal pot, taking care not to bend the justification wedge lever arm rods 15D3.

Do not loosen the clamp bolts 24E2 *too much, otherwise they will foul the casting on their left when the machine is turned.*

REAR PIN JAWS b18CC AND 19CC

Loosen the guide rod expansion screw at end of guide rod, remove clamp screw 23c1, and withdraw guide rod. Take care of guide rod stop a21c.

REAR MATRIX JAWS b8C AND a9C

Turn machine to about 240°, so that locking bars are disengaged from stop racks. Unscrew the cross slide draw rod b5c1 from cross slide, after loosening the lock nut b5c12. Then the two matrix jaws and stop rack may be withdrawn.

CROSS SLIDE g5CC, MOULD BLADE OPERATING ROD a16C AND FORK b16c5, AND MOULD BLADE ABUTMENT SLIDE xd14C

Remove mould blade abutment slide spring 15c. Unscrew operating rod a16c from nut b16c16, and draw rod out without removing the sizing spring 16c10. To do this see that the lock nut is tight on end of mould blade operating rod, and unscrew the rod by means of a wrench on the inside nut. In unscrewing be certain that the *rod* is being unscrewed, otherwise the nuts will be unscrewed, leaving the rod fixed. Next remove the four screws in cross slide guide a7c, and lift cross slide and cross slide guide off together. The mould blade operating rod fork b16c5 and mould blade abutment slide xd14c may now be removed; also the two springs a16c2 and a16c17 and sleeve b16c4.

MOULD BLADE BELL CRANK Xa41E

There is seldom any necessity to remove this, for in doing so the adjustment is disturbed. To remove it when necessary remove nut and washer on top of bell crank stud 42E, take off pin jaw tong spring lever xa62E, unlock the nuts on mould blade connecting rod 45E—one of which has a left-hand thread—and unscrew connecting rod until it comes off.

LOCKING BARS e13B AND d13C AND LOCKING BAR BELL CRANK d28E

Turn machine to about 240° to withdraw the locking bars from the stop racks. Lift up connecting pin a28E3 from rear locking bar d13C, and remove the locking bar in one piece. Next remove the connecting pin from locking bar operating rod eye c33E1, then the connecting pin from front locking bar connecting bar a13B4. Remove bell crank and front locking bar.

TYPE PUSHER BELL CRANK Xa73E

Turn machine until the bell crank is on full rear position (about 360°), and remove the two nuts on end of connecting rod 77E. Do not attempt to remove the lock nut without having a wrench on the inside nut, otherwise the rod will be unscrewed from the bell crank. (*In all cases where there is a lock nut always use two wrenches.*)

JUSTIFICATION WEDGE LEVER ARM BELL CRANKS X4D, X5D, AND X6D

Release wedge lever arm rod springs 16D from their anchorage. Remove bell crank stop screw 6D3, withdraw fulcrum pin a7D and lift bell cranks out.

JUSTIFICATION WEDGE LEVER ARM RODS 15D3 AND JUSTIFICATION WEDGE LEVERS X13D AND X14D

Follow instructions in previous paragraph, then remove the justification wedge lever fulcrum pin 18D, and lift the levers out.

NORMAL WEDGE LOCKING PIN STAND g15B

Take off hexagon-headed bolt 15B1 near path of type pusher, and two small screws 15B6 in path of cross slide. Then drive up the two dowel pins 15B2 from beneath machine base and remove the two screws 15B3 and 15B4. Disconnect the lever arm rod plate 16E2 and remove the transfer wedge shifter lever arm spring 58D. See that the centring pin lever is at its highest position, and lift the locking pin stand off. To do this, lift the stand upward until its base is clear of the pin block, then draw carefully forward until centring pin lever is disengaged from normal wedge locking pin shank a14B7, taking care not to bend the transfer wedge shifter lever arm rod 57D4.

TYPE CARRIER Xd20B

Turn machine to 30°. This may be removed without taking off any part of machine except the bridge. Should the mould happen to be on the machine, it is only necessary to remove the mould crossblock. Take out the eye pin cotter 21B8 and connecting rod forked eye pin 21B7. Next the type carrier shoe long, b23BB, and the type carrier shoe short, b24B. Lift up the spring abutment 21B10, and lift carrier off.

ADJUSTABLE TYPE CHANNEL BLOCK Xa50F

Turn machine until line hook xa19F is clear of type channel and then remove the screw f50F6. Lift block off.

LINE HOOK Xa19F AND LINE CARRYING MECHANISM

First withdraw connecting pin 27F1 from galley cam lever. Remove the stud b28F in line hook by first easing nut at bottom, then holding nut with spanner and unscrewing the bolt with screwdriver till nut comes off, then lift stud out. Take off line hook bar stop a22F at end of galley bracket, remove bar slide and line hook through opening in column pusher (taking care of the small plungers and springs in line hook bar and line hook slide).

COLUMN PUSHER Xc1F

Disconnect line slide, return slide spring box chain. Turn column pusher adjusting cam disc a2F1 to 24 point, lift up the column rule e39FF, and prise up the column pusher spring box x8F. Partly unscrew the two fulcrum screws 4F1 and a4F3, and after having removed the spring attached to the column pusher, lift out the column pusher.

COLUMN RULE e39FF

Screw off all nuts at bottom of lifting rod 39F3 and lift column rule up. In unscrewing the nuts be careful not to bend the column rule guide pin which enters the fixed type channel block a51FF.

FIXED TYPE CHANNEL BLOCK a51FF

If this cannot easily be removed on account of dowel pins having been knocked in too firmly, take off the type channel plate a49F. To do this remove the countersunk screw 49F1 and hexagon-headed bolt a49F2, the head of which will be found underneath the galley bracket. If the dowel pins are not driven in too tightly, there will be no necessity to remove the type channel plate a49F to remove the fixed type channel block.

(For the following instructions it is assumed that all parts on the main stand have been removed with the exception of the parts dealt with.)

AIR PIN PLATE—FRONT a4B

Remove the four screws 4B2. As the two dowels 4B1 are a tight fit in the air pin plate and only a press fit in the pin block, the plate should easily be removed by lightly tapping its end with a piece of wood or lead. If any difficulty is experienced, the four screws 4B2 should be replaced to secure the plate and the dowels removed first by means of the long dowel punch applied from the inside of the machine base.

AIR PIN PLATE—REAR g4C

Proceed in exactly the same manner as for removing air pin plate—front.

AIR PIN BLOCK, JUSTIFICATION COVER PLATE a3D1

Remove the short screw 3D2 and the two long screws 3D3, the cover plate can then be lifted off.

AIR TOWER XXc1G

First remove air tower cam lever stud 53E5, loosen the air pipe expansion elbow nut 1H8 and remove air tower base screws 1G4, a1G22 and four screws 1G14. If it is required to remove air tower whilst retaining some of the parts on main stand the following must be removed in addition to the foregoing: jaw tongs spring box xc26E and mould blade connecting rod 45E.

OIL PAN

To REMOVE OIL PAN turn machine to 150°. Pull oil pan shelf forward, and oil pan may then be lowered and withdrawn. In any other position of machine the cams prevent the oil pan from being withdrawn, even after it has been lowered as described.

ERECTING A 'MONOTYPE' CASTER*

When the machine has been dismantled, as explained, erecting will be made as nearly as possible in reverse order. The operator should now be

---

* These instructions apply to a standard composition caster without optional attachments.

acquainted with the names of parts; if in doubt whilst erecting any section he should refer to the paragraph explaining how that part was to be dismantled.

FIXED CHANNEL BLOCK PLATE a49F

Screw on with cone-headed screw 49F1 and hexagon-headed bolt a49F2. Replace fixed type channel block, and then the column rule, and note that the latter falls freely by its own weight. If it falls stiffly, loosen the screws holding the channel block plate, and tap the plate in the desired direction with a piece of lead or wood, and screw up again. Also see that the column rule lifting rod 39F3 and its guide hole are quite clean.

COLUMN PUSHER XC1F

Place column pusher in position and screw up the fulcrum adjusting screws 4F1 and a4F3 till column pusher has no 'shake' sideways, but will fall back by its own weight. The column pusher is adjusted sideways by the fulcrum screws so that when it is pushed forward the side will just clear the side face of the fixed type channel block by about the thickness of a piece of spool paper, thus allowing a line to be pushed forward without being interrupted by the fixed type channel block, and yet the thinnest type will not get between the end of column pusher and the side of type channel block. Replace the spring that pulls the column pusher back, then with the column rule raised, replace column pusher spring box X8F.

LINE HOOK Xa19F AND LINE CARRYING MECHANISM

First place line hook in an approximate position through column pusher, then insert the line hook slide. Next *partly* insert the line hook bar, with the projecting bar pointing toward the galley cam. Do not forget the plunger and spring. Next get the rear line hook operating slide (the one with the connecting rod attached) and insert the projecting lug into the long slot on lower side of line hook bar, and pass the slides complete in the bearing until the short slot in the line hook bar comes opposite the corresponding short slot in line hook slide. Insert the projecting lug on line hook into the slot of line hook bar. Insert line hook stud b28F and replace lock nut. Turn galley cam to suitable position, and replace connecting pin 27F1. Replace line hook operating bar stop a22F. Turn galley cam until line hook is drawn completely forward, and see that the hooks are adjusted slightly in advance of fixed wall of type channel block; if not, readjust by means of the adjusting screw b22F1. If the line is not drawn sufficiently forward it will not be possible to push it into the galley entrance; if it is drawn too far forward it will cause the line to stop the machine by pressing against the stop slide a44FF.

COLUMN RULE e39FF

Revolve the galley cam b14FF till roller on column rule lever xa40F rests on short flat section of galley cam (underneath), and in this position (which is just before the column pusher recedes) adjust the nuts at bottom of column rule guide rod so that the lower edge of column rule clears top of column pusher by $\frac{1}{64}$″. The order of assembling is: spring, washer, nut, washer, sleeve, washer, nut.

AIR PIN BLOCK, JUSTIFICATION COVER PLATE a3D1

Replace cover plate and secure by means of the two long screws 3D3 and short screw 3D2.

AIR PIN PLATE—FRONT a4B

See that all air pins and springs are assembled in the holes in pin block, particular attention being given to the short spring a2B1 on the underside of the air pin occupying the zero position.

With the two dowels firmly affixed in the air pin plate, press the plate into position on the air pin block and tap lightly with a piece of wood or lead. Secure the plate by means of the four screws 4B2.

AIR PIN PLATE—REAR g4C

Proceed in exactly the same manner as for assembling the air pin plate—front.

When the three air pin plates are assembled and before attaching any other parts to the pin blocks, the air pins should be subjected to an air test to see that all air pins rise and fall quite freely.

NORMAL WEDGE LOCKING PIN STAND g15B

See that the seating is clean, and place in position without force, taking care not to bend the transfer wedge shifter rod. Lightly screw down by two screws 15B4 and 15B3. Replace dowel pins, knock them down firmly, but do not use excessive force, or they may be difficult to remove. Tighten the two screws 15B4 and 15B3. Replace hexagon-headed bolt 15B1 on side near path of type pusher; also the two screws 15B6.

If the dowels are not completely seated they may damage the matrices as they make contact with the mould.

JUSTIFICATION WEDGE LEVER ARM BELL CRANKS X4D, X5D, AND X6D

Assemble the three bell cranks in position, insert fulcrum pin a7D until recess around pin aligns with stop screw hole in casting. Screw up stop screw to secure fulcrum pin. Attach lever arm rod springs to their anchorage on lever arms.

JUSTIFICATION WEDGE LEVER ARM RODS 15D3 AND JUSTIFICATION
    WEDGE LEVERS X13D AND X14D

First see that the screws in fixed centring tooth 12D for justification
wedges are tight, then insert the justification wedge lever X14D, making
sure that the bell cranks are positioned at rear of rock lever b9D1.
Partly insert fulcrum pin 18D, then place on the other justification wedge
lever X13D. Screw up fulcrum pin tightly.

TYPE PUSHER BELL CRANK Xa73E

Place bell crank on fulcrum stud, then see that the ball socket is
properly adjusted. (All ball joints must be quite free, but have no
'shake' over the ball head. If the ball joint is too tight the connecting
rod will quickly break; if too loose there will be a 'hammering' effect
on the ball head.) If not correct, loosen the round lock nut, and adjust
the socket plug; screw the round lock nut up very tightly with pin-
spanner. Place on the connecting rod springs a77E6 and a77E7, then the
small ball socket piece 77E2, and pass rod through eye of cam lever.
Next replace rear piece of ball socket 77E1. Replace two end nuts, but
leave their adjustment until the type pusher is replaced.

LOCKING BARS e13B AND d13C AND LOCKING BAR BELL CRANK
    d28E

Turn machine to about 20° (when type pusher bell crank will be fully
back), and insert front locking bar, then rear locking bar. Then place
the bell crank on its stud. Replace front locking bar connecting pin,
then rear locking bar connecting pin, and finally the operating rod
connecting pin.

MOULD BLADE BELL CRANK Xa41E
MOULD BLADE ABUTMENT SLIDE Xd14C
MOULD BLADE OPERATING ROD a16C AND FORK b16C5
CROSS SLIDE g5CC
CROSS SLIDE GUIDE a7C
CROSS SLIDE EXTENSION SHOE b6CC

Replace mould blade bell crank, and attach the connecting rod 45E.
Leave the adjustment of this connecting rod until the mould is replaced.
(On account of the necessity of re-making this adjustment the mould
blade bell crank should never be removed unless absolutely necessary.)
Next insert the mould blade operating rod ejecting spring abutment
16C3, then from other end of pin block the long ejecting spring a16C2,
ejecting spring sleeve b16C4, mould blade abutment slide, mould blade
operating rod fork b16C5, keeping the large connecting pin hole
towards metal pot. Next place mould blade operating rod nut b16C16
in position in operating rod fork, then the short ejecting spring a16C17.
Connect the cross slide to cross slide guide, and place in position, first

making sure that the cross slide guide cover plate 7c1 is correctly inserted, that is, with recessed section underneath coming towards mould blade. Screw cross slide guide in position. Make certain that the ejecting spring abutment has correctly entered the pin block, then turn machine carefully so that mould blade bell crank is at its full forward position (ejecting position). Prise back the mould blade operating rod fork, so as to compress the ejecting springs a16c2 and a16c17, and screw the mould blade operating rod into the nut in mould blade operating rod fork b16c5. It is possible to tell when the rod has entered the thread of the nut, as it is then not possible to pull the operating rod back. Screw the operating rod tightly into the nut, otherwise it might work loose. Replace cross slide extension shoe b6cc and mould blade abutment spring 15c.

REAR MATRIX JAWS b8c AND a9c
Turn machine until locking bars have receded (about 240°). First replace matrix jaw b8c—the one containing hole for draw rod—then the stop rack, draw rod b5c1 and rear matrix jaw a9c.

REAR PIN JAWS b18cc AND 19cc
Place these jaws one on each side of the stop rack head, place the pin jaw guide rod stop a21c at rear of rear pin jaw. Insert pin jaw guide rod xa20c and fix the clamp screw 23c1. Screw in the pin jaw guide rod expansion screw a20c1 at end of guide rod.

JUSTIFICATION WEDGES 10D AND 11D
If not already done, screw on the centring pin lever plate 16E2. Insert the two justification wedge lever arm rods 15D3 in their slots in matrix centring pin lever, and turn machine until matrix centring pin lever is at its highest position. Place justification wedge 11D in position—the wedge with slight gradient. This wedge will occupy position farthest from galley. Then place justification wedge 10D in position. This wedge will occupy position nearest to galley. Screw on justification wedge stop block 19D. If the justification wedges are transposed, faulty justification will result.

TRANSFER RODS AND TRANSFER WEDGES
From metal pot side of machine pass lower transfer rod b63DD— the longer rod—through eye in transfer wedge shifter 55D, keeping the short slot in rod downward. Before pushing the rod home, place on the lower transfer wedge 62D. Pass the rod through the guide at rear of machine, and place on washer a63D4 *before* passing end of rod into transfer link (short rear link). Fix nuts on end of rod, but in tightening the nuts see that the transfer rod does not become twisted sideways or it will not work freely. Next insert the upper transfer rod. To do this,

keep the short slot in rod facing upward, and insert transfer wedge shifter rod 57D4 into centring pin lever, and turn machine to 60°, so that shifter 55D enters slot in lower transfer rod. Pass upper transfer rod through eye in transfer wedge shifter 55D, on top of lower transfer rod. Attach upper transfer wedge, and pass rod through guide at rear of machine. Insert tufnol washer, and then attach rod to transfer link— long one. Screw up the nuts, taking care that the transfer rod is not twisted as already explained. Turn machine till transfer rod just reaches back position (180°), push rod back by hand, and feel if it springs back freely to its proper position. Both transfer rods should be tested in this manner, as it is essential for perfect justification of lines that these rods work freely. To test the upper transfer rod, the transfer wedge shifter lever arm rod must be inserted in the centring pin lever. When machine is working, look occasionally to see if the nuts have worked loose on end of transfer rods.

JAW TONGS SPRING BOX AND BELL CRANK

Turn machine to 60°, to take paper feed lever to its upper position, and pass spring box along the side of air tower, keeping the bell crank above the justification wedge lever arm rods 15D3. Insert ball extension in cam lever and bell crank on its fulcrum stud simultaneously, and work the two down carefully. See that the square portion of ball extension is square with cam lever, and tighten the cam lever clamp bolts 24E2. Fix nut and washer on bell crank.

FRONT PIN JAWS 16BB AND 17BB

Place one each side of head of stop rack. Put on guide rod, not forgetting the steel abutment sleeve 19B behind rear jaw. Screw up the rod end clamp, also the expansion screw at other end of rod.

FRONT MATRIX JAWS c5B AND b6B

Place matrix jaws in position, one each side of stop rack head. Place packing blocks at each end of jaw race, the square one b10B at rear, and the curved one 11B at front. Place matrix jaw shoe 8B over the jaws, and screw up, preferably the two side screws first, and then the two upper screws. These four screws must be screwed down very firmly. Place on the block cover 11B2 and packing block shoe a9B4, which goes over the hexagon-headed bolt 11B1. See that the jaws are free. If not, there may be grit adhering to them.

TYPE PUSHER AND BUFFERS (REAR)

Reassemble type pusher and rear buffer mechanism.

MATRIX JAW TONGS

The matrix jaw tongs—rear xc38E and front xb37E—may now be replaced. Keep lubricating holes to top. The longer pair of tongs go on front of machine, and shorter tongs at back of machine. Place them over their correct studs, and insert their ends in the matrix jaws. In connecting the tongs to matrix jaws, have machine positioned at 240°, where the jaws may be moved to any desired position, and the tongs will be about parallel at right angles to the matrix jaws. Slide the latches on matrix jaw tongs into position.

PIN JAW TONGS

Place on pin jaw tongs—long xc55E for front of machine, and short xa56E for rear of machine. Lubricating holes to be kept upwards, and studs for spring connecting links to be nearest such spring connecting links. Work tongs down carefully and evenly over the studs; on no account use undue force. Place on the nine washers and ten nuts. Do not forget to place the matrix jaw tongs stud arm a39E3 with spring attached, on the fulcrum stud nearest air tower, the end of plate to rest against front of air tower. No washer is needed on this stud. Screw nuts up firmly, but do not jerk them up, or the studs may break. The pin jaw studs are highly tempered, and will snap easily if too much force is applied in tightening the nuts. Reassemble front buffer mechanism. Place on pin jaw tongs spring lever xa62E and washer and nut.

TYPE CARRIER xd20B

See that the type clamp d26B and type support spring b31B are working freely or type-turning will result. The screws on type clamp shoe must be tight, and beneath the surface of carrier. The type support spring should not touch the type carrier body at the end, nor the type clamp on the sides. Screw the two shoes b23BB and b24B down firmly, but see that the carrier moves freely when tested by hand before connecting it to cam lever, as grit underneath or at the back of the carrier shoes may cause the carrier to become wedged. *Before connecting the type carrier to the cam lever make very certain that the connecting rod spring abutment 21B10 is positioned correctly in its slot.* After connecting the carrier to the cam lever, turn machine gently by hand. If the spring abutment has not been positioned it will make itself known by the machine becoming jammed. *If the spring abutment is not in position the cam lever will be easily broken.* In the long type carrier shoe the left-hand screw is a little shorter than the other two. Connect the type carrier to the cam lever, by passing the connecting pin through the two holes nearest the pin block; the two rear holes are for working the carrier when the DISPLAY TYPE ATTACHMENT is in use.

TYPE PUSHER b29bb

Turn machine to about 360°, so that type pusher bell crank and mould blade bell crank are on full back position, and pass type pusher along, keeping it *above* the mould blade bell crank. If the end prongs of the type pusher have been bent the pusher will not enter its guide. Also if the air pin block has been removed, and the dowel 3b2 has not been driven low enough, it will not be possible to enter the type pusher in its guide. Adjust the travel of type pusher by means of nut 77e3 at end of type pusher bell crank connecting rod so that the end of type pusher comes $\frac{1}{32}''$ beyond the latch a51f3 in type channel. This adjustment is made with machine at 285°. Tighten the lock nut 77e4.

ADJUSTABLE TYPE CHANNEL BLOCK xa50f

Attach this so that type body of the type to be cast is held lightly in the channel.

MOULD BLADE CONNECTING ROD 45e

Fix mould to machine and adjust mould blade connecting rod (if it has been removed) so that at 100°, when type is being ejected into the type carrier, there will be about $\frac{1}{8}''$ clearance between mould blade operating rod distance sleeve a16c1 and mould blade operating rod ejecting spring abutment 16c3. This varies according to wear on mould blade cam and mould blade cam lever roller. When correctly adjusted, after a 4-unit space has been cast (at 340°), the end of mould blade bell crank xa41e will be just clearing the mould blade operating rod sizing spring front abutment 16c13, leaving all wedges free for their next adjustment. Tighten the lock nuts on mould blade connecting rod 45e.

In applying the mould (if numbered below 20,000) screw on the equalizing gear fulcrum block firmly; if these screws become loose they will break. The mould is fixed to machine by three base screws, the shorter one coming underneath mould crossblock. Clean the mould crossblock every morning, and see that the screw connecting the crossblock to the type carrier is not loose.

BRIDGE

Always make certain that there is no dirt or metal adhering to bridge feet, and that the machine bedplate is quite clean beneath bridge feet.

DRAW RODS

Each time the draw rods d9a1 or b5c1 have been removed the first thing to attend to after the bridge is replaced is the adjustment of these draw rods. The draw rod d9a1 attached to the bridge will not get out of adjustment if the nut c9a5 is not permitted to become loose, but each time the rear matrix jaw b8c is removed, the draw rod b5c1 must be adjusted immediately the bridge is replaced, before the machine is turned completely round. Without the air on, turn machine slowly until centring pin begins to seat on the low space 18-unit matrix. Adjust the draw rod until centring pin is approximately central with this low-space matrix. Then turn air on, and position some character matrix over the mould, preferably a matrix in centre of the matrix-case. Turn machine slowly round, and see if centring pin enters matrix coned hole centrally. If not, readjust the draw rod. When correct, very firmly fix the lock nut b5c12. When the draw rods are correctly adjusted the centring pin will enter the matrices without moving the matrix-case. When incorrectly adjusted the centring pin point will become worn on the side; it will also wear the walls of matrix cone holes by having to draw the matrix-case to correct position, which should be done by the draw rods.

PUMP AND GALLEY TRIP MECHANISM XC9D

Remove piston from pump body. Turn machine to 220°, so that pump lever has moved towards rear of machine. Lift piston operating rod crosshead a19H3 by hand, so that the pump rocker arm latch will engage with pump cam lever, taking the latch clear of pump trip tube collar b49D1. Remove the pump trip spring 50D. Place galley trip rod arm rock lever in front of the two ends of justification wedge levers x13D and x14D with flat side of galley trip rod arm rock lever touching the justification wedge levers, and see that the lower end of galley trip rod arm a9D rests between the bars of pump trip operating lever a48DD. Replace pump trip spring 50D.

PUMP TRIP TUBE COLLAR b49D1

When casting type this collar should rest $\frac{1}{32}''$ from side of pump rocker arm latch a33H1 at 100°. If not, move the collar along trip tube a49DD, and tighten firmly. When testing this, the pump hand trip a35H12 should not be latched up. The set screw is reached through hole in machine base just below the mould.

LOCATING DERANGEMENTS

WRONG CHARACTERS BEING CAST

All derangements should be traced to source. For instance, should a caster attendant be getting incorrect characters he must consider all the conditions likely to cause such an occurrence. He should make certain that the keyboard operator has performed his work accurately, *i.e.*, that he has perforated the paper ribbon correctly, that the perforations are in alignment with the side guide perforations, that extra perforations have not been made, that punches have not failed to rise, and that the paper has not been fed on the twist. Being satisfied on these points, place the paper on the crossgirt, as in working position, with paper feed locking lever 12G raised and paper feed pawl ring lug against right-hand stop screw 1G20 and see that the holes in crossgirt are fully uncovered and not partly masked. These conditions being correct, depress the air bar a2GG, and see that the air pins rise and drop quickly. See that the pin jaws do not commence closing before the air pins have blown up. Next examine the jaws to see that they close correctly; also that the spring brakes a26E12 are functioning smoothly, and that no spring box nut or other part has become loose. Also see that the matrix draw rods have not become loose; that the air pressure has not dropped; that the paper is winding up reliably.

Air pins may not be rising or returning freely (test every pin by blowing up each one separately).

On old machines paper dust may have choked the pipes either in air tower or machine base.

Holes in air bar leather packing 2G2 may be choked.

Air-bar clamping lever screw 3G3 may have become loose.

Nuts on the jaw tongs spring box may have become loose.

The characters in matrix-case may not be in the positions as provided for on the keyboard.

Thoroughly examine every detail under the heading of 'PAPER FEED'.

When a line is cast containing incorrect characters, turn machine to 200°, and with paper feed locking lever 12G up, test every row of perforations in that line to see if the perforations come correctly over the holes in crossgirt, and that their corresponding pins rise when the air bar is depressed.

Should the fault be connected with the failure of an air pin to rise or return on the B pin block, the justification will be imperfect.

Should the fault be connected with the failure of an air pin to rise or return on the C pin block the justification will not be affected.

METAL SQUIRTING BETWEEN MATRIX-CASE AND MOULD

When casting large type, or where an unusual number of quads come together, the machine may be running too fast, causing the mould to become over-heated.

Heads of type breaking off in matrix-case, caused through (1) machine casting imperfect type bodies; (2) matrices closed in on the edges of the punching recess.

Bridge not correctly adjusted to mould, or dirt beneath bridge feet.

Centring pin not reaching base of matrix cone holes.

If casting display type the auxiliary spring may not have been applied.

Dirt beneath mould blade, or top of mould badly worn, causing burrs to be cast on type; portions of these burrs gradually adhere to the matrices, preventing the matrices seating perfectly on mould.

The screw in mould crossblock connecting link may have worked loose, or dirt or stray pieces of type may prevent the matrices seating on mould.

When working with a new matrix-case, the matrices may be packed too tightly in matrix-case, preventing individual matrices seating perfectly on mould.

Centring pin may not be entering cone holes of matrices, causing the characters to be cast partly off the type bodies.

The projection or teeth of stop rack may be broken.

Before commencing to cast from a new matrix-case, especially with a new machine, see that the matrix-case hook descends freely over cross slide g5cc from both the quad position and lower-case 'i' position.

Metal too hot, or insufficient water running through the mould.

Metal or oil may be adhering to the faces of matrices, or there may be an accumulation of metal particles on top of mould.

The centring pin may be adjusted incorrectly, or centring pin set too tightly in bushing.

Matrix-case draw rods loose.

Carrying frame guide rods b4A1 not moving freely in bridge bushings a1A6.

Piston spring rod b20H1 may be seized in piston lever operating rod crosshead a19H3.

Matrix jaws failing to close correctly.

METAL SQUIRTING BETWEEN NOZZLE AND MOULD

Assuming the nozzle has been correctly squared up to machine base, and no nuts have become loose on the pump body operating rod a28H, and the spring a27H has not become detached, splashing under the mould is likely to be only due to nozzle not rising exactly in centre of its seating in mould base. In rising slightly out of centre a flat wears on the nozzle, and squirting results, which gradually gets worse. Loosen the nuts on the studs a12H9 beneath each side of pot, take off bridge, mould crossblock, *remove pump body piston,* run pot up, and adjust metal pot until nozzle rises *exactly* in centre of hole in mould base when turning the machine slowly by hand.

HEADS OF TYPE BREAKING OFF

Worn or damaged matrices.

Inferior metal in use.

Hollow type bodies being cast.

Temperature of the metal too high.

Matrix-case not free in sliding frame, or being tight over cross slide plate.

Matrix-case fouling piston guide on pump body (if new pump has been placed in machine).

Piston not working freely or not a good fit, or nozzle and pump body not perfectly clean.

Incorrect setting of sliding frame or cross slide draw rods, preventing centring pin from centring correctly in cone hole of matrix; draw rods may be binding against matrix jaws.

TYPE BEING MARKED OR DAMAGED

Should the type body be scratched, it may be caused by a burr on the fixed or adjustable type channel blocks, by type clamp being burred or not working freely, type clamp spring a26B2 too strong, type support spring b31B too strong or broken, or improper adjustment of type carrier.

In the case of scored type, remove both type channel blocks and cast a few characters. Should they then be perfect, it will prove that the blocks are at fault. The latches a50F2 and a51F3 may be too strong or a burr on either type channel block may cause the trouble. Should the type still be marked when the type channel blocks are removed, the trouble is likely to be connected with the type carrier. This should be removed and examined for the cause.

STOP CASTING—LETTERS NOT BEING CAST, ALTHOUGH PUMP MECH-
ANISM WORKING

Metal too cold; or, when first starting, mould may not have warmed up, thus chilling the nozzle.

Piston not free in pump body; clean off all burnt oil in pump body in path of piston.

Nozzle remaining on mould too long, causing metal to chill in nozzle; lower the upper nuts 28H4 and 28H5, to cause earlier descent of pump body.

Mould blade held up; mould chilled by too much water passing through; defective metal; hole in the nozzle or pump body valve closed.

TYPE TURNING IN TYPE CHANNEL

Adjustable type channel block xa50F may not be properly adjusted to size of type in use.

Latch a50F2 in adjustable type channel block may be strained. The projecting portion of latch should protrude beyond face of block.

Type pusher may not be adjusted correctly. It should push the type $\frac{1}{32}''$ beyond the latch hooks; if pushed too far or not far enough the result will be equally bad.

TYPE FALLING DOWN, BREAKING, AND CHOKING MOUTH OF TYPE
CHANNEL

Read remarks on TYPE TURNING IN TYPE CHANNEL.

Type clamp d26B may be dirty and hanging up.

Type support spring b31B may be strained, too long, or fouling on the side.

The edges of type clamp d26B, or of the carrier (where the type is held), may have become burred.

Type carrier traverse may be wrongly adjusted. (Unlikely if adjustment of connecting rod 21B has not been altered.)

Type may be cast with burrs or hollow at foot.

LINES NOT BEING DRAWN TO GALLEY

When the line hook remains stationary instead of taking the completed line to the galley, and type continues to be cast, examine the following points:

Rock lever b9D1, inside machine base, may have become disarranged.

Rock lever (9D1, if this older pattern is in use) may have been inserted wrong side forward. Keep the curved side towards pulley side of machine.

Galley trip lever adjusting screw 45F1 may have become loose.

Galley cam driving pawl spring 14F5 may have become disconnected.

Nuts on justification wedge lever arm rods 15D3 may have become loose.

Line Hook going to Galley, but not taking line with it.

Stray pieces of type beneath column pusher xc1F may be wedging the line hook.

Dirt in front of line hook projection. This may be cleared after removing the stud b28F and drawing line hook back.

In turning the galley cam b14FF by hand, the line hook will not contact the line if machine has been stopped with the type pusher in type channel. Turn machine till type pusher has receded.

Line not going to Galley (other causes than those mentioned).

When casting large type, after being on small type, the line will stop on reaching the column pusher xc1F if the adjusting disc a2F1 has not been adjusted according to size of type being cast. The same result will also occur if loose type accumulates beneath the column pusher spring box x8F, as the column pusher will not be able to return completely.

The column pusher will not push the line into the galley if the line hook adjusting screw b22F1 is too far in, as the end type will come in front of the channel block a51FF. Neither can the line enter the galley if there is dirt beneath the galley, or if the galley is bent, causing the edge of the galley base plate to be higher than the type channel plate a49F. Also the galley bar x13F should not be adjusted to too narrow a measure at the lower end of galley, or the lines will become jammed.

BURRS ON TYPE

Dirt beneath mould blade, causing mould blade to be slightly higher than blade side blocks. This defect is caused either by working metal

G

too hot, or through having mould blade adjusted downward too loosely; clean the mould.

Matrices not correctly adjusted to mould.

Mould worn on upper surface where matrix is seated. Moulds, especially when they have begun to wear, should be kept to one machine.

Lower end of centring pin bent.

When burrs appear on feet and sides of type, the mould should be sent to The Monotype Corporation Ltd. for repair.

MACHINE CASTING QUADS ONLY

Machine will cast nothing but quads when the air has not been turned on, when the paper feed connecting hook 4G1 is not engaged, or when a piece of blank paper is being passed over air tower.

PUMP NOT FUNCTIONING

Should the pump mechanism remain stationary when it should be operating, i.e., with pump trip handle a35H12 *disengaged from stud* a31F7, *the following are probable causes:*

Pump trip spring 50D in machine base may be disconnected.

Pump trip tube collar b49D1 may have moved along the rod to the front (towards galley side of machine).

Pump trip tube a49DD may have become bent, preventing it sliding freely; or it may require oiling.

PUMP NOT STOPPING, OR MACHINE CASTING ONE OR TWO UN-NECESSARY LETTERS AT END OF LINE

Pump trip tube collar b49D1 may have moved along the rod to the rear (pulley side) of machine.

When the pump trip tube collar is correctly set, the pump mechanism will stop when either justification wedge lever arm rod 15D3 *is inserted in matrix centring pin lever* g16EE, *or when the pump trip hand rod* b35H1H *is latched.*

The nuts on either of the rods 15D3 may have become loose.

PUMP MAKING KNOCKING NOISE

Pump piston hanging up.

Pump body spring rod stop nuts 31H13 set too low down.

PUMP BODY PLUG 23H4 BREAKING

Caused by attempting to remove it when pump body is below molten type metal temperature, and threads are clogged with congealed type metal.

FAULTY ALIGNMENT

This is almost invariably due to running the machine in a careless manner, never troubling to see that essential parts are correctly adjusted or functioning perfectly.

Centring pin not entering cone holes of matrices exactly in centre, or point of centring pin worn or bent.

Matrix-case draw rods allowed to become loose.

Dirt allowed to accumulate in cone holes of matrices.

Locking bars not correctly adjusted.

Matrix-case not correctly adjusted to mould.

Centring pin not correctly adjusted to matrices.

Jaw tongs and spring box incorrectly adjusted, or the spring brakes (wood) a26e12 seized in end of spring box tube.

Mould, the surface badly worn.

Type carrier cam damaged and not holding carrier perfectly still during casting period (seldom likely).

PAPER FEED DEFECTIVE

Paper seating incorrectly on spur wheels. If paper is too wide or too narrow only one side will seat correctly.

See that the character perforations are in alignment with the edge perforations in ribbon.

With the air bar a2GG raised, the locking lever 12G up, and machine turned to about 180°, see that the points of paper feed spurs come exactly in line with centre of holes in crossgirt a1G5G. Should they not do so, examine the following points:

That the pawl spring 13G10 has not become detached.

That the ring a14G works freely, and does not require oiling. If stiff, the projection on the ring may not always reach the stop screw 1G20.

The stop screw (right) 1G20 may have become loose.

The spring and rod in paper feed spring box xc17G may not be working freely.

Connecting the hook 4G1 to stud 3G1 before raising lever 12G.

Air bar a2GG may be clamping the ribbon before it has finished feeding, on account of stop screw 1G20, or studs 2G4, or nuts 2G6 being incorrectly adjusted.

The ribbon may not be winding correctly on paper take-up spool.

IMPERFECT JUSTIFICATION

Assuming the ribbon has been correctly perforated, note that the following are in order:

That the nuts at end of either transfer wedge rod are not loose.

That transfer wedge rods go back freely before mould blade sizing spring 16c10 begins to compress.

That machine is not casting wrong characters. (If so, see points under heading of WRONG CHARACTERS BEING CAST p. 85.)

That the quad is true to size, and galley measure has been correctly adjusted.

That the micrometer adjustment spring 20D7 is not compressed too tightly, thus preventing micrometer wedge seating freely.

That the mould blade abutment adjusting screw c14c1 has not worked loose.

That the transfer wedge shifter lever arm rod 57D4 operates each time a space is required.

That the heads of justification wedges 10D and 11D are being lifted high enough for the matrix jaws to contact them correctly when air is blown through Nos. 13 and 31 perforations.

That the adjusting screw 52D1 in space transfer wedge is not loose, but correctly adjusted.

That the normal wedge corresponds in 'set' with the justifying scale and stopbars used in setting the copy.

That the normal wedge is not damaged, and that the justification wedges are not burred, bent, or transposed.

That the normal wedge locking pin b14BB is not too loose in its bearing.

That the type is being cast without burrs, and that the heads do not overhang the bodies setwise, such as by having, for example, a 10-unit character in a 9-unit row.

That the nuts on the spring-box rod 60D6D have not become loose, and that there is compression on the spring each time the transfer rods are right back or right forward.

PAPER NOT WINDING UP

Flange plate on winding spool x21G may be bent.

Pipe cover plate projection (held by screw 8G4) may be binding on a part of spool flange.

The disc 21G7G in winding spool may have become loose.

Lifting finger 23G3 may not be lifting the pawl 23G1 correctly, or the operating spring 24G may have become damaged or detached.

QUADDING AND CENTRING PISTON NOT RETURNING FREELY

Piston vent gummed up with dried oil.

BLEEDING FEET

Term applied to an excrescence of metal at the foot of a type due to insufficient cooling before ejection from the mould. Happens occasionally on 12-point quad lines. Three remedies are: reduce speed; reduce metal temperature; keep mould cool. *Not to be confused with* SECOND SHOT.

SECOND SHOT
   Term applied to loose pinhead particles of metal in vicinity of the nozzle, or adhering to the foot of an occasional type. Caused chiefly by excessive casting speed or by a weakened pump body spring a31H, either of which may cause a slight overthrow downward flick of the piston, or an upward flick of the pump body at the piston end, whilst the type is being ejected from the mould. End of piston return stroke, 80 degrees; start of type ejection from mould, 70 degrees. *Not to be confused with* BLEEDING FEET.

PISTON SEIZURE
   Mainly due to carbonized oil particles wedging between piston and pump body. Keep piston free of oil or grease before replacing in pump body.

GENERAL INSTRUCTIONS FOR CASTER ATTENDANTS

EVERY MORNING clean the mould crossblock, examine the matrix-case and see that matrix-case draw rods are not loose, that the matrix-case wire retaining plate b8A4 is correctly located, and that the screw in mould crossblock link is not loose.

Before starting machine, remove matrix-case, clean face of matrices and mould with a clean brush or clean rag, and see that all cone holes are perfectly clean.

When changing moulds blow air through mould, water channels, remove crossblock, and carefully clean any foreign matter from mould before placing in its proper box.

Normal wedges should be kept to their respective machines as much as possible; they should not be touched with lap or file, or they will be rendered useless for accurate justification.

Always have the galley gauge set correctly before commencing a job, and then do not alter it.

Always insist that any alteration in the arrangement of the matrix-case layout be written at the end of the spool.

The type as it passes into the galley should be carefully examined to see that no heads are pulled off, and that a perfect face is being cast. The body and feet of type should be examined from time to time to see that they leave nothing to be desired.

Proofs of each galley of type should be pulled as soon as possible after casting, so that any mechanical defect may at once be remedied.

Every time the bridge has been removed and replaced test the alignment before restarting to cast material for use. The surface upon which the types are rested, when testing for alignment, should be quite level, smooth, and free from dirt.

Make certain that the centring pin is entering matrix cone hole exactly in centre.

Centring pins should be tested with a centring pin gauge from time to time, and any burr on point removed.

The pump should always be placed out of action before stopping the machine.

Never attempt to run the metal pot up or down without making sure that the metal is completely molten, or that the nozzle end of pump body is seated correctly.

The metal pot should be lowered away from the mould when machine is not likely to be in use for an indefinite period.

Metal should never be skimmed under casting temperature, and should be thoroughly stirred before skimming.

The metal should be maintained at a constant temperature and level; this is best achieved by fitting the Ingot Feeder Attachment, see p. 234.

Drill the nozzle from both ends daily, whether it appears to be needed or not; if allowed to become heavily carbonized it may be difficult to drill.

Periodically thoroughly clean and drill the pump body.

Drill the pump body and nozzle when cold, in order not to soften the drills.

The caster should be systematically cleaned with dry rag free of grit, and nuts and screws examined occasionally to see that they have not become loose.

Twice a day blow out the water from air tank.

Adjustments of machines must not be tampered with and *in no circumstances should a file be used.*

Never use emery cloth to clean any part of machine.

Cover the machine every night with covers free from dirt or dust.

CLEANING AND LUBRICATING

Lubrication of casters should be carefully attended to daily or excessive wear of parts will take place.

All moving parts should be carefully oiled every morning with good machine oil, and attendants must not forget that the hidden mechanism requires oiling as well as that in view. Special reference may be made concerning the pump bell crank 21H and shaft 21H1, connecting rod yokes 22H1 and 22H3 and pins 22H5, pump operating lever 34H, pump rocker arm latch pin 33H2, and pins 68E5, and galley cam shaft 15FF. *Only special heat-resisting mould oil to be used on moulds.*

The compressor to be lubricated daily.

Jaw tongs spring box wood brakes should be occasionally lubricated by grease gun.

We suggest that users of 'Monotype' casters should allow attendants at least one hour each week for cleaning the machines. The machines should be kept clear of loose or broken type, and surplus oil should be removed with clean rags.

CHANGING FROM ONE SIZE OF COMPOSITION TYPE TO ANOTHER SIZE

THE PARTS TO REMOVE are the mould oiler, matrix-case, bridge, and after unlatching the mould crossblock oiler, the mould, and normal wedge.

Turn machine to approximately zero position (between 360° and 10°). In this position the matrix jaws are just beginning to close and the centring pin lever is at its uppermost position.

Disconnect air bar clamping lever connecting rod connecting hook 4G1.

Cut off water from mould. Run down metal pot, making sure that the metal is completely molten, and swing it clear of mould.

REMOVE MOULD OILER

If screwed pattern lubricating cups are in use, they cannot be removed until the mould is taken off.

Disconnect the crossblock oiler from its anchor and swing clear of the mould.

MATRIX-CASE

Remove bridge lever link pin xa3A, withdraw fibre stop 7A, and disconnect rear end of matrix-case from cross slide g5CC. Slightly depress bridge lever b2AA, keep matrix-case towards centre of carrying frame c4AA, and withdraw matrix-case. The cross-beam lifting lever 42A1 enables matrix-case to be removed for inspection or any other purpose without removing bridge lever link pin.

BRIDGE

Take out the two screws a1A1, and lift bridge off, taking care not to bend the sliding frame draw rod d9A1.

MOULD

Remove mould blade operating rod fork pin c16c6, and link connecting mould crossblock to type carrier. Remove the three screws from mould base, then the two mould clamps a48E and a49E. Lift mould off carefully. Remove the two lubricating cups (if screwed pattern) from mould, also the equalizing gear fulcrum block if mould below 20,000 is in use. Thoroughly clean mould, blow water out of the water course, oil the mould, and store away in proper box.

NORMAL WEDGE

Press forward the matrix jaw latch c7BB and turn latch upward so that it will rest on top of matrix jaw. Hold mould blade abutment slide forward by pressing mould blade abutment slide spring post b14c8 towards mould, and withdraw normal wedge from left of machine.

REPLACING MOULD, MATRIX-CASE AND NORMAL WEDGE

NORMAL WEDGE

Partly insert normal wedge of required 'set', then hold mould blade abutment slide forward by pressing mould blade abutment slide spring post b14c8 towards mould, and slide the normal wedge to position until the end projection comes between the matrix jaws. Push forward the matrix jaw latch c7BB and turn the latch downward so that it will be in position for operating the normal wedge, taking care that the pin b7B1 is under the matrix jaw.

MOULD

Screw on the equalizing gear fulcrum block very tightly, and affix the two lubricating cups (if screwed pattern is in use). If mould oiler is in use it should be replaced after the bridge is screwed on. Make base of mould very clean, and also machine base where mould is positioned. Slightly oil base of mould to prevent rusting in case the water should leak between mould and machine base. Screw on the two mould clamps a48E and a49E but do not use too much force, as they are only meant to position the mould and not to fix it. Screw up very tightly the three mould base screws; the two long screws go into the mould on the mould-blade side of mould, and the short screw on the crossblock side of mould. Connect the mould crossblock to type carrier, and firmly tighten the screw. Replace the mould blade operating rod fork pin c16c6.

Engage crossblock oiler with its anchor attached to rear pin block.

BRIDGE

Lift on the bridge, and in doing so see that (1) the end of the sliding frame draw rod d9A1 is in position in groove of matrix jaw; (2) that the centring pin spring abutment d5A5 enters the fork at end of matrix centring pin lever; (3) that the low space lever and character lever on bridge come one on each side of the low space lever on mould; (4) guide the low space cam into the slot of low space actuating lever. When correctly in position replace bridge screws a1A1.

MATRIX-CASE

Withdraw fibre stop 7A and insert matrix-case, keeping it towards centre of bridge; engage it with cross slide g5CC. Connect bridge lever connecting link 2A1 to bridge lever b2AA.

METAL POT

See that the piston is sliding freely in pump body, and that the nozzle is correctly seated. Hold piston in its uppermost position, and swing metal pot carefully forward; screw up. Turn on water.

Turn column pusher adjusting cam a2F to position according to point size of mould on machine.

Adjust the type channel block according to size of mould. Size up the type, align up, reset draw rods if necessary, adjust galley measure and proceed.

PISTON HANGING UP

Main cause of piston hanging up is the presence of foreign matter between piston and pump body bearing. This may be caused by wiping piston with gritty rag, or by the piston receiving grit as it is passed through the dross on surface of the metal.

It is an incorrect assumption to think that a surfeit of grease on the piston may be effective over a prolonged interval. Grease on a piston is quickly transformed to a residue, which adheres to the pump body bearing and metal channel, wedging the piston and in time choking the pump body and nozzle channels. A brush seems to be most suitable for cleaning a piston, but this should be free of grit.

CAUTION

Never attempt to run the metal pot up or down without making sure that the metal is completely molten, or that the nozzle end of pump body is seated correctly.

SIZING

Should the type be more than one or two thousandths large or small, adjust the mould blade by turning the adjusting screw in the mould blade abutment slide. One nick of adjustment on this screw increases or decreases the size of the type by .002″. If the type is almost correct an adjustment of the micrometer wedge adjusting screw will be quite sufficient. For this reason the micrometer wedge should be in an approximately central position vertically before adjusting the mould blade abutment slide.

ALIGNING

After the mould blade has been correctly adjusted, the face of the type should be correctly aligned on the body of the type. This is done by loosening the centring pin stand bolts 6A3 and turning the centring pin adjusting screws in the desired direction. One complete turn of these screws alters the alignment of the character by .010″ and one nick in the screw gives a difference of .0002″. Each time this adjustment is made the centring pin stand bolts must be tightened before casting type. Keep repeating until correct. It is most important to be assured that all newly-cast type aligns perfectly with type already in use, otherwise any corrections made from the old types will be out of alignment. *The importance of this cannot be impressed too strongly upon attendants.* In the case of a machine being installed, no type should be cast for the cases until the correctness of the alignment has been thoroughly proved, as all future founts must be cast to that standard. The characters must not in the slightest degree overhang any side of the type body.

TYPE LINE

The specimen book of 'Monotype' type faces gives the matrix 'line' of all matrices (such as Series No. 327, 10 point, Line .1338″). This indicates the distance from the rear side of matrix body to the serif line of the character. When correctly aligned the matrix body during casting is exactly central (pointwise) over the mould blade; therefore, where the position of the line on the matrix is known, it is a simple matter to find the position of the line from the rear of the type body. *Example:*

SERIES NO. 327, 10 POINT, LINE .1338″

Line	.1338″
Half of matrix body	.1000″
Line below centre of matrix	.0338″
Half of 10 point (.1383″)	.0692″
Line below centre of 10-point type ..	.0338″
Serif line from rear of 10-point type body	.1030″
Serif line from front of 10-point type body	.0353″
	.1383″

ALIGNMENT GAUGES

Although the use of the set mark matrix has for long been the recognized means of obtaining correct alignment, the present method is to use the special steel flat type alignment gauges sold by The Monotype Corporation Ltd. These are produced for composition matrices in increments of .0005″.

CASTING FOUNTS ON NON-STANDARD BODIES

When casting founts on non-standard bodies such as 10 point on 11 point or 12 point, the matrices should be aligned relatively to the centre of the type body.

In these cases the alignment gauge to use must be equivalent to plus half the difference between the two point sizes. For example: when casting 10 point on 12-point body the alignment gauge should be equivalent to 1 point (.014″) more than that used for the 10 point. When casting 10 point on 11-point body the addition to the 10-point gauge should be ½ point (.007″).

By always casting to the centre of the matrix body excessive alteration in the adjustment of the centring pin and front draw rod is avoided.

ADJUSTING MATRICES TO MOULD

Do not let the matrices hammer on the mould, but let the guide-post bushes take the force of the descent. The matrix wires should never be pressing on the bottom of matrix holes or the matrix face will become hammered, which in time will result in the type heads becoming lengthened or pulled off as the matrix recedes from the mould. It may also cause undue wear on mould surface.

CENTRING PIN

Never commence a job without seeing that the centring pin is entering the matrix correctly, both as to time and position, as an imperfectly adjusted draw rod is the worst cause of mould surface wear. If the bridge setting is correct, the timing need not be considered, but *it is imperative that the pin be tested for entering centrally each time a fresh matrix-case is inserted, or after the adjustment of a draw rod may have been altered.* Should the pin enter the cone slightly to one side it will wear the cone on that side where it strikes, and in time the alignment will be affected. The lock nuts on the matrix-case draw rods should be occasionally tested to see that they have not become loose.

Periodically see that the centring pin is not loose in its bearing. It must not have the slightest side shake, although it must move up and down freely. Test centring pin point with its gauge from time to time. Do not allow any burr to occur, neither must it be too pointed. The point should be slightly ball-shaped to prevent cutting the cone hole walls of the matrices. Defective alignment can be caused by the centring pin point becoming eccentric, or the point becoming worn causing the pin to seat on the matrix-case rods.

To test the truth of the centring pin, cast a roman lower-case 'm'; then turn the pin 90° and cast another 'm'. Repeat until the pin has been turned completely around and four 'm's' have been cast. If they are all of the same alignment the pin is true. (Before making the test be sure that the matrix and point of centring pin are both in good condition.)

TIMING OF CENTRING PIN SEATING AND MOULD BLADE OPENING

The mould blade must be drawn completely back before the centring pin is seated, or there will be undue wear on mould blade and matrices.

LUBRICATION AND GENERAL CARE OF MOULDS

When applying a mould, very slightly oil the mould base and slide it up to its position. Adjust the movable type channel wall to suit the body of type to be cast; also the column pusher.

Upon removing the mould, blow out all water, taking care that this is done thoroughly. If a mould is likely to remain out of use for a considerable time it is advisable to blow a little machine oil through the water-ways. Always put the mould away clean, with the base slightly oiled to prevent rusting. When replacing mould and bridge, see that all the surfaces of contact are *scrupulously clean*. Examine the crossblock to see that the jet piece is clean and working freely, and, in replacing, take care the jet piece does not fall out. Oil the link connecting crossblock to carrier. In replacing the bridge take care not to knock the centring pin on the mould, or the latter may become seriously damaged should the blade or blade walls be struck. If the screwed-on mould lubricators are in use always insert these in the mould before placing mould on machine. Should the mould be over-lubricated, wipe the matrices and the upper surface of the mould with a piece of clean rag, or particles of metal will gradually adhere, causing the type to be cast with a burr. Regulate the water flow so that there is no undue pressure in the mould, or the water may work between parts of the mould where it should not be.

GALLEY MEASURES

The galley measure should be set correctly according to the pica ems to which the keyboard measure was adjusted. The galley measure must be slightly wider than the required pica measure, in order to allow the line to enter the galley easily and to allow for 'squeeze' when the type is locked up later on. (The Monotype Corporation Ltd. supplies sets of standard pica measure gauges, which include special gauges to allow for 'squeeze'.)

If the lines are being cast too long or too short the micrometer wedge may need a slight readjustment, but it is bad practice to alter the adjustment of micrometer wedges excessively in an attempt to rectify an incorrectly adjusted keyboard measure, or an incorrect galley adjustment, as this upsets the justification. For example: assume the type has been sized .001″ large, and that one line containing 100 characters and spaces is followed by a line with 120 characters and spaces, the latter would come out .020″ longer than the former.

POINT MEASURE GAUGES

When locked up in a chase, it is essential that composition, whether hand or 'Monotype', should be compressed uniformly to correct standard measures. To ensure uniformity of galley measures, a set of 'Monotype' point measure gauges should be purchased, as each gauge is machined correct to length, and any measure may be obtained in $\frac{1}{4}$, $\frac{1}{2}$ or complete ems up to 60 ems of pica (the width limit of composition on a 'Monotype' caster).

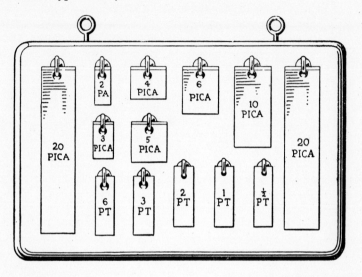

TYPE SQUEEZE

To allow for definite amounts of 'squeeze' (the compression of type in the lock-up) gauges of $\frac{1}{2}$, 1, 2 and 3 points are provided, so that these definite amounts may be added as desired to the column measure in the casting machine.

Allowing for squeeze by *unduly* increasing the galley gauge and adding to the type measurement to correspond is not good practice, as it affects the justification, most noticeably by causing quad lines to be short. Any increase beyond the correct measurement of type puts that increase on *every* type cast, and as quad lines have fewer pieces than non-quad lines the former will be cast shorter than the type lines. In lesser degree this applies to type lines where there is frequently a considerable variation in the number of types in two adjacent lines. In the forme lock-up type lines should squeeze up evenly to the quad lines, and should not be shorter or longer than the correct pica measure.

If adding units at the keyboard to allow for squeeze is adopted, different allowances must be made according to the set in use. For example: if it is accepted that the allowance for squeeze for a 60-pica measure should not exceed three units for 12 set, the allowance for the same pica measure in 6 set should be six units of set, and a proportionate allowance for any other set. A 20-pica measure would thus require one unit allowance for 12 set, or $1\frac{1}{2}$ units for 8 set—the operator in this case choosing between one or two units.

The necessity for providing for squeeze in lock-up is usually evident in wide measures, and is generally due to a worn mould casting microscopic burrs on the corners of the type bodies, or to over-lubrication of the mould causing the types to be covered with an excess of oil. The types are consequently not closely packed, and appear too long to enter the galley gauge. The operator then reduces the type size to cause the line to enter the galley gauge freely, but when the forme is locked up the lines naturally appear to be unduly short of the required pica measure.

The moral is: *keep the mould in good order.*

CARE OF MATRICES

PROPERLY TREATED these will last for years.

To provide against undue wear take care that the matrix-case draw rods are adjusted so that the matrix-case is brought exactly into position for the centring pin to enter a matrix without pulling it sideways in any direction, and that the timing of the centring pin for seating in the matrix is correct; also particular attention must be paid to the setting of the bridge and to all adjustments connected with the positioning of the matrix-case. Having done this, the parts concerned should be examined daily in case any may have become loose; any slackness is sure to cause imperfect results.

The correctness of matrix-case adjustments should be tested on matrices at opposite ends of the matrix-case before causing the machine to make one single revolution by power.

Careful attention should be paid by the attendant to the adjustment of the matrix jaws, pin jaws and the centring pin. The latter should always enter centrally in the cone holes, or a set of matrices may very quickly be rendered useless for good work.

To enable the centring pin to function correctly it must be seated in the matrix just *before* the matrix has descended sufficiently to touch the mould, otherwise undue wear on both mould and matrices will be the inevitable result. Undue 'hammering' on the mould bruises the faces of the matrices in time, causing the heads of the types to lengthen or break off as the matrix-case rises after each casting.

Matrices should be thoroughly brushed before being inserted in the machine, and cleaned every morning when in continual use, otherwise grit may accumulate between them and cause excessive wear. Examine the cone holes to see that no metal or other foreign matter is deposited there, *as this will affect the alignment of the type cast from such matrices.*

The best method of cleaning matrices is to wash them in clean paraffin, and then to blow out from the cone holes and faces the loosened dirt by compressed air.

Oil should be kept from the face of matrices as much as possible while the machine is running, as it causes burrs to be cast on the type between matrix and mould.

If by chance a character breaks off in its matrix, the matrix should not be dipped in the metal pot, as this softens the matrix. The following procedure should be adopted: place both justifying wedges in the 18-unit position, perforate the paper ribbon so as to locate the matrix which is to be cleared, bring the space transfer wedge into operation, and give machine a few revolutions with the pump mechanism in action. This generally clears the matrix.

On no account should the matrix be struck against anything hard. Should a matrix become damaged in a manner likely to affect the precision of the type to be cast from it, it should at once be discarded and replaced. The use of a scriber for clearing damaged matrices should not be permitted.

When not in use, store loose matrices in a dust-free cabinet. If stored flat, keep the cone holes facing downward.

The tendency to grow careless in handling matrices as soon as the sheen of newness has worn off must be resisted. They have more bearing on the appearance of the product than any part of the machine, not excepting the mould.

Before inserting a matrix-case in the machine:

(1) Be certain that every matrix wire has been inserted, and that the spring clip which prevents these wires from working out has been placed securely in position.

(2) See that matrix-case enters the bridge freely.

(3) Make it a rule, where possible, to use the same mould, matrices and normal wedge together on same machine.

When the bridge has been removed, wipe the centring pin before replacing the bridge on machine.

New matrices should not be used on a mould that is indented by wear on matrix seat, as this will cause the type to be cast with burrs on its upper corners, and the corners of the matrices will be damaged. The matrix seat on mould should always be flat; this will greatly prolong the life of the matrices.

It is not advisable to cast type on a worn mould of larger point size than the body size of matrices (such as 10 point on a 12-point mould), as the indentation on the mould may damage the face of the matrix bodies. In these cases 'leading' the type is preferable, and avoids the necessity for special cases of type for corrections.

On no account should a matrix wire be visible through the base of a cone hole. This indicates a worn centring pin.

To prevent matrices becoming damaged, spare matrix-cases should be kept sideways in racks in a dust-proof cabinet, which is preferable to keeping them loosely in a drawer or cupboard.

When oiling the centring pin, care must be taken that the oil does not run into the cone holes of the matrices.

When removing or replacing the bridge, be careful not to strain or bend the centring pin. A bent centring pin point is a principal cause of mould wear and of burrs between matrix and mould, as the bent centring pin causes the matrix to meet the mould at one edge.

IMPERFECT JUSTIFICATION

PROVIDED THE KEYBOARD has been functioning and operated correctly, imperfect justification is unlikely if the following conditions exist. The wedges must not be damaged, and must be kept clean; the type must be cast true to size; the normal wedge locking pin must not be a 'loose' fit in its bearing. The transfer wedge rods must be drawn freely back before the mould blade is operated, and the nuts at the end of transfer rods must not be loose. The upper transfer wedge must be correctly adjusted. Justification wedges must be taken to correct positions. The mould blade must slide freely, and type must be cast without burrs.

Lines will be cast incorrectly justified if the keyboard and caster measures do not correspond, or if the wrong justifying scale has been used. On the caster a similar result will take place if the wrong normal wedge is in use, if the type has not been sized correctly, or if the space transfer wedge is not correctly adjusted. With a badly adjusted machine there are other causes. It is to be assumed the moulds are maintained in good working condition.

CONVERTING DECIMALS TO JUSTIFICATION WEDGE ADJUSTMENTS

A simple method of converting decimal measurements to half-thousandths for justification wedge adjustments is as follows:

Part off the 'thousandths' (first three decimal figures), and multiply these by 2. If the 4th and 5th figures are under .00025 ignore them; if .00025 and under .00075, add 1; if .00075 and over, add 2. Divide the total by 15, and the *quotient* will indicate the movement required on the .0075 wedge, and the *remainder* will indicate the movement required on the .0005 wedge.

Find 'constant' for 9¾ set.

$$.014.98 = 2 \text{ units } 9¾ \text{ set}$$
$$\times \quad 2$$
$$\overline{\quad 28 \quad}$$
$$+ \quad 2$$
$$15)\overline{30} \text{ half-thousandths}$$
$$\quad\quad 2 \quad 3/8 \text{ minus } 2/0 = 1/8.$$

Find 'constant' for 8½ set.

$$.013.06 = 2 \text{ units } 8½ \text{ set}$$
$$\times \quad 2$$
$$15)\overline{26}$$
$$\quad 1/11 \quad 3/8 \text{ minus } 1/11 = 1/12$$

When increasing or decreasing widths of type start from 3/8 (the positions of the justification wedges at which the space transfer wedge is adjusted). This adjustment is equivalent to 2 units of 12 set.

$$.018.44 = 2 \text{ units } 12 \text{ set}$$
$$\times \quad 2$$
$$\overline{\quad 36 \quad}$$
$$+ \quad 1$$
$$15)\overline{37} \text{ half-thousandths}$$
$$\quad 2/7 \quad 3/8 \text{ minus } 2/7 = 1/1$$

Find justification for line 8½ set, 10 units short, 8 spaces. 'Constant' 1/12.

$$8).065.32 = 10 \text{ units } 8½ \text{ set}$$
$$\overline{.008.16} = \text{ addition per space}$$
$$\times \quad 2$$
$$15)\overline{16}$$
$$\quad 1/1 \quad 1/12 \text{ plus } 1/1 = 2/13$$

NORMAL WEDGE MARKINGS

A 'MONOTYPE' STANDARD MATRIX-CASE contains fifteen rows, and all the matrices in each row are of a given unit value. In general practice the progression of units is from the smallest unit (5) to the largest unit (18), some rows (such as 9 units or 10 units) being duplicated, on account of the large number of characters usually designed to these two thicknesses. Each normal wedge is marked to indicate the unit arrangement to which the wedge is designed.

Wedges based on 12 point at .166″ are marked with a single capital letter, such as A, B, K, S, etc.; wedges based on 12 point at .1667″ are marked with double capitals, such as AB, AT, BC.

H

NEW STYLE

Normal wedges are now marked with two numbers near the lug which is engaged by the matrix jaws, thus: 364–6¾.

The first number (such as 364) indicates the number of the stopbar case to be used with the wedge. The second number (such as 6¾) indicates the set.

A further number (such as 18), on the same face of the wedge but near the other end, indicates the unit value of the quad position.

Standard wedges are based upon 12 point = .166″. Where the wedges are based upon Pica = .1667″, 'E' follows the set number, thus: 364–6¾E.

PRODUCTION OF GOOD TYPE

TO BE CONSIDERED PERFECT a type must possess the following attributes:

(1) It must be quite solid, have sharp corners, a solid and flat foot, the face sharp and well defined, and cast from metal neither too soft nor too brittle.

(2) It must be *square* in all directions, exact to size pointwise and setwise, and of correct height from foot to face of character.

Of first importance in governing the quality of the type produced is the adjustment of the pump connections; after that everything depends on the attendant and the metal he is using.

Principal causes of imperfect type are: (1) poor quality metal; (2) foul nozzle or pump body channel; (3) worn piston or pump body bearing; (4) insufficient piston pressure to overcome air resistance in mould; (5) some part of pump mechanism not working freely; (6) water leakage below mould blade side blocks.

In the case of imperfect type, make sure of the following points: that a suitable quantity of metal enters below the pump body piston, and that no dross has accumulated in the piston inlet, piston base, valve face and seating, pump body channel, or nozzle channel. The pump body should be cleaned regularly, and a drill run up the main channel till it can be seen at the nozzle end. The nozzle should be drilled every day whether it appears to require it or not. If dross is allowed to accumulate unduly in the nozzle it may become difficult to drill.

All pump connections should be free and kept well oiled. The piston must slide freely in pump body, but should never be filed or cleaned with an abrasive. Before replacing a piston, warm it, and see that it is clean.

Never attempt to run the pot up or down without making sure that the metal in it is completely molten, or that the nozzle end of pump body is seated correctly.

CARE OF METAL

The metal in the pot should be kept clean and completely molten when the caster is in use. In molten printing metal, the tin and antimony are completely dissolved and do not tend to separate. However, the metal may get chilled, for example, by the addition of fresh ingots, or by a current of cold air passing over the surface. It may then happen that some parts of the metal cool below the temperature at which freezing commences, with the result that crystals of tin-antimony form. These crystals being light, float upwards and collect as a scum on the surface. Severe separation not only leads to loss of the hard tin-antimony constituent but interferes with the proper working of the pump and leads to the production of hollow type. The important points, therefore, are to maintain the temperature, to avoid chilling by the sudden addition of a lot of cold metal and to puddle the metal occasionally to help dissolve any tin-antimony crystals which may form. Do not attempt to clean the metal in the caster melting pot; any skimmings should be remelted with type. Be careful of nostrums advocated for cleansing the metal. If they contain acids or salts the pump body valve may become corroded, and the small hole in the latter will become enlarged. The main point is to keep the antimony well mixed with the lead. Being lighter, it has a tendency to rise and oxidize. Occasional puddling maintains the mixture, and assists the dirt in the metal to rise to the surface. The practice of dipping the piston in vaseline and other lubricants is much overdone, as the oil carbonizes on the piston and in the pump body channel, in time causing the latter to become choked. Simply brush the piston end with a brush, and before inserting the piston, skim away any dross above the pump body boring so that the piston may enter clean metal and not carry dross down with it.

Regulate the metal passing through the piston so that the type is solid and too much metal does not remain in nozzle. In the latter event, stop-casting may result. When casting small type the piston should have a short, sharp stroke, which will slightly lengthen when casting larger type. As it is impossible to see the metal entering beneath the piston any idea of the action that takes place must be based on theory, and this gives the attendant scope for reflection and deduction.

Never attempt to run the pot up or down without making sure that the metal is completely molten, or that the nozzle end of pump body is seated correctly. The nozzle should be a perfectly vertical fit in mould base. The dross which accumulates on the surface of the metal near the nozzle should be cleared away so as to allow the jet pieces from the mould to melt quickly. In the case of metal squirting over the nozzle, or the jets not being melted, the latter may accumulate so that it is not possible to eject any more, and the crossblock will in consequence become wedged. In this event do not force the machine round, as this might break the type carrier lever; run the pot down and clear away all the jet pieces from the opening in the mould through which they fall.

TYPE HEIGHT

The height of type depends upon the height of the mould blade and the depth of matrix punching. These are fixed quantities, and will only alter through wear, which should be very slight over a prolonged period if care and attention are given to the adjustment of matrix-case to mould, and to matrix-case draw rod adjustment.

The standard height for English 'Monotype' type, from foot to face of character, is .918″, and when moulds are producing type more than .002″ less than this they should be sent for repair.

Low space height is .750″, so that low quads may be used for mounting electros and stereos 12 points thick. The depth of composition matrix punching (under 24 point) is .050″.

DISPLAY TYPE CASTING

THE PRODUCTION of display type on a 'Monotype' caster, equal to the best type sold by typefounders, is possible by employing high pump piston pressure. In addition to obtaining the advantages of solid type, the application of strong spring pressure enables casting to be made at a lower temperature, thereby increasing the life of the matrices, which may be damaged by casting from overheated metal.

Excessive caster speed results in hollow display type, as the return stroke of the piston sucks back any molten metal not thoroughly sealed at the foot of the type body. This backflow is assisted by expansion of the compressed air which becomes trapped in the type body during casting. The speeds given in the CHANGE SPEED GEAR TABLE (p. 213) are maximum speeds, and on no account should they be exceeded. In some cases one speed less should be employed, according to the quality of metal in use.

HOLLOW TYPE BODIES

The presence of hollow type bodies is due to two main causes: (1) insufficient piston pressure to expel the air which rests above the metal in the pump body channel and in the mould; (2) back suction of the return stroke of piston before the foot of the type is sufficiently sealed.

In favourable conditions the piston pressure overcomes air resistance, either expelling it or compressing it into almost undetectable globules. The pressure of these globules is temporarily increased by the heat of the molten metal, so that if there is any relaxing of air imprisonment conditions, such as by a too early return of the piston, or too early ejection of the type from the mould, the compressed air in the type body starts to expel any molten metal through the weakest point of sealing, which is usually where the jet has been sheared.

When casting large display type at an excessive metal temperature, or at too fast a rate, the trapped air may bulge or burst the type immediately it is ejected from the mould.

The inference, therefore, is not to sacrifice quality for speed, but to keep the temperature of the metal at a reasonable level, and see that pump body and piston conditions are satisfactory and that the quality of metal is up to a reasonable standard.

SORTS CASTING ON A 'MONOTYPE' MACHINE

A greater production is obtained in a given time by casting type from a complete set of matrices arranged in the matrix-case than from a matrix-holder containing a single matrix. In the former case, the change from one matrix to another can be made so quickly that overheating the matrices may be avoided by not casting too continuously from any individual matrix.

The position of the matrix is indicated on the layout sheet and the matrix-case is positioned accordingly, as indicated on the 'B' and 'C' air pin blocks.

The normal wedge corresponding with the set of matrices in use must be positioned according to the unit row that the matrix occupies in the matrix-case.

METAL HINTS

THE FIRST USE of a 'Monotype' caster was for composition work and metal containing 6–7 per cent tin, 15 per cent antimony, remainder lead was found to be suitable and was generally adopted. The development of Display machines and Display attachments led to the practice of using a separate, harder metal for case type, frequently 9 per cent tin, 19 per cent antimony, 72 per cent lead. In the course of time, many 'Monotype' users adopted one grade of metal for composition and case type, using the higher grade 9 per cent tin, 19 per cent antimony alloy with obvious advantages. It was recognized, however, that while the harder metal can give excellent results, it is rather more difficult to cast solid type consistently day in and day out.

More recently, the alloy 10 per cent tin, 16 per cent antimony, 74 per cent lead has become popular as a dual purpose metal in preference to the 9 per cent tin, 19 per cent antimony alloy. The fundamental importance of solidity of the type has been more clearly realized and it is easier to maintain such solidity with the 10 per cent tin, 16 per cent antimony alloy which allows for a lower casting temperature and is easier to handle. This is particularly the case in ordinary commercial conditions and the alloy is especially advantageous for the production of rule and leads.

When it is known that a job, such as a catalogue or time table, will be reprinted with additions or corrections it is often worth while to use a special high grade and wear-resistant metal. Thirteen per cent tin, 17 per cent antimony, 70 per cent lead is an excellent formula for this purpose. The relatively high proportion of tin makes the metal tough as well as fluid. It is an easy metal to cast and produces very clean, hard-wearing type.

For display type, 14 to 36 point, the formula for a good hard metal is 12 per cent tin, 24 per cent antimony, 0.5 per cent copper. The copper content gives additional hardness but must be carefully controlled as too much copper will cause trouble in casting. For this reason, foundry type, which often contains an appreciable proportion of copper, should not be re-melted with 'Monotype' metal.

The characteristics and properties of the alloys are discussed in greater detail later, p. 196 onwards.

SKIMMING

Never skim metal under a temperature of 730°, for if this is done a large part of the skimmings will be antimony. Always stir and puddle the metal thoroughly before skimming. The dross should be taken off in a perforated ladle, pressed to free the good metal and put into a suitable container.

RE-MELTING

Do not make use of the melting pot on a 'Monotype' caster for re-melting used metal into ingots. A suitable re-melting pot of reliable make should be installed for this purpose.

The type for re-melting will carry ink and may be mixed with paper, dirt and other matter. The object is to separate these non-metallic materials and produce good clean metal for re-use. To achieve this, it is essential to raise the temperature above that normally used for casting, to stir the metal thoroughly and to use a suitable flux.

Although the metal can be cleaned in this way, the re-melting operation should not be expected to free the metal from metallic impurities picked up in handling. Such work cannot satisfactorily be carried out without complicated equipment.

The greatest care is therefore required to keep any metals other than the type metal out of the re-melting pot. On no account should half-tone plates, brass rule, zincos or aluminium cuttings, etc., be allowed to become mixed with used type before re-melting, as the metal may become so polluted that it must be returned for refining. Zinc in particular is 'poisonous' to type metal.

The quality of the alloy obviously changes if mixed with line-cast slugs, stereos or other differently constituted alloys; these also should be kept out of the melting pot when type is being treated.

The final requisite in good re-melting practice is to bring the composition of the metal up to standard. In use, the tin and antimony contents of the alloy tend to fall, for reasons which are explained in the section on metal, p. 196. If this depreciation is not made good, there will be a progressive deterioration in the quality of the alloy. This explains the need for rejuvenation by the addition of 'reviving alloy', which has high tin and antimony contents to counteract the loss.

The composition of the reviving alloy is based on experience of the depreciation which occurs in average working conditions. The best procedure is to add a suitable quantity of the reviver to each potful of metal as it is melted. In this way, the stock is kept uniform. If the depreciation is allowed to continue until its effects are noticed in the quality of the type, a large addition of reviver will be required and furthermore, the stock, which will not all have been used to the same extent, will not be uniform.

The whole subject of re-melting equipment and procedure is dealt with in the notes on metal, p. 196. It may suffice here to say that the operation is an important one which, while not difficult to carry out, should be in the hands of a competent melter. The primary object is the maintenance of a supply of good clean metal to the composing room. The secondary object is to collect the dirt and oxides into a dross containing as little good metal as posible. This dross can be accumulated and sold. Losses in dross are kept to a minimum by attention to temperature, neither overheating nor underheating the metal, and by proper fluxing treatment.

To summarize, keep the metal up to standard; avoid contamination from foreign metals or alloys: revive the metal regularly, and have an occasional analysis made to check the composition and do not over-heat it nor skim it at too low a temperature: remember that a deficiency of tin results in poor type face, a deficiency of antimony produces softer type bodies.

CARBONIZING OF PISTON END AND PUMP BODY CHANNELS

It has been customary to remove the piston from the metal pot before periods of rest, such as the lunch-hour or when work is finished in the evening. It has also been considered beneficial to wipe the piston with a clean oily rag and then to dip it in some heat-resisting lubricant before replacing the piston in the pump body.

But a new line of thought has been advanced by several competent attendants who claim that it is a more practical proposition not to remove the piston all the while it is functioning satisfactorily. This suggestion is based on the theory that when the piston is being replaced particles of surface dross get taken down with it, and these are apt to become wedged between the piston and pump body bearing. Also oil adhering to the piston after being wiped with an oily rag, or by dipping the piston in so-called heat-resisting preparations containing a high percentage of graphite, soap, or other ingredients, is quickly converted to a grease-charged vapour which flows with the metal and settles in a carbonized layer on the surface of the metal passages in the piston, pump body, and nozzle, rendering frequent drilling an imperative necessity.

These arguments seem perfectly logical, because if there is no substance on the submerged section of the piston that can be completely or partially vaporized or oxidized the passages for the metal cannot become clogged. No oil or grease can function as a lubricant in the highly heated metal for more than a few seconds. Also in replacing a piston, it is difficult not to take down with it a percentage of surface dross, in spite of efforts to provide a clean entry for the piston.

As there is much to be said in favour of these arguments they are included in this book.

TEMPERATURE OF METAL AND MOULD

These temperatures are variable, and no exact rule can be given that will answer in *all* cases; they vary with different sizes of type and according to the speed of the machine. This most particularly applies to the mould, for the larger the type cast or the higher the rate at which the machine is running the greater the quantity of metal that will be passed through it in a given time; a greater flow of water will consequently be necessary to keep the mould at the proper casting temperature. The mould should be kept at a heat consistent with good working. It must not be so hot as to cause the mould blade to hang up or the cross-block to bind; on the other hand, the types must be sufficiently cooled whilst in the mould to ensure that they do not burst or swell during their transit from mould to type channel. There are two limits to the temperature of the metal in the pot: (1) the lower limit, at which the machine will not cast, and (2) the higher limit, at which the mould becomes overheated to such a degree that the types are insufficiently cooled before being ejected from the mould, causing them to blister and burst. Between these limits lies the correct temperature.

The proper temperature is judged from the appearance and quality of type produced. If the type has a frosted appearance, and the corners are not well defined, the temperature is too low; if, on the other hand, the type is very bright but shows signs of blistering, the temperature is too high. The ideal to be aimed at is that in which the type is solid and not blown and the corners are well defined. Having obtained type fulfilling these requirements, attention must be paid to the face, that is, the character, which must be sharp and well defined, every part of the outline showing clear and distinct. If defective, the fault most likely lies in one of the following causes: the temperature of metal or mould too low, the metal dirty, the nozzle not clear, oil on the face of the matrices, or a foul piston. Examine the piston first; then raise the temperature of the metal and regulate the flow of water through the mould accordingly. By strengthening the piston spring, the face of the type is often improved, but care should be taken in this connection as extra spring pressure results in an increased load being put upon the machine at one particular point of its revolution, making it work in a jerky manner, besides causing excessive wear on the pump levers and their connecting eyes. The pump spring should be worked with the minimum compression consistent with good results.

Given satisfactory type metal, the main factor in obtaining good results is the temperature, which, in turn, depends upon the intelligence and care of the attendant. When the temperature has been arrived at which gives the best results it should be noted and maintained throughout the run. As a general rule, it may be taken that best results are obtained with a temperature ranging from 660° F. for 12 point to 700° for 6 point. The latter is the maximum temperature for composition and should not be exceeded.

ELECTRIC MELTING POT ATTACHMENT

THIS ATTACHMENT CONSISTS of a melting pot in which two elements are attached to a connecting box, and a box containing an automatic temperature regulator, double-pole switch and ammeter.

The connecting box is inverted on machines equipped with lead and rule attachment.

CHANGING THE ELEMENTS

If an element gives trouble, unscrew the cover of the connecting box and detect the faulty element with the aid of a testing lamp. Having done this, remove the pump body and plunger and empty the melting pot, remove the pump body lifting levers c25HH and b26HH, disconnect the cable on connecting box, release element from connecting box and release the clips holding element in position. Then attach a new element and reassemble all parts.

If facilities are not available for quickly detecting the faulty element, it is advisable to disconnect the two wires on the connecting box, remove both elements complete with box and replace with a spare set.

AUTOMATIC TEMPERATURE REGULATOR

A steel bulb containing mercury is inserted in the melting pot and connected to the automatic regulator by a metal tube of very fine bore; the other end of this tube is connected to a spiral. As the mercury in the bulb is expanded by the heat the spiral tends to unwind and press against a lever, which will then start to tilt a small glass tube containing mercury. In this glass tube there are two pockets into which the terminals are fixed. When the tube is horizontal, the mercury content extends from one pocket to the other and makes contact. When the tube is tilted by the movement of the spiral, the mercury accumulates over one pocket and breaks contact with the other.

The temperature at which the metal is to be kept can be adjusted by loosening the locking nut and moving the indicator to the desired position on the graduated scale.

'ROTOTHERM' THERMOMETER

A useful adjunct to the gas heat regulator or electric heater is a 'Rototherm' thermometer, which is used as an occasional check on the reliability of the automatic heating fixtures. The 'Rototherm' registers the temperatures plainly, in large figures on a flat horizontal disc.

The thermometer should not be immersed in the type metal for indefinite periods, as the type metal penetrates the sealing compound used on the lower end of the thermometer, with subsequent damage to the sensitive bimetal multi-helix element.

If the thermometer is required for continual use it should be used in conjunction with the sheath 12CT5T which protects the delicate mechanism.

The sheath is supported by a modified support b12CT3 opened out to make the necessary accommodation.

CENTIGRADE AND FAHRENHEIT

To convert Fahrenheit to Centigrade: deduct 32, multiply by 5, divide by 9. To convert Centigrade to Fahrenheit: multiply by 9, divide by 5, add 32. *Example:* 60° Cent. = 140° Fahr.

TYPE FEATURES

THE FOLLOWING DIAGRAM illustrates all the main features of a type:

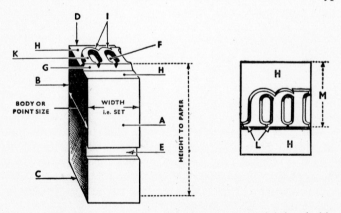

(A) front (of body), (B) back (of body), (C) foot, (D) head, (E) nick, (F) counter, (G) beard (shows depth of drive), (H) shoulder, (I) hair line, (K) main stroke, (L) serif, (M) type line.

DEPTH OF PUNCHING

For 'Monotype' composing machines the depth of matrix punching for 24 point and under is .050″; for hand composition 36 point and under, .050″; over 36 point, .065″.

MATRICES

SIDE WALLS ON COMPOSITION MATRICES

Composition matrices are punched a certain distance from one particular side of the matrix body. With a few exceptions the following side walls apply:

In English founts from 5 point to 11 point inclusive, the standard side wall measurement is .035″; in 12-point founts it is .025″. In some large type composition matrices the side wall is reduced to .015″.

Didot roman founts from Didot 5-point to Didot 10-point inclusive have .035″ side wall; Didot 11-point .025″; and Didot 12-point .015″.

Didot Fraktur founts correspond with the English: Didot 5-point to Didot 11-point, .035″; Didot 12-point, .025″.

TYPE HEIGHT

ALL ENGLISH 'MONOTYPE' composition moulds are made to cast type .9195″ high. This is slightly higher than foundry type height, which is .9185″. Display type moulds are made to cast type .918″ high, as there is practically no wear on the upper surface of these moulds.

The amount that a mould can be lower than this and yet be used depends entirely upon the class of matter run with it. If the type made by the mould is to be used with foundry or other 'Monotype' type with cuts, or to correct standing matter, the mould should not be allowed to wear so that it casts type less than .916″.

A useful form for a monthly record of checkings of the heights of moulds is shown on p. 292.

'MONOTYPE' TYPE UNITS

THE BASE UNIT of 'Monotype' founts is .0007685″. This is 1 unit of 1 point. A 'unit' is the 18th part of an em quad. By multiplying the measurement of 1 unit of 1 point by any number the unit value of any larger set is obtained. Thus: .0007685″ multiplied by 8½ gives .0065324″ as the measurement of 1 unit of 8½ set, and the em quad would be .1175″ (taken to the fourth decimal position).

An em quad in printers' language is a space which in width equals the point size of the type; in other words, it is perfectly square in section. 'Monotype' ems are 18 units wide, and are only square when the 'set' equals the body point size, such as 8 point 8 set. They are *not* square when the 'set' does not equal the body point size, such as 8 point 8½ set, or 8 point 7¾ set, the width of the former being greater than the body point size and the latter narrower. 'Monotype' figures are usually 9 units wide, or half the width of the em, but figures of various unit widths are available.

TYPE BODY SIZES

Lines to Inch		Pts.	Eng. & Amer.		English (Old)				Didot Pts.	
14.4	..	.. 5	.0692	..	.066	Pearl ..	..	..	.074	5
13	..	.. 5½	.0761	..	.0725	Ruby ..	..	..	.0888	6
12	..	.. 6	.083	..	.0833	Nonpareil	..	..	.1036	7
10.3	..	.. 7	.0969	..	.0972	Minion	..	..	.1184	8
•9	..	.. 8	.1107	..	.1083	Brevier	..	..	.1332	9
8	..	.. 9	.1245	• ..	.118	Bourgeois	..	..	.148	10
7.2	..	.. 10	.1384	..	.135	Long Primer	..	..	.1628	11
6.5	..	.. 11	.1522	..	.145	Small Pica	..	..	.1776	12
6	..	.. 12	.166	..	.1667	Pica ..	..	..	.2072	14
5.1	..	.. 14	.1937	..	.188	English	..	..	.2368	16
4.5	..	∴. 16	.2214	..	.2166	2-line Brevier		..	.2664	18
4	..	.. 18	.2490	..	.235	Great Primer		..	.296	20
3.6	..	.. 20	.2767	..	.2626	Paragon	..	..	.3256	22
3.2	..	.. 22	.3044	..	.289	Double Pica ..		..	.3552	24
3	..	.. 24	.332	..	.3362	2-line Pica	..	..	.4144	28
2.5	..	.. 28	.3874	..	.375	2-line English		..	.444	30
2.4	..	.. 30	.415	..	—	———	..	..	.4736	32
2.2	..	.. 32	.4428	..	.469	———	..	..	.5328	36
2	..	.. 36	.498	..	.498	3-line Pica	..			

TYPES (EVEN SET ENS) PER LB.

			6 pt.	7 pt.	8 pt.	9 pt.	10 pt.	11 pt.	12 pt.
1 lb.	..	..	1,152	844	648	512	412	340	288

Four square inches of solid type = 1 lb. in weight (approx.).

NUMBER OF ENS IN SQUARE INCHES OF TYPE

Sq. In.		6 pt.	7 pt.	8 pt.	9 pt.	10 pt.	11 pt.	12 pt.
1	..	288	212	162	128	104	86	72
2	..	576	424	324	256	208	172	144
3	..	864	635	• 486	384	312	258	216
4	..	1152	847	648	512	415	343	288
5	..	1440	1058	810	640	519	429	360
6	..	1728	1270	972	768	623	515	432
7	..	2016	1482	1134	896	726	600	504
8	..	2304	1693	1296	1024	830	686	576
9	..	2592	1905	1458	1152	934	772	648
10	..	2880	2116	1620	1280	1037	857	720
20	..	5760	4232	3240	2560	2074	1714	1440
40	..	11520	8464	6480	5120	4148	3428	2880
50	..	14400	10580	8100	6400	5184	4284	3600
100	..	28800	21159	16200	12800	10368	8568	7200

FOUNT SCHEMES

REQUESTS ARE FREQUENTLY made to provide tables showing how many sorts of each character of a fount should be cast so as to produce complete founts of certain weights.

There are so many possible variations in any such scheme that no definite ruling on this subject can be laid down. For example: type-founders have accustomed the trade to order founts by weight; every point size of a given weight must therefore have a proportionate difference in the number of each sort supplied. Even in the same point size given weights must contain different numbers of sorts according to whether the face is normal, narrow or extended.

Again, the number of types required of the various alphabet characters may vary through special circumstances, according to the general nature of the work done by individual firms. Even a town's name may cause a run on certain letters, for a London, Liverpool, or Pontypool printer would need more o's than a Walsall or Llangollen printer, who would stipulate for extra l's. A Loughborough printer would have an inordinate run on o's, u's, g's, and h's. Consequently it is recommended that users of 'Monotype' composing machines consider founts in terms of numbers of characters, and not by weight.

Today founts for hand work are necessarily small, being used mainly for corrections or short settings.

In casting founts of type for case work, some effort should be made to maintain the correct relative proportions of the various characters of the alphabet, both upper- and lower-case.

A table of the standard proportions of characters is given at the end of this book, p.224, and founts of any strength may be built up from this. The strength of the founts given is based upon a fount containing 1,000 lower-case characters, and this may be multiplied or divided at will.

Where trade typecasting is done, and printers insist on ordering by weight, proportions of different characters may be obtained by first casting a complete fount according to the figures given, and then weighing the total. The proportions of the characters in the required fount will be relative to the difference between the known fount weight and that of the required fount weight. For example: if a fount of 74 'a's' weighs 15 lb., and a 10 lb. fount is ordered, the latter will carry 49 of 'a' ($74 \times 10 \div 15 = 49.3$), 12 of 'b' ($18 \times 10 \div 15 = 12$), 23 of 'c' ($34 \times 10 \div 15 = 22.6$), and so on.

To find relative weights of founts the formula is $\dfrac{A \times B}{C}$ where A is body multiplied by set of required fount, B is weight of known fount, C is body multiplied by set of known fount.

Example: Fount of 12 point 11 set weighs 20 lb.; find weight of similar fount in 8 point 8½ set.

$$\frac{8 \times 8\frac{1}{2} \times 20}{12 \times 11} = \frac{1360}{132} = 10.3 \text{ lb.}$$

PUMP BODY SPRING ROD STOP PLATES a63H1
(FOR PLATE SEE P. 282)

THE OBJECT of the stop plates is to enable the piston to be adjusted according to point and set of type to be cast.

When stop block 63H1 is in operation it alters the timing of the piston and is used when types of large body are being cast. By means of the four plates which replace the single stop block 63H1 a gradual difference can be made according to the volume of metal required to fill the mould.

The following table gives the approximate number of plates to be used when casting various sizes of type:

   4 plates when casting 36 point by 36 point.
   3 plates when casting 36 point by 27 point.
   2 plates when casting 36 point by 18 point.
   1 plate when casting 36 point by 9 point.
   3 plates when casting 30 point by 30 point.
   2 plates when casting 24 point by 24 point.
   1 plate when casting 14 point by 14 point.
   2 plates when casting 12 point lead and rule.
   1 plate when casting 6 point lead and rule.

COMPOSITION IN SETS OVER 12 SET

ALL JUSTIFYING SCALES for sets above 12 set are based on a 5-unit minimum space. This avoids alteration of transfer wedge adjustment for sets above 12 set.

When the justification wedges are in the positions indicated by the justification scale 'constant' on all sets above 12 set up to 24 set, it implies that only 1 unit of set will be deducted by bringing the space transfer wedge into operation, instead of 2 units as in all sets under 12¼ set. The space matrix is located in the 5-unit row of matrix-case.

LETTER-SPACING

THIS TERM IS APPLIED to composition where characters are cast upon bodies wider in set than that for which the characters were designed. This enlargement is brought about by bringing the space transfer wedge in operation, so that the position of the justification wedges decides the extra thickness to which any character shall be cast. The accuracy of the justification of this form of composition depends upon correct adjustment of the space transfer wedge. When the justification wedges are in their neutral positions (3–8) the measurement of type bodies should be exactly the same whether cast with the type transfer wedge in use or the space transfer wedge in use. Should this not be the case it indicates that the space transfer wedge is not correctly adjusted (assuming all other adjustments which affect the type sizing being correct).

Letter-spacing is principally applied in narrow measures where there may be insufficient spaces to fill out a line. No alteration to caster is required.

UNIT ADDING ATTACHMENT (c20CU)

THIS ATTACHMENT is for adding one, two, or three units of set to any standard set unit. The usual addition is two units. In English composition it is customary to space small capitals two units of set; in German composition, words with spaced letters are used in place of italics for emphasis.

Where this attachment is applied the justification perforations in the ribbon (.0075″ and .0005″) are used to operate it, and a combination of perforations NK and NJ are used to operate the two justification wedges.

The 'set' units are added to the normal type sizing adjustments by the interposition of a distance piece between the micrometer wedge and the transfer wedges. The distance piece 25D66D is usually sufficiently wide to hold the transfer wedges back so that the mould blade opens an additional two units of set.

The distance piece varies with every set.

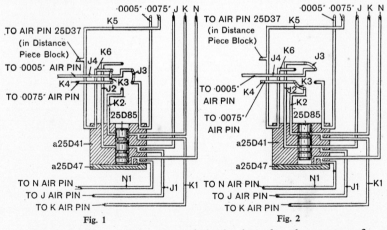

Fig. 1   Fig. 2

In diagram (Fig. 1) it is assumed the keyboard and caster are functioning in the normal manner. On the keyboard the knob 77KB33 must

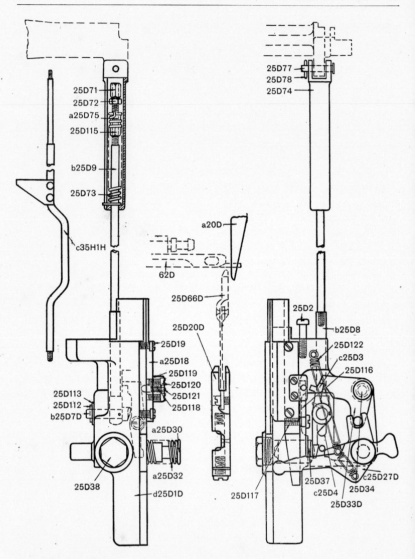

be pushed to the rear and the auxiliary valve bars 77KB89 and 77KB85 must be lowered out of action; on the caster the valve switch must be turned clockwise.

.0005″ *perforation.*—Air goes to valve box through switch, thence to .0005″ air pin.

.0075″ *perforation.*—Air goes to valve box, through switch, thence to .0075″ air pin; a branch pipe also leads to air pin 25D37 in unit distance piece block. (This places the unit distance piece into operation but when the character perforations are reached the distance piece will be placed out of operation.)

J perforation.—Air goes to valve box, is checked by valve and branches to J air pin.

K perforation.—Air goes to valve box, is checked by valve and branches to K air pin.

N perforation.—Air goes to valve box, raises valve 25D85, and branches to N air pin. Raising the valve 25D85 does not affect anything, as in ordinary composition the perforations J and K never occur in combination with N.

In diagram (Fig. 2) it is assumed the keyboard and caster are arranged to compose and cast unit spaced composition. On the keyboard the auxiliary valve bars 77KB89 and 77KB85 must be raised into action. The operating knob 77KB33 must be pushed to the rear, and then the unit dial handle 77KB56 must be turned until one of the figures 1, 2, or 3 (according to the number of units required to be added), comes opposite the positioning line on the housing 77KB57; after adjusting the latter pull the operating knob 77KB33 to the front each time unit spaced copy is required, and push it to the rear before composing ordinary composition; on the caster the valve switch must be turned anti-clockwise.

.0005″ perforation.—Air goes to valve box, and its exit is blinded by the switch. It therefore does not function.

.0075″ perforation.—Air goes to valve box, and its normal exit to the .0075″ justification air pin is blinded; a branch pipe leads to air pin 25D37 in unit distance piece block, so that the unit distance piece will be raised when the character is cast, causing 1, 2, or 3 units of set to be added to the character, according to the unit distance piece in use.

J perforation.—When this perforation is not in combination with N perforation the air goes to valve box, is checked by valve (as in Fig. 1), and is branched to J air pin. When J and N perforations are in combination the air passing through N raises the valve (as in Fig. 2), and this permits the air in J pipe to pass along the groove in the valve, thence to the switch, and thence to the justification .0005″ air pin. A branch pipe leads to the J air pin, which also is raised.

K perforation.—When this perforation is not in combination with N perforation the air goes to valve box, is checked by valve (as in Fig. 1), and is branched to K air pin. When K and N perforations are in combination the air passing through N raises the valve (as in Fig. 2), and this permits the air in K pipe to pass along the groove in the valve, thence to switch and thence to the .0075″ justification air pin. A branch pipe leads to the K air pin, which is also raised.

N perforation.—Air goes to valve box and raises valve; a branch pipe leads the air to N air pin. Raising the valve does not affect anything unless air is in the pipes J or K (see two preceding paragraphs).

I

J, K, *and* N *perforations in combination.*—When J and N perforations are in combination the .0005″ justification air pin is raised; when K and N perforations are in combination the .0075″ justification air pin is raised; when J, K, and N perforations are in combination both .0005″ and .0075″ justification air pins are raised (used when double justification is required).

UNIT ADDING VALVE BOX a25D41D

The caster portion of the unit adding device is provided with a special valve box, which may be placed 'in' or 'out' of action by means of a switch.

In the following description turning the switch 'clockwise' implies placing the valve 'OUT' of action; turning 'anti-clockwise' implies placing the valve 'IN' action.

Instead of the .0075″ and .0005″ air pipes being led direct to the justification air pin block c3DD, they are connected first to the unit spacing valve box and thence to the justification air pin block. The J, K, and N air pipes are also branched to the valve box.

When the switch is turned clockwise the air from all these perforations (.0075″, .0005″, J, K, and N) functions in the normal manner.

When the switch is turned anti-clockwise the air from the .0075″ and .0005″ perforations is shut off from the justification air pin block, and the air from the .0075″ perforation is conducted by a pipe from the valve block to an air pin 25D37, in the unit distance piece block, causing the distance piece 25D66D to be placed in the return path of the transfer wedges, thereby preventing them from going back to their normal positions, and permitting the mould blade to be opened further according to the thickness of the distance piece used. (The air from the .0005″ air pipe becomes inoperative, as there is no exit for it.) Therefore every time a .0075″ perforation is associated with a combination of character perforations the type will be cast 1, 2, or 3 units wider in set, according to the distance piece in use in front of the micrometer wedge.

Also, when the switch is turned anti-clockwise to the left the air from the N air pin is conducted to *beneath* the valve in the unit spacing valve box, causing the valve to be raised, so that should air at the same time be in the J or K pipes it will be led into the .0005″ or .0075″ air pipes which connect the unit spacing valve block to the justification air pin block. Therefore when air is at the same time in K and N pipes it will raise the .0075″ air pin; when air is at the same time in J and N pipes it will raise the .0005″ air pin; when air is at the same time in J, K, and N pipes it will raise both .0075″ and .0005″ air pipes simultaneously, thus providing for 'double-justification'.

As the J, K, and N perforations are never used in combination during the composition of characters they function in the usual manner when used alone; but at the end of the lines they are used in combination to operate the justification air pins.

UNIT ADDING OPERATING STAND d25D1D

This block is located inside the machine base just under the micrometer wedge, and is connected by a lifting rod b25D9 to the centring pin lever. Any overthrow on the up stroke of the centring pin lever is absorbed by a spring 25D14 in the spring box 25D74.

The lower end of the lifting rod b25D9 is connected to a rock lever c25D3, which therefore moves up and down with the movement of the centring pin lever.

Normally the upper end of this rock lever is held to the front by the action of a torsion spring c25D4 anchored between the rock lever and rock lever fulcrum pin.

When the rock lever is held in this (the normal) position it will, when lifted, be in position to strike against a projection on the operating stand latch 25D33D, causing the other end of this lever to rock the slide operating lever c25D27D, and thus pull to its lowest position the unit slide 25D20D.

To the upper end of the slide 25D20D is attached the unit slide distance piece 25D66D.

When this unit distance piece is moved to its lowest position as just described, it rests against the micrometer wedge with its upper end just below the type transfer wedge. Both transfer wedges therefore may be drawn against the micrometer wedge in the usual manner, the unit slide distance piece being inoperative; the operating stand rock lever c25D3 is now free to slide up and down without opposition, whilst the machine casts ordinary composition.

When a unit-spaced type body is required, compressed air passes through the .0075″ perforation in the paper ribbon, and is conducted to behind the operating stand air pin 25D37, causing it to press against the operating stand rock lever c25D3, pushing its lower end to the rear. Whilst the rock lever is held in this position it is drawn upward, and a projection on the lower right-hand side of the rock lever c25D3 engages the slide operating lever part two b25D28 causing it to rise. The slide operating lever part two b25D28 is anchored to the lever c25D27D by means of a spring, but is prevented from rising by a projection on the slide operating lever delaying latch 25D116 until the upper portion of the rock lever, in its upward movement, contacts a cam face on the delaying latch and releases the operating lever part two. When the lever part two is released it carries the slide 25D20D and interposes the unit distance piece between the transfer wedges and micrometer wedge, thus permitting the mould blade to be opened further on account of the transfer wedges not having been drawn back to their normal positions.

This action is repeated all the while a .0075″ perforation is in the paper ribbon, but on the return down stroke of the centring pin lever (should there be no .0075″ perforation in the paper ribbon and the operating stand air pin 25D37 has been returned), the upper end of the rock lever c25D3 gets under a projection on the operating stand latch 25D33D, so that as the centring pin lever again rises, the rock lever c25D3 rocks the stand latch 25D33D, and this in turn rocks the slide operating lever c25D27D, pulling to its lower position the unit slide distance piece 25D66D, where it will remain until another .0075″ perforation in the paper ribbon is reached.

The unit slide distance piece must be changed to produce 1, 2, or 3 units of set, according to the set to be composed.

HOW TO INSERT AND REMOVE UNIT SLIDE 25D20D COMPLETE WITH UNIT DISTANCE PIECE

To insert unit slide.—Turn the machine to the casting position, as in this position a transfer wedge is seated against the micrometer wedge, acting as a stop for preventing the unit distance piece and slide being pushed up too far. Insert right hand through aperture in main stand and pull slide operating lever c25D27D to the right; turn the front end of the lever down until it will lodge on operating stand. Next insert unit slide (complete with unit distance piece) in the slot in operating stand, keeping one finger under unit slide; use other fingers to move the left-hand end of slide fulcrum lever upward so that it springs into slot in unit slide.

If any difficulty is found in placing unit slide in the operating stand it may be necessary to wind up micrometer wedge adjusting screw a20D2 to give unit distance piece more clearance past micrometer wedge; after inserting unit slide return a20D2 to its original position.

ADJUSTMENT

Remove the spring box pin 25D77. Adjust the lower nuts a25D75 and 25D115 on spring box rod so that top of nut a25D75 is $\frac{3}{4}$″ from top of spring box rod. Lock the nuts together with the slots in nut a25D75 facing to left and right.

Turn machine to 220° and adjust the upper nuts 25D71 and 25D72 so that a clearance of $\frac{1}{64}$″ is obtained between the top of nut 25D71 and underside of projection on centring pin lever. Lock the two nuts together. If this clearance is not obtained the spring box rod and operating stand mechanism will be subjected to excessive strain by the centring pin lever.

Engage the end of spring 25D73 in the slot of nut a25D75 and give the spring box 25D74 a quarter of a turn clockwise and engage the spring box to centring pin lever by means of the pin 25D77.

See that slide distance piece 25D66D is in its lowest position and set machine to 0°.

Pierce hole in paper for .0075″ air pin and turn machine steadily one revolution to 5°, taking care not to over-run; in this position the slide distance piece should not have moved from its bottom position.

Continue to turn machine to 10°; in this position the slide distance piece should be in the upper position.

If the slide distance piece is raised before 5° release the pressure on spring 25D73 by decreasing the distance between nuts 25D71 and a25D75 and if the distance piece has not risen before 10° increase the pressure on the spring by increasing distance between nuts.

It is most important that the distance piece should not be early in its operation, or the space transfer wedge will not have moved sufficiently away from micrometer wedge to allow the entry of distance piece, and damage will be inflicted upon the head of transfer wedge adjusting screw.

When the adjustment is correct insert the cotter 25D78 in the pin 25D77.

MORE THAN 20 JUSTIFYING SPACES IN WIDE-MEASURE COMPOSITION

IN VERY WIDE MEASURES it may happen that more than 20 justifying spaces are needed, whereas the justifying scales are based on a maximum of 20. In these cases the keyboard mechanism automatically cuts out the 'S' perforation and registers any justifying space after 20 as 6-units.

The average difference between the correct justification and the 6-unit space is scarcely noticeable.

An alternative method is to adjust the keyboard to half measure, and single justify the first half of each line, and double justify the second half.

QUADDING AND CENTRING ATTACHMENT

OBJECT OF THE ATTACHMENT

Two separate mechanisms are fitted to the casting machine. To distinguish them one is called a 'quadding' mechanism, and the other a 'repeating' mechanism. The Quadding mechanism will repeat the signal for a quad (or character) five or ten times for each quadding perforation in the paper, the mechanism being previously set to a repeat of five or ten. The Repeater mechanism, put into action by the 'repeater' perforation, enables the casting of a quad (or character) to be repeated until a selected measure has been completed. The two features can be used singly or in combination. The Quadder and Repeater are both used for centring, and both mechanisms can be used for casting lines of sorts.

HOW IT FUNCTIONS

Two recessed control plates, adjustable so as to present two or four recesses in their common periphery, have been added to the air tower. The paper feed pawl arm is extended to the periphery of these control plates, and in its normal function passes in and out of one of the recesses. The control plates are rotated by a ratchet wheel and pawl, driven by air from the quadding signal in the paper. When this signal is given the ratchet wheel turns the recessed control plate, and presents the periphery instead of a recess to the paper feed pawl arm, preventing its movement and thus stopping the paper feed. If the Quadder is set for a repeat of five, the machine will make five casts before the control plate has rotated sufficiently to present the next recess to the paper feed pawl arm, to release the paper feed. If the Quadder signal has been repeated in the paper, the control plates will continue their movement, and a further number of quads will be cast. (Should the mechanism be set for a repeat of ten, the outer recessed control plate is moved round, converting the four recesses into two.) The signal used for quadding is the combination BC.

The Repeater action differs from that of the Quadder. The Repeater signal locks the paper feed, so that the machine will repeat whatever character is combined with this signal until the paper feed is released, when the line being cast has reached a predetermined measure. The Repeater signal air is taken to a control box (paper feed) lock piston on the air tower housing (front), which raises a control box (paper feed) lever in the path of a paper feed pawl ring arm, stopping the paper feed. (As the machine continues to run, one character will be repeated.)

The release is effected by a small cam face on the line support coming into contact with an adjustable trip carriage, and raising a trip gauge bar mounted on top of the column pusher. The quad (or character) selected is repeated until the line support raises this bar and thus opens a valve (mounted on the end of the main galley stand) controlling the supply of Repeater signal air to the control box (paper feed) piston, mounted beside the lock piston, but larger in diameter. When air is thus supplied to both pistons, the feed piston actuated from the galley mechanism will overcome the lock piston and release the paper feed. The attachment can be used to cast lines from nine to sixty pica ems.

TWO LINE SUPPORTS NECESSARY

To cast the shorter measures it is necessary for the line support to be extended into the type channel; one long and one short line support are, therefore, supplied in each of the two usual thicknesses. The long support is used for measures nine to twenty-four picas, and the short for twenty-four picas and upwards. The gauge bar has two sets of gradations marked on it; one for use with the long line support, and the other with the short line support. When setting the adjustable trip carriage, set the trip carriage gauge to the measure indicated on the gauge bar (taking care to use the scale corresponding with the line support in use). Place two quads of the set to be cast against the gauge and bring the trip carriage up to them and secure.

'TRY-OUT' LINES

'TRY-OUT' LINES

To prevent the stoppage of the paper feed when 'try-out' line perforations pass through the caster air tower the 'repeater' control box feed piston is made in two parts, i.e. lower and upper 'BC' air is diverted from the air pipe connecting block, through an air pipe to the 'repeater' control box cover (bottom). The air pipe then passes through the control box body to the upper feed piston.

If, as can happen, air is supplied to both pistons (i.e. feed and lock), the upper feed piston will overcome the lock piston and thus prevent stoppage of the paper feed.

This does not affect the normal use of 'BC' air for quadding and 'AC' air for repeating.

When 'killing' a line in which the 'repeater' perforations 'AC' occur in combination, either the 'A' or 'C' perforation must be pasted over, otherwise the ribbon will remain locked.

SIGNAL COMBINATIONS

The signal used for Repeating is the combination of perforations 'AC', and for Quadding, 'BC'. The 'A', 'B', and 'C' air pipes are branched to a valve box, causing the 'A' air to be switched to the Repeater piston, and the 'B' air to the Quadder piston. The normal use of 'A', 'B', and 'C' air is not affected when the perforations occur singly.

ADJUSTMENTS

REPEATER MECHANISM

Adjust the screw 28G10 in the lever on air tower to give .010″ clearance between the head of the screw and the paper feed pawl ring arm when the lever is raised by air from the Repeater signal.

Adjust the height of the valve 220F1 at the end of the main galley stand, so that it clears the tappet attached to the trip gauge bar by .020″ when the bar is not lifted. To make this adjustment, slacken the screw securing the bracket to the main galley stand and move the bracket until the valve is in the correct position; then secure it. Check that in its forward position the front of the type pusher is 20 picas from the column pusher (adjust if necessary). To set the adjustable trip carriage 218F2F set the trip carriage gauge 218F8 to the measure indicated on the gauge bar (taking care to use the scale corresponding with the line support being used). Place two quads of the set to be cast against the gauge and bring the trip carriage up to them and secure.

If difficulty is experienced in obtaining the correct measure it may be necessary to modify the gap between the tappet on the trip gauge bar and the top of the valve.

QUADDER MECHANISM

See that the air tower operating rod 54E, the paper feed pawl ring b14GG, and the paper feed spring box are set correctly to the standard adjustments.

Lock the paper feed. Adjust the eccentric 19G6 in the air tower lever to its middle position on the longest side of its throw.

Perforate holes 'C' and 'B' in paper. Remove the lower paper feed pawl arm 13G14. Turn machine until the ratchet wheel pawl lever piston is raised by air, loosen the detent spring a29G2, and adjust its position so that there is a gap of approximately .020″ between the pawl and a tooth on the ratchet wheel. Lock the spring in this position and slowly turn machine to see that the pawl remains engaged until the detent spring has dropped into the next tooth, but is clear of the ratchet wheel when it has reached the end of its movement. (It may be necessary to slightly readjust both the spring and eccentric to obtain this condition.)

Release the paper feed and turn machine so that there is no tension on the paper feed spring box. Assemble the paper feed pawl arm (lower), and adjust it so that vertically its lower end is approximately .010″ clear of the lower edge of the recess in the control plates 29G31G, 29G23G; horizontally the arm should just clear the periphery of the plates.

Position a piece of spool paper perforated 'BC' and rotate machine to see that the ratchet wheel is moved one tooth at each revolution of the machine, and that the front of the tooth contacts with the end of the detent spring; also check that all tension is off the paper feed spring box just before a notch in the control plate lines up with lower end of paper feed pawl arm.

FOUNT AND SORTS CASTING
USING QUADDING AND CENTRING ATTACHMENT

A TABLE is appended for the casting of small founts from a ribbon, in which each line contains only one kind of character, so as to simplify transference to the type case. The measure selected is twelve set ems, and the same table and ribbon will do for any point or set size of the same matrix-case character and unit arrangement.

The twelve set-em measure is assumed to be divided into two sections, one of two set ems and one of ten set ems. The former starts with a space sufficient, when added to the characters, to make two set ems (36 units). As two characters are always ejected into the type channel after the ribbon feed-wheel has been released, these two have been deducted from the number to be composed in the first column. The Repeater gauge is adjusted so that when ten complete ems (180 units) have been ejected into the type channel the release valve opens just sufficiently to release the ribbon feed-wheel.

When the ribbon is perforated, the Repeater key must be depressed in combination with the desired character, followed by a unit-space sufficient to make the characters of the second section of the measure total up to ten set ems (180 units),

The Repeater should be used for all characters and spaces, except those in the A, B, and C columns of matrix-case, which will be tapped out for the full number required.

The narrow measure of twelve set ems has been selected so that complete lines of sorts may be cast, without casting too many of the characters not frequently used.

In the table non-surplus characters are marked with an asterisk (*), and a small figure beneath some of the characters indicates where more than one line is required.

(*These numbers should be increased where there is a special local run on certain characters.*)

If a double-strength fount is needed it will only be necessary to cast double the number of lines of those characters marked with an asterisk. Therefore, in preparing the ribbon, first tick off the characters required, then compose the required characters against which no asterisk appears, and then those marked with an asterisk, so that if a double-strength fount is needed it will be sufficient to cast only the latter section twice.

SPECIMEN TABLE FOR CASTING FOUNTS IN JUSTIFIED LINES

The table given represents approximately a 50 lower-case 'a' fount, with an excess of characters not frequently used. (To produce a 100 lower-case 'a' fount, cast double the number of characters marked with an asterisk.) Measure to be twelve set ems. A figure against a character indicates the number of lines to be cast; all other characters one line only.

UNIT ARRANGEMENT No. 1

A	‡	‡	‡	B														C	D	E	F	G
5	′	î	ï	l	t^*	'	,	!	:	□	;	.	,	l	i^*			6	4	Rr	0	42
6	I	:	;	j	f	i^*	]	)	(	-	j	f	□					0	4	Rr	0	36
7	°	″	‖	§	?	z	s^*	r^*	c^*	e_2^*	'	'	r^*	t_2^*	s^*			8	2	Rr	5	29
8	z	J	s	ç	é	q	v	b	g	o_2^*	?	I	z	c_2^*	e_3^*			12	1	Rr	12	24
9	ö	*	†	$\frac{1}{3}$	$\frac{1}{6}$	$\frac{3}{4}$	$\frac{1}{2}$	$\frac{1}{4}$	.	9	7	5	3	1	0			0	2	Rr	0	24
9	ä	à	‡	$\frac{2}{3}$	$\frac{7}{8}$	$\frac{5}{8}$	$\frac{3}{8}$	$\frac{1}{8}$	-	£	8	6	4	2	□			0	2	Rr	0	24
9	P	T	L	F	C	I	x	k	y	d^*	h^*	a_2^*	g	a_2^*	o_2^*			0	2	Rr	0	24
10	Q	B	O	E	ü	u^*	n_2^*	J	S	x	q	b	y	u^*	n_2^*			6	1	Rr	0	21
10	V	G	R	A	ñ	fl	fi	p	fl	fi	k	v	p	h^*	d^*			6	1	Rr	0	21
11	Y	X	U	K	N	H	D	¶	J	S	ff	$	Z	C	ff			14	0	Rr	15	17
12	M	Z	Q	G	O	L	C	œ	æ	w	æ	P	L	F	T			0	1	Rr	0	18
13	P	R	B	F	E	T	&	Q	V	B	G	O	E	A	w^*			10	0	Rr	11	15
14	Œ	Æ	W	V	D	A	ffl	ffi	m^*	œ	Y	U	R	N	D			8	0	Rr	12	14
15	&	X	Y	K	U	N	H	℔	ffl	ffi	X	K	M^*	H	m^*			6	0	Rr	0	14
18		$\%_c$	%	℔	@	Œ	Æ	W	M^*	Œ	Æ	..	—	W	□			0	0	Rr	0	12

A=character unit; B=characters in matrix case; C=space at beginning of line to make characters in column D, plus two, equivalent to 36 units; D=number of characters to compose before using Repeater key (two more will be added automatically in casting); E=Repeater key to be depressed with character; F=unit space to add before justifying, to make column D up to ten set ems (180 units); G=number of characters in each line; Rr=Repeater key; ‡=characters in these three columns must be tapped separately. Double justify at end of each line (two revolutions).

EXTENDED MATRIX-CASE ATTACHMENT

ORIGINALLY 'MONOTYPE' CASTERS were equipped with 15 × 15 matrix-cases as standard, but owing to the general increase in 7-alphabet composition (which includes upper- and lower-case and small caps. in roman, and upper- and lower-case in italics and bold face), present casters are equipped with 15 × 17 matrix-cases.

This involves considerable alterations in the structure of the caster, but the innovation has been a great convenience, especially for foreign composition, where a great variety of accent matrices is needed.

The special parts of an extended matrix-case attachment include a new rear pin block, a set of rear tongs, and a new matrix-case; on the keyboard additional keybars have been introduced to provide for the 30 extra matrix-case positions.

In the extended matrix-case there are 15 rows of 17 matrices.

On the rear pin block there are, for dealing with these two new rows of matrices, two additional air pins, and on the side of the pin block an air-transferring device is fitted. Beneath each air pin 'I' and 'L' is an air channel which, by means of the air-transferring device, conducts

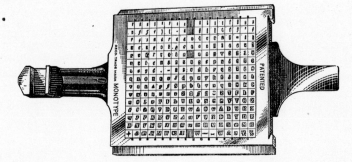

the compressed air to the two additional pins 'I1' and 'L1' (see diagram).

Additional keybars are provided in the keyboard, each making three perforations in the ribbon, one for raising an air pin on the front pin block and *two* for raising two air pins on the rear pin block.

When air pin 'N' is raised, the air beneath it is conducted along channel 'Na' to beneath piston valve 'b' in the air transferring device 'a', causing two grooves around its circumference to connect two air channels, 'Ia' from air pin 'I' to air pin 'I1', and 'La' from air pin 'L' to 'L1'. When air is beneath either air pin 'I' or air pin 'L' alone it cannot escape, as the grooves around the piston valve will not be in alignment to complete the air circuit. The air pins 'I', 'L' and 'N' therefore function in the ordinary manner when each is elevated separately, but when air pins 'L' and 'N' are raised simultaneously the air beneath 'L' pin is directed by means of the transferring device to beneath air pin 'L1', which is thus also raised. Similar action takes place when pins 'I' and 'N' are raised simultaneously; the air is then directed to beneath air pin 'I1'. There are therefore occasions when three pins are raised simultaneously on the rear pin block, namely: 'NL' and 'L1', *or* 'NI' and 'I1'. The leading pin jaw is arrested by the foremost raised pin, and the matrix-case is then taken to that position. The raising of these two supplementary air

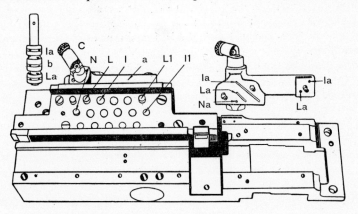

pins can only be effected by the simultaneous elevation of the pins 'L' *and* 'N' or 'I' *and* 'N'; when the pins 'L' or 'I' are raised separately the extra pins remain seated. When working from the 15×15 matrix-case (225 matrices) the stop 'C' can be brought into operation; this prevents the possible elevation of the two supplementary air pins ('I1' and 'L1'). Either the 15×15 matrix-case or the 15×17 matrix-case may therefore be used as desired.

LARGE TYPE COMPOSITION

LARGE TYPE COMPOSITION implies mechanical composition for sizes above 12 point up to (and including) 24 point. Matrices for this work are made in two sizes, $.2'' \times .4''$, and $.4'' \times .4''$, and the storage area of the matrix-case is enlarged to $3.2'' \times 3.2''$. Setwise, the matrix-case will carry 16 of the narrow matrices, or 8 of the larger size; pointwise, it will carry eight rows. Before starting to cast with this matrix-case in use see that the draw rods are correctly adjusted to bring matrix cone-holes central with the centring pin.

NUMBER OF CHARACTERS

The number of characters varies according to the 'set', as more matrices may be included in a 14-set fount than in a 24-set fount. The average number of characters is about 90, and includes upper- and lower-case, punctuation marks and figures.

The extended matrix-case (15×17) will carry an extra row of $.4''$ matrices.

MATRIX LOCATING

Matrix locating is obtained in the same manner as with ordinary composition matrices (see diagram of matrix-case).

Pointwise, the cone holes are central in the matrix body, and the matrices may be arranged so that all 15 positions of the normal wedge are utilised.

Setwise, the cone holes of some matrices are $.2''$ and some $.4''$ apart. Other cone-hole positions are ignored, except for positioning the justification wedges during composition.

JUSTIFICATION SCALE CONSTANT

For large type composition the justification scale 'constant' produces a transfer wedge difference of 1 unit of 'set' instead of 2 units. A 4-unit variable space is therefore obtained from a 5-unit position (see COMPOSITION IN SETS OVER 12 SET p. 118). Above 24 set all 'constants' will be 3/8, and the variable space will be positioned in the smallest unit row.

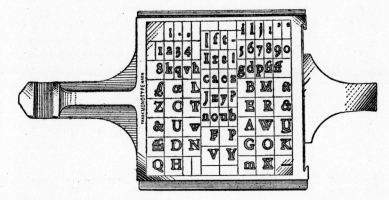

VERY WIDE CHARACTERS

Characters wider than the maximum unit row of matrix-case are sometimes cast in composition with an overhanging face. This overhang is supported by a high space, composed in advance of any such letter. The overhanging characters are usually capitals 'M' and 'W'. When casting sorts only, the mould blade should be adjusted to open wide enough to cast these sorts without overhang.

ACCESSORIES REQUIRED

When using normal wedges of large 'set' for the first time see that the corner of mould blade abutment slide anvil a14c3 (during type sizing) does not foul an adjoining step on the normal wedge, thereby causing imperfect line justification.

Accessories required on caster for use with large type composition equipment:

Mould (inset pattern, composition nick position).

Matrix-case and matrices.

Normal wedge.

Nozzle No. 2.

Centring pin auxiliary spring xb36A, etc.

Mould blade cam lever compound lever locking screw distance piece (stepped) d44E9, pump trip latch 57H1, etc.

Speed-reducing gear or pulleys.

Line hook (adjustable).

TRANSFER WEDGES

No alteration needed in adjustment of transfer wedges.

LOW QUAD MECHANISM

Large type composition moulds are not made to be used in connection with the old style form of low quad mechanism.

MOULDS FOR LARGE TYPE COMPOSITION

For large type composition special 'inset' moulds are provided. These moulds have a frame common to all sizes, and the mould blade side blocks are made interchangeable so that they may readily be changed from one size to another.

Printers in possession of the older style sorts moulds may use them for sorts casting in conjunction with 14, 18 and 24-point composition matrices, but the nick will be cast on the back of the type body instead of on the front; for this reason this practice is not recommended. Before first using the older style sorts moulds in conjunction with large size composition matrices, the moulds should be returned to The Monotype Corporation Ltd. for adjustment. Display type moulds cannot be used for composition. When casting sorts from the older style (T.A. & U.A.) display moulds in conjunction with 24-point composition matrices a 2-point packing piece must be placed between the mould and B pin block, in order to obtain the necessary adjustment on centring pin stand.

When first positioning new moulds for large size composition, see that the type pusher guide xa28b permits the mould to seat correctly.

ON STANDARD COMPOSITION CASTER

The matrix-case will be positioned in exactly the same manner as when casting from the ordinary matrix-case, and the normal wedge will be automatically carried to its required position.

CASTING SPEEDS

The speed of the caster should be reduced for large type composition according to the 'set' and point size of matrices. For sorts casting, the machine should be run slower when casting capitals than when casting lower case. The gears shown below are those for use on the speed regulating attachment (see p. 163).

TYPE	R.P.M.	GEAR
24-Point 24 Set	50 to 65	1-B-E or 2-B-E
18-Point 18 Set	65 to 80	2-B-E or 3-B-E
14-Point 14 Set	100	2-C-E

Speeds are largely governed by the 'set' and the amount of capitals in the copy.

Where large type composition is limited to two or three founts of one point size, the speed of the caster may be reduced by changing the pulley on the primary driving shaft to suit the size of the type to be cast.

If only 14 point and 18 point sizes are required, it is advisable to use the change-speed gear described on p. 135.

It is not advisable to cast for too long a period from any given matrix, otherwise the matrix may become overheated and be spoiled. Allow plenty of water to flow through the mould.

CHANGE-SPEED GEAR FOR LARGE TYPE COMPOSITION

A special change-speed gear is provided for large type composition up to 18 point only, which must be cast at speeds much lower than the minimum required for 12 point.

The driving motor is fitted with a V-belt pulley. This drives a speed-changing pulley combination consisting of two laterally fixed outer discs with angled inner surfaces, between which may be moved laterally a third disc with both sides angled. As the inner disc is advanced towards one of the outer fixed discs it reduces the angled gap between these two, and increases the angled gap formed from the other fixed disc.

The V-belt from the motor runs in the V gap formed by the proximity of the movable disc to the first fixed disc, so that the closer these two discs are, the further from the axis will the belt be crowded, and the nearer to the axis will the belt be crowded on the other side of the centre adjustable disc.

The second V-belt contacts a V groove in a pulley of considerably enlarged diameter on the caster.

To vary the speed a quadrant is provided, so that according to the adjustment of the quadrant, indicated by a scale, the speed may be regulated as desired, and the belt tension accommodated to the changed conditions.

COMPOSITION WITH OVERHANGING CHARACTERS

THIS IS OF TWO KINDS:

1. Newspaper Smalls, for which a small type (such as 5 point) is composed with a larger type (such as 10 point). The two sizes are arranged in the same matrix-case; the mould used is that of the smaller size. The large-type characters are cast overhanging from the back of the type bodies, and this overhang rests upon quads and spaces of the line previously composed on the keyboard, but cast in reverse order. The size limit of the large fount is 12 point, the punching limit of .2″ × .2″ matrices.

2. Characters of large-type body used in the same matrix-case with a fount of smaller body size. The 'set' limit of the large type is the limit of the mould blade opening for .2″ × .2″ matrices. When considering

the maximum amount of mould blade opening the measurement of the wall on the matrix, mould crossblock side, must be taken into consideration.

The following is a specimen of matrix-case combination for 'Newspaper Smalls' layout, 163 series (5½ point), 9 set, with 7-11 caps:

HOTEL DE L'UNIVERS, 10 Rue Croix des Pts. Champs. All modern comfort. Moderate terms.

FAREBROTHER, ELLIS & CO.,
26 DOVER-STREET, W.1

PARK-LANE (within a stone's throw of).—SERVICE FLAT in modern mansion building; central heating, constant hot water, &c., for DISPOSAL; three bed, bath, two sitting rooms; full service charge 5½ gns. a week; £600 required for long lease.

RENT

£775 P.A.

Specimen of a matrix-case combination of 115 series (7 point), 177 series (7½ point), and 141· series (12 point), cast on 8-point body, 12½ set:

BLACKPOOL. Mrs. Dennett, 46 Frampton House
High-street, homely public and private apartments. Beds for one or two persons.

EGYPT AND INDIA
ELLERMAN'S CITY AND HALL LINES
Frequent service of fast passenger steamers from Liverpool to Egypt, Bombay, Karachi, Colombo and Madras

Specimen of matrix-case combination of 115 series (7 point) and 193 series (7 point), cast on 7-point mould, 12½ set:

CROMWELL HOTEL
145 and 146 CROMWELL-PLACE, facing South Kensington Station ; every comfort ; excellent cuisine and catering ; gas fires ; lift ; night porter. 'Phone, Western 2015.

GROSVENOR COURT HOTEL
Davies-st., Mayfair, W.1, Comf. FURNISHED SUITES, bath enclosed. 199 double and single rooms ; gas fires. Moderate terms. Mayfair 7172.

The following specimen of price-list work contains special figures from matrices .2″×.4″. These figures have the centring pin cone hole .1″ from end of matrix, so that they will align with the cone holes of the .2″×.2″ matrices:

ALL WOOL HIMALAYA FLEECE for Sports Coats and Wraps. Light in weight and fleecy in texture, this splendid fabric is now genuinely worth 7/11 per yard. In shades of Tan, Fawn, White and Sand. Special Price 5/11¾

OVERHUNG TYPE ATTACHMENT

THIS ATTACHMENT consists of a special type channel block, fixed, d51FF, to which is attached at one end a guide for carrying the rear end of the rule e39FF. This guide is movable in a direction towards the galley, that is, in a right-hand direction.

The type, after being pushed from the type carrier, is supported between the walls of the channel blocks. When nearing the end of the channel blocks, the overhang on the type comes into contact with a curved face on the guide. Any further travel of the type results in the guide being moved by an amount equivalent to the overhang on the type. Since the rule moves with the guide it follows that the rule is in such a position as to enable the overhung type to be pushed across behind the rule for delivery to the galley in the usual manner.

The rule is supported by a distance piece 39F30 which takes the load off the guide and allows it to move freely.

The thin line support should be used with this attachment.

ADJUSTMENTS

Adjust the column pusher spring box so that the projections on the thin line support just clear the stop slide a44FF when column pusher is in its extreme right-hand position and the operating lever a32F is in its working position.

Set the type channel block xa50F and column pusher adjusting cam disc a2F1 to suit the body size of type to be cast.

IMITATION TYPEWRITER COMPOSITION

EQUIPMENT NECESSARY to compose imitation 'Typewriter' founts, whether lines are to end ragged or to be justified to even lengths, consists of:

Typewriter normal wedge,* suitable for all typewriter founts.

Typewriter stopbar case, suitable for all typewriter founts.

Typewriter justifying scale† of set required.

* The sizing section of this is parallel; for convenience of reference it is termed a wedge.

†Typewriter justifying scales have constants of 3/8. If standard justifying scales are used the difference between constant and 3/8 must be added to the indicated justification. Example: $9\frac{3}{4}$-set constant is 1/8; adding 2/0 to indicated justification becomes equivalent to having 3/8 constant.

K

LINES TO END RAGGED

If the measure is to be in pica ems, adjust keyboard measure to nearest number of 'set' ens to pica measure required. Use 9-unit spaces between words, and at end of last word of line, or syllable, compose 9-unit spaces to complete measure.

On the caster manipulate the micrometer wedge to bring line to nearest pica measure, if required. The greatest difference can only be 8 units, which will be divided amongst all the characters and spaces in a line, and every line will have the same number of pieces. For example: the measure of this page is 25 picas, the fount is Series 127, 8 point, 10 set; keyboard measure 30 ems.

If measure is not to be in pica ems, adjust keyboard to number of set ens required.

LINES TO END JUSTIFIED

Adjust keyboard to equivalent of pica measure (this page 30 ems in Series 127, 8 point, 10 set). Compose 9-unit justifying spaces between words, and justify according to justifying scale at end of line.

TYPEWRITER CHARACTERS

Founts contain upper- and lower-case, points and figures, fractions and commercial signs in common use, and can be laid out to any keyboard and matrix-case arrangement.

Here are six lines composed with the lines ending in the usual ragged manner:

```
To calculate the revolutions per minute of driven shaft-
ing on a driven pulley, multiply the diameter (in inches)
of the pulley on the driving shaft by the number of the
revolutions per minute that pulley makes and divide by the
diameter (in inches) of the driven pulley; the result will
be the answer required.
```

Where composition of justified lines of a typewriter face is required it may just as easily be done, as illustrated by the following six lines of the same measure:

```
To calculate the revolutions per minute of driven shaft-
ing on a driven pulley, multiply the diameter (in inches)
of the pulley on the driving shaft by the number of the
revolutions per minute that pulley makes and divide by the
diameter (in inches) of the driven pulley; the result will
be the answer required.
```

COMBINED SPACING ATTACHMENT

THIS ATTACHMENT PROVIDES a choice of three methods of word spacing:

1. *Normal Spacing,* with separate low or high spaces of a minimum thickness of four units.

2. *Combined Standard Spacing,* with spaces of a minimum thickness of four units, the spaces being cast to the first letter of a word.
3. *Combined Close Spacing.* In this composition the spaces are cast to the first letter of a word, but no units are registered for them on the keyboard, the justification being decided entirely by the justifying scale; in other words, the space thickness starts from nothing instead of from four units.

HOW IT FUNCTIONS AT THE KEYBOARD

The attachment is operated by an air pipe connected to the justifying space air channel, which conducts the air in one direction to a piston for cutting off the paper feed, and in the opposite direction to a plunger for preventing the unit wheel advancing. Connected to this air pipe is a three-way air valve, which may be moved to one of three positions, marked N, C, or O.

N—To prevent air entering this attachment pipe, so that keyboard functions normally when a space key is struck, i.e., the unit wheel registers four units and the paper ribbon advances.

C—To permit air to lock the paper feed so that when the space key is struck the unit wheel will register four units but the paper ribbon will not advance. In this case the space will be cast to the first letter of the following word. The width of spaces between words will be based on 4-unit minimum.

O—To permit air to lock both paper feed and unit wheel so that when the space key is struck the ribbon will not be advanced, and no units will be registered. This is for very close spacing. (In this case the operator must finish his line before zero is reached, otherwise there will be no space between words.)

For 'combined' spacing two special keybars (1–S15) must be used in connection with the two adaptable justifying space bars 12KU. (These adaptable space bars are fitted to modern keyboards.)

NOTE.—*When operating for combined spacing, only nineteen justifying spaces can be included in any line. After the nineteenth justifying space has been included in a line the 'fixed' 6-unit space key must be used instead of the justifying space key.*

HOW IT FUNCTIONS AT THE CASTER

When copy has been perforated with three-way valve at N, the casting machine functions normally; that is, separate spaces of normal width are cast between words.

When the copy has been perforated with three-way valve at C, the 'S' perforation is produced in combination with the perforations for the first letter of the following word, so that character and space will be cast in one piece, and width of space portion on character body will be equivalent to a normal space. The space transfer wedge must be changed for one adjusted to add four units of set to the width of the first letter of words when the justification scale 'constant' figures are reached.

When the copy has been perforated with three-way valve at O the spaces will also be cast on the first letter of the following word, but very close spacing will be possible as the width of spaces will start from nothing instead of from four units of set. The space transfer wedge must be changed for one adjusted so that nothing will be added to the width of the first letter of a word when the justification scale 'constant' figures are reached.

ADVANTAGES

When spaces are cast to the body of the first character of a word there automatically follows a 16 per cent saving of paper ribbon at the keyboard, and 16 per cent increase in output at the caster.

A further advantage due to spaces being cast to the first character of a word is the spaces cannot rise in printing. Against this advantage must be considered the possibility of extra time which may be taken in hand correction of the proofs, on account of the absence of movable spaces.

With this device text may be composed with the closest possible spacing, finer than so-called 'hair-spacing'. This is especially useful in composition of very narrow measures, where it frequently happens there are not more than two or three spaces in a line, and a satisfactory word division cannot be negotiated. Also invaluable for 'line-for-line' reprint composition, where very close spacing is often required.

THE MOULD

Moulds to be used for casting combined-space composition must be sent to The Monotype Corporation Ltd. for alteration so that the *lower* blade will open to over two ems of set, and to limit the opening of the upper blade so that it will come safely within the range of the matrix seating; the latter is necessary when the first letter of a word is an 18-unit character, to which may be combined the widest space. All moulds over 6 point need altering.

When casting 12-point 'open' composition with combined spacing, the caster should be run slightly slower to allow extra time for the enlarged type bodies to cool.

The space transfer wedge is reduced in width to enable the space to be cast to the first character of a word, without altering the justifying scale figures.

To adjust a special space transfer wedge for casting 'combined standard spacing' (with a 4-unit minimum space), proceed as follows:

Put justification wedges in positions indicated by the 'constant' of the justifying scale of the 'set' to which the transfer wedge is to be adjusted. Cast a number of 18-unit characters; then cast a similar number of 14-unit characters with the space transfer wedge in operation. When the two lines are exactly similar in length the adjustment is correct.

To adjust a special space transfer wedge for casting 'combined close spacing' (with a minimum of 0), put the justification wedges in positions indicated by the 'constant' of the justifying scale. Cast a number of 18-unit characters; then cast a similar number of these 18-unit characters with the space transfer wedge in operation. When the two lines are exactly similar in length the adjustment is correct.

The operator must write on his spool whether 'normal', 'combined standard' or 'combined close' space transfer wedge adjustment is to be used, and give the justifying scale 'constant' figures. To avoid repeated adjustments it is advisable to keep special transfer wedges for each caster already adjusted.

SPECIMEN OF CLOSE SPACING

> My excellent father died about five years ago; and his attachment to Mr. Wickham was to the last so steady, that in his will he particularly recommended it to me, to promote his advancement in the best manner that his profession might allow—and if he took orders, desired that a valuable family living might be his as soon as it became vacant. There was also a legacy of one thousand pounds. His own father did not long survive mine, and

HEBREW COMPOSITION

IN HEBREW COMPOSITION the characters read from right to left, and this is provided for on a 'Monotype' composing machine by punching the characters of matrices in a direction reverse to the punching of matrices for English composition, and equipping the caster with a reversed galley mechanism, which stacks the lines of type in a galley arranged over the sorts tray position of the standard casting machine. When the galley of type is proofed it is read from right to left, proceeding downward, without further manipulation beyond any necessary correction of the composition. But for this reverse delivery arrangement the matrices would have to be punched in the same direction as English matrices, and each line after casting would require to be turned into the opposite direction by hand. Hebrew composed on a 'Monotype' reverse delivery caster may contain all the 'points' or 'accents' associated with correct Hebrew literature. Here are a few lines of 'pointed'

Hebrew composed on a 'Monotype' Hebrew machine, followed by ordinary (imperfect) Hebrew.

וְהַזְקֵנִים רָאוּ כִּי שָׁבָה חֲמַת הַמֶּלֶךְ מֵעֲלֵיהֶם
וַתְּחִי רוּחָם, וַיָּקוּמוּ מִן הָאָרֶץ וַיִּשְׂאוּ כַּפֵּיהֶם
הַשָּׁמַיְמָה וִיאׁמְרוּ:

והזקנים ראו כי שבה חמת המלך מעליהם ותחי רוחם,
ויקומו מן הארץ וישאו כפיהם השמימה ויאמרו:

REVERSE DELIVERY ATTACHMENT

THE REVERSE DELIVERY ATTACHMENT enables composition matter reading from right to left to be cast on the composition caster and delivered to a galley positioned on the left of the caster instead of the right as in English composition.

To equip the caster with this attachment the following parts must be removed from the machine:—

Rule xe39F.
Type channel block, adjustable, xa50F
Stop slide xb44F.
Column pusher spring x7F.
Column pusher spring box x8F.
Column pusher xc1F.
Type channel plate d49F.
Sorts tray support bar 43FF.

Assemble complete the lifting mechanism on the galley bars and secure with screws. The lifter must be flat on the type channel plate when at rest. By lifting vertically, the lifting frame latch secures the mechanism, thus preventing it from falling back.

Replace type channel plate, front, screw and bolts, and see that friction plunger is in place on line hook operating bar.

Assemble type channel block (adjustable) bracket, wing bolts and washer.

Assemble type channel block, adjustable.

Assemble rule lever with lifting frame lifting rod.

Assemble column pusher guide bar lever rod ball plunger to column pusher spring box with column pusher guide bar lever and galley pan spring post.

Assemble complete galley pan shelf. Place a galley in position, making the necessary adjustments by means of the support tray support bar stud nuts to allow the mouth of galley to be approximately $\frac{1}{64}''$ under the level of type channel block, adjustable. The galley is adjusted for side position by means of the clamps provided.

Assemble rule, stop slide mechanism and sorts tray.

ADJUSTMENTS

Set the type channel block, adjustable, to suit point size of type to be cast, making sure that it is parallel with type channel block, fixed. Adjust if necessary, using clamp tongue and channel block bracket wing bolts.

Secure the lifting frame plate in the correct position for size of type to be cast, No. 1 position for 6 to 8 point, No. 2 for 9 to 12 point, and No. 3 for over 12 point.

The lifting frame should be located on galley pan support bars to give approximately .008″ clearance between the lifting frame plate and the type channel block, adjustable. This clearance should be checked when lifting frame is being raised. Check that lifting frame plate is parallel with type channel block before securing frame in position with set screws. Set column pusher cam adjusting cam to position according to point size of mould on machine.

Adjust column pusher guide bar lever rod so that face of column pusher is .008″ to the right of type channel block, fixed.

Release lifting frame adjusting lever bell crank eccentric nut and adjust eccentric to give approximately $\frac{3}{64}''$ clearance between lifting frame adjusting lever bell crank and lifting frame adjusting lever bell crank slide.

Release lifting frame lifting rod nut and adjust the rod to give approximately $\frac{1}{8}''$ clearance between end of the rod and lifting frame adjusting lever bell crank.

Trip the galley mechanism by hand and turn machine until lifting frame is in its highest position. Adjust the lifting frame adjusting screw nut to bring upper face of lifting frame plate .008″ above the upper face of the type channel block, adjustable.

Turn machine until column pusher is in its forward position and the vernier reads 160°. Adjust rule lifting rod nuts to give $\frac{1}{32}''$ clearance between bottom face of rule and column pusher. Check that rule is parallel with left hand face of column pusher, adjust if necessary, using lifting rod bracket wing bolt.

With machine in same position, adjust column pusher stop adjusting nuts to allow column pusher to project $\frac{1}{32}''$ beyond left-hand face of rule.

Engage operating lever and adjust stop slide trip bar pin to remove all slackness from stop slide trip bar.

NOTE.—*With the exception of the lifting frame vertical adjustment, all adjustments must be made whenever point size of mould is changed.*

When changing from reverse delivery to English composition the entire attachment should be removed with the following exceptions:

Sorts tray support bar stud, long, b43F1.

Rule Lever xb40F.

Type channel plate, rear, b49F5.

To detach type channel plate, front, remove bolt and screw and gently knock channel plate towards front of machine, taking care that line hook operating bar friction plunger and spring are not lost. Replace with channel plate for English composition.

DUAL TYPE MOULD ATTACHMENT

WITH THIS ATTACHMENT the low quad operating mechanism is controlled by air signals, and gives $4\frac{1}{2}$ or 9 point at will, in place of low spaces or characters.

For this purpose the signals 'N' and .0075″ are used; .0075″ giving 9 point, and 'N' and .0075″ giving $4\frac{1}{2}$ point.

The main parts of the attachment consist of a valve box secured to the main stand at the rear of the machine, a selecting lever switch box attached to a new fulcrum bracket on the bridge and a new selecting lever.

The switch box consists of an air operated piston connected to a diamond-shaped switch, air passes from the valve box to either end of the piston as dictated by signals from the paper. This occurs simultaneously with the positioning of the justification wedge.

The switch, which is held in position under spring tension, controls the selecting lever, causing it to contact with the character lever, to give 9 point openings and with the space lever to give $4\frac{1}{2}$ point.

The valve box consists of a spring loaded valve. This can be put out of action by means of a locking screw which is screwed down to its fullest extent and secured by a clamp screw.

The 'N' and .0075″ pipes are tapped and connections made with the valve box and a tee is fitted to each of these pipes, which enables 'N' and .0075″ air to function normally when the attachment valve is locked.

Main stand air pipes 'N', .0075″, and 'N' and .0075″ connect the valve box to selecting lever switch box and the tees on the .0075″ and 'N' pipes.

When .0075″ signal only is used air passes across the valve box valve and through the main stand and bridge .0075″ air pipes to rear of switch box piston. This moves the switch into such a position that selecting lever contacts with character lever, which in turn moves the mould blade lever and causes the auxiliary blade to be brought back into contact with the main blade allowing a 9-point type to be cast.

When 'N' and .0075″ signals are used together, the valve box valve is raised by 'N' air and cuts off supply of air from .0075″ pipes to rear of switch box piston and diverts it to the front of piston. This moves the switch into such a position that selecting lever contacts with space lever, which in turn moves the mould blade lever and causes the auxiliary blade to be held forward. When a cast is made under these conditions only the main blade moves and a 4½-point type is produced.

There are no special adjustments necessary for this attachment, except to ensure that the switch situated on the fulcrum bracket of bridge is operated freely so as to prevent damage to the selecting lever. When replacing bridge, care must be taken to ensure that the feet of bridge are making good contact with main stand in order to obtain an air-tight joint.

The valve lock on valve box should be unscrewed and clamped into position to allow valve to move to its upper position. Turn the .0075″ air cock on.

To revert to the standard low quad operating mechanism, the following parts must be removed from the selecting lever switch box: the split cotter, spring, pivot and switch. Remove the dual type mould selecting lever and replace by the standard selecting lever, fulcrum pin and spring. Lock the valve box valve and turn off the .0075″ air cock.

The following additional adjustments are necessary if the machine is fitted with the reverse delivery attachment:

The type channel block, adjustable, xe50F must be adjusted to suit the smaller point size produced by the dual type mould.

The lifting frame plate must always be located in the forward position.

DUAL TYPE MOULD

IN THIS MOULD the two blades are so designed that the front ends, the ends against which the cast is made, are side by side, each blade being 4½ points wide. One, equivalent to the lower blade of the standard composition mould, is moved each time a cast is made. The other, like the upper blade of the standard composition mould, is an auxiliary blade, and is used only when casting 9 point.

For Hebrew composition this pattern of mould is used. The accents are cast separated from the characters by having a single blade in operation. When characters are being cast, both mould blades are in operation, the two forming the body measurement of the characters.

This auxiliary blade is held back against the main blade by the mould blade lever f29A13 in the same way that the upper blade is held back against the lower when casting characters in the standard composition mould.

When the auxiliary blade is held forward by the mould blade lever, $4\frac{1}{2}$ point is cast, whereas in the standard composition mould it would be a low space.

DUPLEX MOULD ATTACHMENT
FOR
EXOTIC LANGUAGES

WITH A NUMBER of the Eastern languages, such as Arabic, the characters are cast on type bodies larger than 14 point and the normal requirements necessitate the use of $.4'' \times .4''$ and $.4'' \times .2''$ matrices to provide an adequate metal-tight matrix seating on the mould. This method considerably limits the number of matrices which can be accommodated in the matrix-case.

To increase and include as many matrices as possible in the case for mechanical composition, those characters in exotic faces with short or no ascending or descending strokes are now punched in $.2'' \times .2''$ and $.2'' \times .4''$ matrices.

A mould is provided to give a seating surface for these different styles of matrices, and to enable it to be used on the caster, the duplex mould attachment must be fitted.

In the duplex mould there are two blades. The top half of the main blade is cut away to allow an auxiliary blade to operate by its side, this is provided with a projection, formed in such a way that the opening of the mould at the top would be, for example, 18- or 12-point bodywise. By this method and operation $.4'' \times .2''$ or $.2'' \times .2''$ matrices can be used in the matrix-case. The auxiliary blade is held back against the main blade by the mould blade lever in the same way that the upper blade is held back against the lower when casting characters from a standard composition mould. When the auxiliary blade is held forward by the mould blade lever, a 12-point character with 18-point body is cast, whereas from the standard composition mould a low space would be produced.

With this attachment the low quad mechanism is controlled by air signals and gives 18 or 12 point at will in place of characters or low quads. For this purpose the signals 'N' and $.0075''$ are used. 'N' and $.0075''$ together give 18 point. No signal gives 12 point.

The main parts of the attachment consist of a valve box secured to the main stand at the rear of machine, a selecting lever switch box attached to a new fulcrum bracket on the bridge and a new selecting lever.

The switch box consists of a spring-loaded piston connected to a diamond-shaped switch; air passes from the valve box to rear of the piston as dictated by 'N' and .0075″ signals from the paper.

The switch controls the selecting lever, causing it to contact with character lever to give openings of 18 point and with space lever to give 12 point.

The valve box consists of a spring-loaded valve. This can be put out of action by means of a locking screw, screwed down to its fullest extent and secured by a clamp screw.

The 'N' and .0075″ pipes are tapped and connections made with the valve box, a tee is fitted to 'N' pipe enabling 'N' air to function normally when the valve is locked, the .0075″ air pipe is diverted to the valve box. Main stand .0075″ air pipes connect the valve box to selecting lever switch box and to 'D' pin block.

When .0075″ signal is used air passes across the valve box valve and through the pipe to the .0075″ position in 'D' pin block. When the 'N' and .0075″ air signals are used together, the valve is raised by 'N' air and cuts off supply of air from .0075″ pipes to 'D' pin block and transfers it to rear of switch box piston. This moves the switch into such a position that selecting lever contacts with character lever, which in turn moves the mould blade lever, causing the auxiliary blade to be brought back into contact with main blade, allowing 18-point type to be cast.

There are no special adjustments necessary for this attachment except to ensure that the switch situated on the fulcrum bracket of bridge is operating freely and so preventing damage to selecting lever. When re-securing bridge to machine, the feet must always make good contact with main stand to form an airtight joint.

See that valve lock on valve box is unscrewed and clamped into position to allow valve to move to its upper position.

To enable composition to be cast using the duplex mould the caster must be equipped with the following:

Nozzle a14H2.

Speed regulating attachment a9cu(B).

Duplex piston springs 75cu or 75cu1.

For composition reading from right to left the reverse delivery attachment must also be fitted.

The duplex piston springs enable composition up to 18 point to be cast without the use of centring pin auxiliary spring group xb36A, thus reducing the downward pressure on matrices during the casting period and also permits type to be cast without the use of latch 57H1.

Alloy	Point Size	Speed	Temp.	Duplex Piston Spring Pressure	Water	Nozzle	Pump	Piston
9–19	14	135 r.p.m.	700°	—	Plenty	No. 2	Std. $\frac{7}{8}''$	$\frac{7}{8}''$–$\frac{13}{16}$ stroke
9–19	16	130 r.p.m.	700°	$\frac{3}{4}''$	Plenty	No. 2	Std. $\frac{3}{4}''$	$\frac{7}{8}''$–$\frac{13}{16}$ stroke
9–19	18	115–120 r.p.m.	700°	$1''$	Plenty	No. 2	Std. $\frac{7}{8}''$	$\frac{7}{8}''$–$\frac{13}{16}$ stroke

To revert to standard low quad mechanism: remove pivot switch with collar and split cotter; these parts cannot be used with low quad mechanism.

Remove duplex selecting lever and replace by the standard selecting lever and readjust where necessary.

Lock the duplex mould valve box valve.

DUPLEX PISTON SPRING 75cu1

The duplex piston springs may be applied to composition casters fitted with display type attachment and for casting large type composition.

To enable this to be effected a longer rod is provided graduated in inches and the adjusting nut can be screwed down to give a pressure of approximately 490 lb.

SQUARE EMS AND HALF-SQUARE FIGURES

IN COMPOSITION from 'Monotype' keyboards normal figures are registered and cast to nine units of set, or half of the set em, which is eighteen units.

This is a perfectly satisfactory basis for general composition and most tabular work, but cases arise where half-square figures are more convenient. This is exemplified usually in the composition of railway time-tables, where the headings may run at right angles to the cross lines, or where otherwise blank columns are filled with explanatory remarks. For this class of work it is possible to compose the stub in an expanded face, and to use half-square figures for the train times. For example: the stub may be composed in 8 point $8\frac{1}{2}$ set and the figures required are nine units of 8 set.

The following example (with stub in $8\frac{1}{2}$ set) is sufficient to explain the use of half-square figures, as it is obvious that if the time columns were composed in $8\frac{1}{2}$ set figures, the vertical 8-point lines would need a $4\frac{1}{2}$-point make-up on each side to bring these columns up to 17 points.

Three Bridges	..	1245	1257		1 15	1 13		1 33		1 46	2 2		4 10
Balcombe	..	1253	1259		1 22	..				1 52	2 8		
Haywards Heath		1259			1 28	1 24				1 58	2 14		
Wivelsfield	..	1 4			1 32	..				2 3	2 19		
Burgess Hill	..	1 7		To Horsham, etc.	1 35	..	Table A		To Reading—	2 6	2 21	Refreshment Car	
Hassocks	..	1 12			1 39	..				2 10	2 33		
Preston Park	..	1 19			1 47	1 40				2 18	2 35		
Brighton..	arr.	1 22			1 50	1 43				2 21	2 37		
Hove	arr.	1 29			2 7	1 53				2 32	2 50		
Shoreham	arr.	1 36			2 20	2 4				2 45	2 57		
Worthing	arr.	1 46			2 31	2 12				2 56	3 5		

The stub measure is 8 ems of 8½ set; other columns 2 ems of 8 point, divided by 2-point rules.

Keyboard measure is adjusted to 8 ems 8 units. The stub lines are single justified, and the balance of the measure is composed with four 'letter-spaced' figures or ens in each column (without any reference to the em scale), and double justified 3/1. Nine-unit figures of 8 set replace the 8½-set figures in the matrix-case.

The normal wedge in use is 8½ set, and there are four figures or spaces in each column. The difference between 9 units of 8 set and 8½ is .00346", the amount to be deducted from each 9-unit figure (or 9-unit space) to make two figures equal one em of 8 set. Seven *minus* moves on the fine justification wedge make the justification wedge positions 3/1 (3/8 minus 0/7=3/1).

Following shows the amount to be added to or deducted from 3/8 for ens of ¼, ½, ¾, or 1 set so that 'letter-spaced' two figures (or en spaces) may make square ens: ¼ set, 0/3; ½ set, 0/7; ¾ set, 0/10; 1 set, 0/14.

In the three columns containing 8-point alphabetic type, two of the spaces in each line cast in place of figures would be discarded, and the type lines inserted. (To make these types easily removable, two figures should be composed in each line in place of spaces.)

THE UNIVERSAL 3/8 CONSTANT

The method of selecting 3/8 as the starting point for adding or deducting type measurements is to be encouraged, as it rules out the necessity of having to refer to the various justifying scale constants. The transfer wedges on the caster are adjusted to a justification wedge difference of 3/8, in which positions types are cast to the same width, no matter which transfer wedge is in operation. Therefore: any alteration to the designed measurement of any type or space can start only from 3/8.

By this method (for figure columns) 9-unit figure matrices may be placed in any matrix-case row within the limits of the justification wedge adjustment above or below 3/8. The reduction limit on any type body is 2/7 (3/8 minus 1/1=2/7), and the limit to be added to any type body from any unit row is 12/7 (3/8 plus 12/7=15/15), provided, of course, that the increased measurement does not exceed the mould blade opening limit.

INCREASING SETS TO OBTAIN SQUARE EMS

Where the set is less than the body (such as $7\frac{3}{4}$ set, 8 point), square ems and half-square figures may be obtained by composing half sets or quarter sets to the next higher whole number set; but where the set is greater than the body point (such as $8\frac{1}{2}$ set 8 point) this implies casting the type on a mould one point larger than that for which type has been designed, so that the composition appears leaded. The limit of increasing sets should be one-half set, otherwise the type becomes visibly spaced. Except for special kinds of tabular work there is no advantage in having square ems. Figures should be proportionate to the type design, whether of normal, condensed or expanded face.

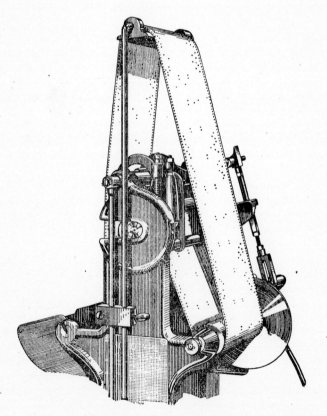

Copy repeating attachment.

REPEATING LINES OF COMPOSITION

WHEN A QUANTITY of justified lines of type or quads is required, perforate and justify on the Keyboard a few of these lines to occupy a
short length of ribbon, about 2 ft. long; place the ribbon on caster air
tower, and join the ends together, thereby making an endless band from
which any number of lines can be cast. To join the ends of the paper a very
thin application of seccotine is found best, care being exercised that the
join is made at the correct place. It should be noted that the marginal
holes overlap each other exactly. Any perforation 'blinded' by the overlap at the join should be re-pierced with a bodkin.

COPY REPEATING ATTACHMENT

With this attachment it is possible easily and accurately to join the
ends of a strip of keyboard 'copy', thus making it continuous for
repeating lines indefinitely.

Attach it near the upper end of the air pipe a6G and see that the collars
on the support rod 26G8 are approximately central with the pin wheels
on air tower.

When a strip of 'copy' is to be joined, lock the paper setting plate
26G1G so that the pins 26G7 are projecting upwards; insert 'copy'
under air bar in the usual manner, bring the two ends of 'copy' to the
setting plate, and register them by means of the justification perforations. Then gum the ends together.

The paper setting plate is then unlocked, turned under the support
rod and re-locked in this (the working) position. The horizontal portion
of the rod between the two collars serves as a guide for the paper ribbon.

GALLEY AUTOMATIC TRIP ATTACHMENT

(FOR SORTS CASTING)

WITH THIS ATTACHMENT sorts matter may be stacked automatically in
any given measure between 22 and 30 ems pica.

When the caster is operating and the galley has been set to the
required measure, the line of sorts that is being withdrawn to the galley
has its forward end supported by special line supports xk29F for 5 point
to 8 point inclusive or xk30F for 9 point to 12 point inclusive. When
sufficient types have been cast, the line support will be pushed against
the curved end of an operating lever 71F1, causing the lever to fulcrum
on its bar 71F2. This bar is attached to a special sorts tray support bar
stud a43F1, which replaces the standard part 43F1. The motion is
transmitted by means of a link 71F4 to the trip lever d45FF and so

pushes the trip lever out of engagement with the galley cam driving
pawl. The pawl is thus released and galley mechanism is put into
operation.

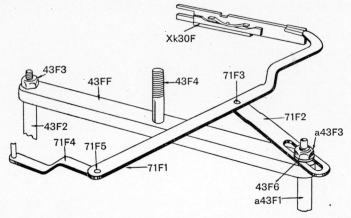

To adjust the device for the required measure, remove the sorts tray,
release the nut at top of special support bar stud a43F1, and adjust the
position of the fulcrum bar 71F2 under the nut until the galley mechanism trips at required measure; tighten fulcrum bar firmly in position.

MOULD BLADE COVER FOR USE WHEN
CASTING WHITE LINES AND SPACES

SHOULD A QUANTITY of quads and spaces or of white lines of any measure up to 60 ems pica be required to be cast, considerable time can be
saved on the keyboard, paper economized, wear and tear of mould,
matrices, and bridge prevented by using a mould blade cover a60AA.

With the bridge removed this cover is screwed to the mould, so that
it is placed on the mould where ordinarily the matrix is positioned
during casting. Before finally screwing this cover to the mould see that
there is clearance for the carrier when the latter is in its forward position.

A screw adjustment is provided so that correct pressure can be put
on the mould blade to prevent it rising. The importance of this will be
appreciated when thin spaces are being cast.

The mould blade lever is held back by the spring 60A5 which is
anchored to bridge screw 1A21. In the event of high spaces and high
quads being needed, the pull of this special spring must be reversed
by anchoring it to the space casting spring post, thereby holding the
upper mould blade open.

LEADING ATTACHMENT

A SPECIAL ADVANTAGE of this attachment is the avoidance of casting founts on bodies larger than that for which a type face has been designed in order to save hand leading. For example: a given point size of face may be cast to its correct body size, or 1 point, $1\frac{1}{2}$ point or 2 point larger body, thus necessitating four different sets of type cases for corrections.

The attachment will lead 5 to 24 point composition matter with 1 to 6 point leads, or place rules between the lines, in any length from 6 picas to 48 picas, but is limited to either leads or rules of one particular point size at one setting.

The special equipment includes: lead galley xa201F, column rule xm39F, column pusher spring box xa8F, valve box, galley cut-out valve, etc.

LEAD GALLEY Xa201F

This operates above the composition galley and is moved towards the column rule for leading, when air from a valve box causes the lead galley operating lever piston 202F9 to act on its lever 202F1. The galley must be adjusted so that its edge is exactly parallel with the column rule when working freely without shake.

COLUMN RULE Xm39F

This is fitted with depressors for transferring the leads or rules from the lead galley to the composition galley below. Adjust as described for the standard column rule, and see that it is quite free throughout its movement.

COLUMN PUSHER SPRING BOX Xa8F

When the lead galley advances towards the column rule it depresses a stop 44F25F attached to the stop slide c44FF. This allows the spring box to push the line of type just cast sufficiently far for a lead or rule to be inserted beside it.

When the leading attachment is not in use the special spring box must be replaced by the standard part. Adjust the column pusher adjusting screw nuts as described for the standard caster whenever the spring boxes are changed.

VALVE BOX

This includes a valve a206F18, upper trip 206F22 and lower trip 206F21. When the valve is free of both trips, i.e., 'up', air can pass to the galley operating lever piston 202F9 and so advance the lead galley towards the column rule. When, however, the valve is held down by either trip, air cannot pass to the piston; consequently the lead galley does not move and 'leading' cannot take place.

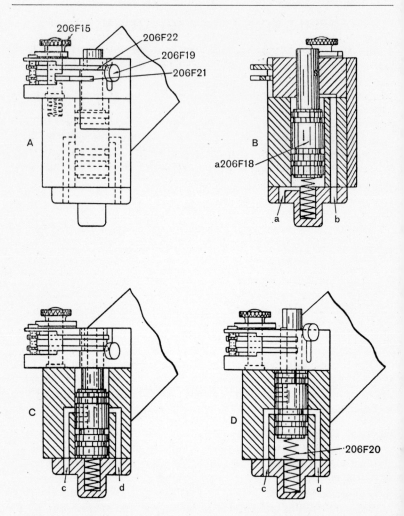

The upper trip is always in use. A plate 14F13 attached to the galley cam pushes the valve down under this trip at a suitable moment *before* the galley cam comes to rest. A pin 14F12, also fixed in the galley cam, releases this trip at a suitable moment *after* the galley cam has started, and the valve is raised by a spring.

The lower trip is available only when the switch is at 'S' ('signalled' leading), and holds the valve down after the valve has been depressed by air from .0005″ perforation.

A second pin 14F12 fixed in the galley cam is positioned so as to release this lower trip just before the galley cam comes to rest, whereupon the valve rises to engage under the upper trip, from which position it may be pushed down or released up, according to whether the leading device is signalled to remain at rest or to function.

When air from 'S' perforation is admitted to the under face of the valve at the same time as air from .0005″ perforation is admitted above it, the valve is not pushed down but remains under the upper trip ready to be released up when freed by the trip pin during the next revolution of the galley cam.

'REPEAT' LEADING

The valve box switch must be set at 'R'. The device will then automatically insert the lead or rule each time the galley mechanism is operated.

'SIGNALLED' LEADING

The valve box switch must be set at 'S'. The device will then insert a lead or rule only when specially signalled by perforations 'S' and .0005″.

ADJUSTMENTS

The valve box must be adjusted for vertical relation with the plate on galley cam so that the plate depresses the valve a further $\frac{1}{64}$″ after the upper trip has dropped in.

GALLEY CUT-OUT X208F

This cuts off the air supply to the lead galley operating lever piston 202F9 if the line of type is shorter or longer than the galley entrance.

The lead galley then returns to its extreme position away from the column rule, and the operator can correct the line of type without allowing the caster to stop.

The cut-out is placed in the pipe line from the valve box to the lead galley operating lever piston 202F9 and is operated by the operating lever latch c33F.

The hook and valve should be uncoupled if the operator wishes to prevent movement of the lead galley when turning the machine with the galley mechanism tripped.

With the operating lever a32F in running position, disconnect the valve coupling hook 208F7. Press the cut-out valve 208F4F into its cylinder to contact on the bearing bracket 39F24, and adjust the hook so that when its lock nut 208F9 is tightened, the hook enters freely in the slot in valve and engages with the pin without withdrawing the valve or moving the operating lever latch c33F.

LEAD GALLEY GUIDE BARS a201F4 AND a201F5

Two setting gauges 201F13 for 1 to 1½ point, and 201F14 for 2 to 6 point, are supplied for setting the bars to suit the point size of lead or rule. Two leads or rules of the correct length must be used to set the bars the correct distance apart.

LEAD DEPRESSORS a200F1, a200F9 AND 200F13

These are adjusted horizontally by being located as near as possible to the ends of the lead or rule. Their vertical position is determined by tripping the galley mechanism, turning machine until the column rule is in its highest position, and then adjusting them so that they just clear the upper edge of leads or rules when lead galley has advanced to the column rule. Lock the depressors firmly in position.

LEAD GALLEY OPERATING LEVER STOP, ADJUSTABLE 202F16

Load the galley with the leads or rules to be used. Set the valve switch knob at 'R'. Trip the galley mechanism, and turn machine so that the column rule is in its highest position and lead galley has moved towards it. Then adjust the lead galley stop so that the depressors have a maximum bearing on the lead or rule to be pushed into the composition galley without engaging the next one.

AIR THROTTLE VENT SCREW 207F29

This must be adjusted so that the air supply causes the lead galley to make a sure and steady movement.

When the attachment is not in use, turn off the air by means of cock, to avoid valve becoming gummed up.

When using 6-pica measure, slide the front depressor well clear of lead galley. Remove rear depressor. Attach the 6-pica depressor, using the existing slide 200F12 and locking screw a200F11.

Locate the 6-pica depressor horizontally in the centre of the lead or rule in the lead galley. The vertical adjustment is determined by placing one of the leads or rules to be inserted with its lower edge flush with the lower edge of the rule, making sure that the depressor is in contact with the upper edge of the lead or rule.

RULE SPRING CLIP 39F33

The rule spring clip should be attached to the rule as near as possible to the front end of the measure.

The clip supports the previously dropped lead or rule against the line of type and obviates the possibility of the lead or rule creeping forward between the stop slide and galley rule and causing an obstruction when the next line of type is being pushed into the galley by column pusher.

OVERHUNG TYPE FOR CASTERS EQUIPPED WITH LEADING ATTACHMENT

This attachment consists of a rule guide which is free to slide in a right-hand direction on top of type channel block, fixed. A tension

spring returns the rule guide to the normal position. The rule is cham-
fered at the guide end so that when the overhang of type contacts with
it the rule moves over with guide by a distance equivalent to the overhang of the type.

When leading with 1-point leads or rules or reverting to standard
composition without overhung type the rule guide should be prevented
from sliding by attaching it rigidly to the channel block. To do this the
rule guide screws must be removed and replaced by the two spare screws
provided. Before tightening these screws care must be taken that guide
is in its normal position, that is to the left.

NOTE.—*The thin line support* XN29F *should be used with this attachment.*

REMINDER

*Any matrix-case that is to be used with this device should be returned to
The Monotype Corporation Ltd. for alteration to clear the column rule
guide* 205F1.

MOULDS

COMPOSITION MOULDS UP TO 14 POINT INCLUSIVE

Designed for use on 'Monotype' Composition or Display Type
Machines, for casting type in any size up to 14 point inclusive from .2″
matrices. A separate mould is required for casting type of each point
size. The 13-point and 14-point moulds produce type with bevels on
the upper edge; this is to give the matrices a larger seating area on the
mould.

Blade Openings on Composition Moulds 22,000—*Point or Didot.*

	Upper Blade		Lower Blade	
Standard Mould	.157	.200 quad	.350 (with character)	5 to 11
	.167	.200 quad	.350 (with character)	12 to 14
When used for	.142	.200 quad	.350 (with character)	5 to 11
Combined Spacing	.152	.200 quad	.350 (with character)	12 to 14
By fitting Special Blade Stop	.250*	.200 quad	.350 (with character)	5 to 14

* These moulds are specially designed for use with extended matrix faces. An
additional stop is supplied so that blade movement can be restricted to standard
opening.

All new pattern, loose-nick moulds are converted to square nick when restored
to full height; the blade openings then conform to above table. Old pattern, loose-
nick moulds cannot be converted to square nicks if for use with old-style low quad
attachment on machines still fitted with 'G' cams.

LARGE TYPE COMPOSITION MOULDS, 14 POINT TO 24 POINT

Designed for use on 'Monotype' Composing Machines, for casting
type in 14 point, 18 point and 24 point from .4″ matrices. These consist

of a base containing interchangeable mould blade insets, one for each point size. The type nick is on the right-hand mould blade block, similar to that of 5-point to 14-point composition moulds.

Large Type Composition Mould Blade Openings:

14 point	..	..	..	..	.. .360
18 point	..	..	..	..	.. .360
24 point	..	..	..	..	.. .392

DISPLAY TYPE MOULDS, 14 POINT TO 36 POINT

Designed for use on 'Monotype' Display Type Machine, for casting type in 14, 18, 24, 30, and 36 point from display type matrices. These consist of a base containing interchangeable mould blade insets, one for each point size. Type nick is on left-hand mould-blade block, as display matrices are positioned on mould in a direction reverse to that of composition matrices.

Coupling hook 56B1 is required for 14- and 18-point display mould insets.

LOOSE NICK MOULDS

14 and 18 point	..	..	Blade opening .422
24 and 30 point	..	..	Blade opening .498
36 point	..	..	..	Blade opening .532

SQUARE NICK MOULDS

14 and 18 point	..	..	Blade opening .422
24 point	..	..	..	Blade opening .498
30 point	..	..	..	Blade opening .581
36 point	..	..	..	Blade opening .664

SHORT LEAD AND RULE MOULD

Designed for use on the Composition Caster or Display Type Machine, for casting short leads and rules in any body size from $1\frac{1}{2}$ point to 3 point, in any length from 2 point to 36 point. These moulds consist of a base fitted with interchangeable insets. A matrix is fitted to and supplied as part of the mould blade. A change of blade and matrix is therefore required for any change of rule face, and a different inset is required for each body size. A special low blade and corresponding cap for each inset converts the inset into a short low lead mould.

QUAD AND SPACE MOULD

For casting quads and spaces (low) in any set width from 1 point to 36 points, by using interchangeable blades in any body size from 5 point to 12 point.

If used on the Composition Caster, the Speed Regulating Attachment (see p. 163) and mould blade cam lever compound lever b44E7 (see p. 165) must be fitted to the machine.

SPLIT FRACTION MOULD

For casting figures for split fractions of half the body size for moulds from 8 point to 12 point. These figures will produce fractions for every possible combination. The mould is equipped with interchangeable blades in 4, 4½, 5, 5½, and 6 point.

ARABIC COMPOSITION MOULD

This mould has a main blade and an auxiliary blade. The upper edge of the auxiliary blade overlaps the main blade, and both blades can be operated independently of each other.

The nominal body size of the mould is always that of the main blade. When both blades are operated together the body size at the top will be that of the main blade, and requires the use of .4″ matrices.

When the auxiliary blade is automatically held forward, the body size at the top is reduced by the thickness of this blade, and permits the use of .2″ matrices.

The bodywise openings are: 11 and 14 point for 14-point moulds; 12 and 16 point for 16 point; 12 and 18 point for 18 point.

The set-wise blade opening limits for 14, 16 and 18 point are: lower blade .360″, upper blade .250″.

HEBREW COMPOSITION MOULD

These moulds are equipped with two blades, either of which may be worked separately. Both blades are in operation when casting the body characters of a line (as in Hebrew composition), and only one blade is used for casting the accents in separate lines of reduced body size. See also instruction under heading DUAL TYPE MOULD p. 145.

INSTRUCTION ON 'MONOTYPE' COMPOSITION MOULDS
(FOR PLATE SEE P. 287)

These notes and instructions should be carefully read by all responsible for the care and efficient working of 'Monotype' moulds.

1. Efficient lubrication is of utmost importance. Always have the mould equipped with mould oiler b11cT1 and crossblock auxiliary oiler x32cT.

2. Do not experiment with mould oils, but use only the oils recommended.

3. The blades of all composition moulds are the same length within a limit which will not affect the adjustment of the mould blade connecting rod 45E, but it is advisable to check this adjustment occasionally.

4. Before placing a mould on the machine fill the hollow screw (11581) at the end of mould with warm mould oil.

5. Secure the mould to the machine after making sure that the mould abutment faces of the pin blocks are perfectly clean. Make

sure that the shortest of the three holding down screws is in the front position.

6. Lubricate the mould coupling hook (6338).

7. Place the bridge on machine and check the adjustments. Pay particular attention to the ascent and descent of matrix-case, the timing of the centring pin and length of draw rods. All moulds are made to the same over-all height within a very small limit, so that it should not be necessary to readjust the bridge each time a mould is changed, but *regular checking of these adjustments will save considerable wear on the matrix seat of mould.*

8. When a mould is taken off the machine always blow the water out of the waterways. Then blow a few drops of oil through the waterways before putting the mould in its box.

9. Do not leave a mould lying where dirt or grit can get into it. Grit in a mould will start scoring of the various parts and render a major repair necessary, therefore always keep the mould in its box when not in use. It is also important occasionally to clean the mould oiler.

TAKING THE MOULD APART FOR CLEANING

Never take a mould apart so long as it continues to cast satisfactory type. Should it become necessary to take a mould apart for cleaning, prepare a suitable place, cover it with clean paper and proceed in the following manner:

1. Remove the crossblock.
2. Loosen nut (1053) and hollow screw (11581) on end of mould.
3. Remove blade stop (13620–3) and support (5637).
4. Remove cover plate (13613) (22,000 series mould).
5. Remove blade holding-down plate (13612).
6. Take off cover springs (6328, 6329).
7. Withdraw the blades, keeping them down on the intermediate plate while doing so in order not to damage the nick or nick recess.
8. Insert a few thicknesses of paper between the side blocks (6857, 11420) in place of the mould blades and remove the side blocks by canting them towards the blade opening.

This is as far as it is safe for a mould to be taken apart by the operator. The two eccentric dowels (3575) which position the side blocks must not be interfered with in any way. If the dowels of these moulds are moved the slightest amount, the side blocks will not go back in correct adjustment.

Wash all parts thoroughly in clean benzine. Metal or burnt oil adhering to the parts can be scraped off with a piece of type metal rule, care being taken not to damage the sharp corners of the side blocks, blades, etc. On no account attempt to lap or polish the parts with oilstones or other abrasives, the effect of which would be to destroy the sharp corners which are so essential if clean, burrless type is to be cast.

REASSEMBLE THE MOULD IN THE FOLLOWING ORDER:
1. Place screw side block (11420) in position.
2. Place nick side block (6857) in position.
3. Replace blades and insert mould blade lever (4010) whilst doing so. Exercise the same care in replacing the blades as when withdrawing them so as not to damage the nick or nick recess.

NOTE.—*In order that the blades should open to their fullest extent, it is essential that the distance pieces should be located in the rear ends of their slots in the blades. To ensure this, advance the blades to a position slightly in advance of the side blocks by a continuous forward movement. If the blades are pushed too far forward the distance pieces will also be carried too far, so that when the blades are pulled back to a position slightly in advance of the side blocks, the distance pieces will be left somewhere in the middle of the slots and the movement of the blades will be restricted accordingly.*

4. Advance the hollow screw in the end of the mould until the side blocks just nip the distance pieces.
5. Replace the blade holding-down plate.
6. Replace cover plate (22,000 series moulds only) and screw down firmly.
7. Replace cover springs and screw down firmly.
8. Apply tension to the side blocks as follows for the different styles of moulds:

22,000 *series moulds with spring tension on side blocks.* Tighten up the hollow screw by screwing firmly home.

22,000 *series moulds and old pattern moulds which have been converted to square nick and have a hollow plug in place of the spring.* Tighten hollow screw, applying no more pressure than can be exerted by hand without undue strain.

Old pattern moulds, either converted or not converted to square nick, which have spring tension on the side blocks. Advance the hollow screw until it just grips, and then give it three half turns.

In those cases where the hollow screw has a lock nut see that this is tightened.

9. Replace blade stop and support.
10. Oil the mould thoroughly and replace the crossblock.

ADJUSTING THE GIB PLATE OF MOULDS WITH NEW STYLE CROSS-BLOCK

The crossblocks of these moulds are fitted with a back plate (13243) without spring pad.

After the mould has been in use some time a slight burr may appear on the crossblock side of the type, rendering a slight adjustment of the gib plate (14612) necessary.

To adjust, proceed as follows: loosen the gib plate adjusting screw lock nuts (13419) and slide crossblock into casting position.

Tighten the left-hand screw (13418) just sufficiently to permit the crossblock to be moved freely by hand, but so that the pressure of the gib plate can be felt. Then slide the crossblock to the right, so that right-hand edge is flush with edge of mould base.

Repeat the adjustment to right-hand screw (14549).

Slide the crossblock backwards and forwards a few times to allow it to settle itself to its new adjustment.

Repeat the adjustment if not satisfied that the crossblock is free or tight enough, or if crossblock is tighter at one end than the other.

Tighten the lock nuts by using wrench 6CT4, holding the screws with a screwdriver to prevent them turning with the lock nuts. Only slight pressure is necessary in tightening the lock nuts.

NOTE.—*When the gib plate is properly adjusted, the crossblock should work much more easily than was the case with the old style crossblock with a spring button in the back plate.*

This readjustment of the gib plate on a new or overhauled mould may become necessary as a result of initial 'running in' wear. Once made, further adjustment should not be necessary for a long period, provided of course that the crossblock is kept properly lubricated.

For the better working of 'Monotype' moulds the use of the auxiliary mould oiler X32CT in conjunction with the mould oiler is recommended. This oiler not only ensures that both sides of the crossblock do not run dry, but also wipes off excess oil, thus preventing the top of mould from becoming flooded.

HINTS FOR MAINTAINING THE ACCURACY OF COMPOSITION MOULDS AND QUAD AND SPACE MOULDS

The blade support should be positioned so that it is almost, but not quite, in contact with the blade. Bad ejection may result from an incorrectly positioned blade support.

Incomplete ejection of the types may be caused by particles of type metal between lower blade and rear end of upper blade.

The shortest of the three mould holding-down screws must be used in the hole under crossblock. If this screw protrudes through the mould base into contact with the crossblock back plate it will be found that the counterbored face of hole in main stand is worn. A worn counterbore can also allow the screw under the screw block of moulds prior to 20,000 series to contact the round key which locates the screw block.

The matrix seating of side blocks in moulds up to and including 12 point is surfaced with a wear-resisting material. This material is a proved advantage when used with a correctly adjusted bridge, etc., but faulty adjustment of the matrix-case stops and draw rods, worn centring pin and matrices, all tend to cause wear on the mould surface. The only matrix under pressure on the mould should be the one directly under the centring pin. Marking on the remaining surface of the mould is usually an indication that the matrices are under pressure applied by the matrix-case back plate or retaining wires.

The blade distance pieces should determine the body size of the product but these can only be effective if held rigidly between the side blocks. An insecure spring block (6322) is a likely cause of 'plus body' as movement of this part allows the distance pieces to become free.

Poor quality types do not arise from a fault in the mould but from a defective pump action, or lack of cleanliness in pump well or nozzle.

The surface of the metal in melting pot should be kept clean. Jets may pile up on dirty type metal until they prevent free movement of the crossblock.

Type from moulds equipped with solid back plate may develop a slight burr on crossblock side. This is caused by the initial wear on the cast-iron gib plate and can be remedied by an adjustment of the gib adjusting screws. If burr persists after making this adjustment it is probable that the side blocks are out of line and mould may then have to be returned for attention.

Product which is tapered setwise can be caused by a faulty mould, but it is usually found that the mould blade is being influenced by defects in the blade sizing mechanism. The adjusting screw c14c1, against which the mould blade abuts, should be domed at the end. A flat-ended screw or loose mould blade abutment slide can tend to strain the mould blade out of its perfectly horizontal line of travel so that the front of blade does not produce parallel types.

DISPLAY TYPE ATTACHMENT
(FOR PLATE SEE PP. 280–283)
ADJUSTMENTS

WHEN THE SPEED REGULATING ATTACHMENT is applied to a machine outside of The Monotype Corporation's Works it is advisable to go over all the regular adjustments of the machine before attachment is put into use. Worn driving cams should be replaced before the display type driving gear is fitted.

To cast display type of 14 point or larger the following changes are necessary:

The speed of the machine, which depends on the time required to cool the type in the mould, must be reduced. Nineteen speeds are obtained at will by changing the position of three levers on the speed regulating attachment. No calculation is necessary to determine the positions of these levers, as a plate on the attachment translates the marks for point size and wedge settings, as given on each display matrix, into positions for these three levers.

Refer to Fig. 1, *Page* 280.—With tumbler in No. 4 position, adjust the belt shifter operating bar lever bracket 100E2 so that the face of the shoulder on the rear end of the belt shifter operating bar a97E1 comes $\frac{1}{32}$" in front of the belt shifter ring b5E when the operating lever is to the right—the position it occupies when machine is not running. With tumbler in No. 1, 2, or 3 position, engage operating lever and see that recessed face of clutch gear 104E1 is almost touching the face of clutch pin a65E3. If necessary, readjust the bracket 100E2 to obtain this condition.

Put the tumbler handle in its No. 1, 2, or 3 position, and adjust the speed bracket guide post nut 122E15 so that there will be $\frac{1}{64}$" clearance between the lug at the lower end of the belt shifter ring and the bottom of the notch in the clutch shifter plate lever a105E7. Note that the belt shifter operating rod does not engage the belt shifter ring when the operating lever is thrown over to start.

Put the tumbler handle in its No. 4 position, with the operating lever to the right (the position it occupies when machine is not running), and adjust the length of the clutch control operating rod 102E1 to give $\frac{1}{64}$" clearance between the under face of the rear end of the belt shifter operating rod a97E1 and the bottom of the slot in the belt shifter ring b5E.

Refer to Fig. 2, *Page* 281.—With the operating lever to the left (in running position) adjust the interlocking lever operating rod a109E1 to give $\frac{1}{64}$" clearance between this rod and the operating lever spring box cam a37F5 when the rod is pushed down by hand as far as it will go. This adjustment should be tested with tumbler handle 133E1E in its No. 1, 2 and 3 positions and the speed bracket quadrant shaft handle 129E4 in each of its three positions.

With tumbler handle in No. 4 position and the operating lever to the left, in running position (on display machines the starting handle should be pushed to the rear), see that the interlocking lever x108E does not bind against the tumbler.

TYPE CARRIER

The stroke of the type carrier must be increased so that its right end will travel far enough to the right to be able to receive the largest point type. This is accomplished by changing the type carrier connecting rod yoke pin 21B7 in the type carrier connecting rod yoke a21B5 and type carrier cam lever extension a72E4.

When casting 14- to 36-point display type, using the curved type channel blocks xb50F and xj51F, the yoke pin should be inserted in the left-hand hole of connecting rod yoke, and left-hand lower hole in cam lever extension.

For 14- to 18-point display type, using the type channel block fixed xh51F, the yoke pin should be inserted in left-hand hole of connecting rod yoke and left-hand upper hole in cam lever extension. This latter position is also used for casting 14- to 24-point large composition type, with the standard composition type channel blocks and the mould coupling hook 56B1.

TYPE CARRIER SHOE PLATE a24B2

The type carrier shoe plate a24B2 has a tongue $\frac{9}{32}''$ wide and is used to obtain a wider opening of the type clamp for type over 14 point in both display and large type composition sizes. The shoe plate c24B2 with the $\frac{3}{16}''$ tongue is for use when casting type from 5 to 14 point.

TYPE CARRIER SHOE, LONG, xc23B

When producing type in set sizes of 24 points or less the type is prevented from falling on its side by type support spring, but for type over 24 points setwise the cam on type carrier shoe should be raised so that the type support spring is not in action. Failure to do so may result in the spring being badly strained.

To accommodate the larger type bodies, and because of the change in the position of the stroke of the type carrier, the regular type channel blocks must be replaced by the display channel blocks. The standard fixed block is replaced by the fixed display type channel block xj51F, using the front screw 51F5 of the standard block in the front hole of the display block. The pawl 14F1F should be reversed, as this obviates all danger of the galley mechanism working. To replace the adjustable type channel block it is necessary to draw the line hook xa19F as far forward as possible, taking off the line hook operating bar stop a22FF and taking out the pin 27F1 which connects the line hook operating slide rod 27F7 to the line hook operating slide lever 25FF. The column pusher adjusting cam a2F should be in the 12-point position. The adjustable display type channel block xb50F is clamped down with the screw f50F6 used with the standard adjustable block.

MOULD BLADE CAM LEVER COMPOUND LEVER

Refer to Fig. 3, *Page* 282.—The mould blade must draw back far enough to permit type 36 points wide to be cast. This change in the stroke of the mould blade is made by taking the screw a44E8 and its distance piece d44E9 from the compound lever b44E7, and screwing it into the stud a44E10, placing the distance piece between the compound lever and the stud.

For casting type from small composition moulds, the compound lever must be locked to its cam lever.

For casting type from large type composition moulds and display type up to 19 points setwise, the compound lever and distance piece must be connected to the abutment a96E1 so that the *low* level of distance piece contacts on the lever.

For display type over 19 points setwise to the maximum opening, the compound lever and distance piece must be connected to the abutment so that *high* level of distance piece contacts on the lever.

THE PUMP

Two pistons are supplied for type casting; the longer of these (similar to the standard piston supplied for ordinary composition) is designed for a stroke not exceeding $\frac{1}{2}''$ and is used with display and composition moulds up to 18 point. The other is for a maximum stroke of $\frac{13}{16}''$ for use with display and large type composition moulds from 24 to 36 point.

NOZZLE a14H2

The nozzle a14H2 is provided for use with display and large composition moulds and has an $\frac{1}{8}''$ hole drilled through its entire length.

PUMP BODY LIFTING SPRING a27H

Greater pressure must be exerted between the nozzle and the mould. This is accomplished by connecting the upper hole in the lower spring plate a27H2 of the pump body lifting lever spring to the spring post a37H6.

PISTON OPERATING ROD CROSSHEAD STUD a19H5

In order to ensure the nozzle has seated in the mould correctly, the piston operating rod crosshead stud must leave the operating lever before the piston acts. To adjust the stud, engage the pump, turn the machine by hand until the latch abutment plate 58H2 contacts latch plate 57H2 and rotate the stud to clear the pump body operating lever by approximately $\frac{1}{64}''$.

PUMP TRIP LATCH 57H1

The pump trip latch must be in action when casting large type bodies in order that the piston spring may be compressed and then suddenly released, so causing a stronger and quicker pressure to be applied to the piston.

The nuts 62H4 and 62H5 at the top of latch stand shaft must be adjusted so that latch will drop freely into position with as little clearance as possible.

DUPLEX PISTON SPRING 75CU1

A composition caster equipped with display attachment has the duplex piston spring suitable for any size of product that can be cast on the machine.

The piston spring rod is graduated in inches and the adjusting nut can be screwed down to give a pressure of 490 lb.

The most suitable position of the adjusting nut can only be decided by the machine operator, as much depends on the condition of mould, pump body, piston, quality of metal and heating equipment.

NOTE.—*Special attention must be given to correct tension when changing from display type casting to composition.*

CENTRING PIN AUXILIARY SPRING xb36a

Refer to Fig. 6, *Page* 283.—A centring pin auxiliary spring is placed between the centring pin spring abutments g5a4 and d5a5 when casting large type composition or display type so that the pressure applied cannot cause the molten metal to raise the matrix off the mould.

The auxiliary spring is attached and removed from the machine by means of the gag provided.

PUMP BODY SPRING ROD STOP PLATES a63h1 (See p. 282)

For large type improved results are obtained by means of the stop plates, which can be placed in the path of the spring rod stop nut in order to vary the stroke of the piston for different point sizes and sets.

While there can be no hard and fast rules about these instructions, the following table gives the approximate number of plates to be used when casting the various sizes of type:

4 plates when casting 36 point by 36 point
3   „   „   „   36 point by 27 point
2   „   „   „   36 point by 18 point
1   „   „   „   36 point by 9 point
3   „   „   „   30 point by 30 point
2   „   „   „   24 point by 24 point
1   „   „   „   14 point by 14 point

DISPLAY TYPE SIZING

The variations in set sizes are obtained by a display normal wedge xb21D and a display justification wedge a11D1. These wedges replace the regular normal wedge 21D and the rear justification wedge 11D respectively, the front justification wedge being the standard wedge 10D.

The display normal wedge is designed to increase or decrease the size of product by 1 point for each tooth of its movement and the justification wedge a11D1 by $\frac{1}{8}$ of a point for each two teeth of its movement.

The packing piece 32c1 rests on top of the mould blade operating rod fork, straddling the mould blade abutment slide. A lug on the packing piece goes in front of the abutment slide adjustment screw c14c1. When casting set sizes from $2\frac{1}{4}$ points to 19 points inclusive the 17 point packing piece 32c1 must be in position. For set sizes from

19¼ points to 36 points the packing piece must be removed and for sizes above 36 points the mould blade adjusting screw must be adjusted.

Refer to Fig. 7, Page 283.—These two type-sizing wedges are positioned by hand with gauges. The justification wedge stop block 19D must be removed to allow the justification wedge gauge a69D1 to be used. The .0075″ justification wedge is always at its extreme left position (No. 8 on gauge a69D1). The marking on the gauge must coincide with the *left-hand* edge of the space transfer wedge operating rod guide cap 54D1. The space transfer wedge a52D must always be in operation. This is accomplished by swinging the centring pin lever gag block a140E1E to the rear to engage the space transfer wedge shifter lever arm rod 57D4 and hold it forward so that it will be lifted by the centring pin lever at each revolution of the machine. This gag block, when turned towards the front, acts as a packing piece beneath the normal wedge locking pin nut to cause it to rise out of the normal wedge at each revolution, and when turned to the rear (to engage the shifter lever arm rod) it releases the normal wedge locking pin, permitting it to drop until its nut rests on its abutment on the centring pin lever; this ensures that the locking pin shall not lift out of the normal wedge unless raised by hand when it is required to shift the wedge.

For machines not equipped with the gag block, screw down the bell crank stop screw 4D3 until the shifter lever arm rod is held forward so that its nut will always be engaged by the centring pin lever. For such machines it is necessary to readjust the normal wedge locking pin adjusting nut 14B1 as follows: with the centring pin lever at the top of its stroke, unscrew the locking pin adjusting nut until there is clearance between it and its abutment; screw down the nut until it just touches the abutment, give it half of a turn more, and lock it.

Use the display matrix holder instead of the regular matrix-case. Bring the matrix holder to its central position by means of a paper ribbon perforated for the central character of a matrix-case (H–9 perforation), and uncouple the locking bar operating lever. This should be done for safety, because if the air supply should cease, the matrix-case would resume its zero position. When inserting the matrix in the holder be sure that no dirt is between the matrix and the holder.

After inserting the matrix holder, loosen the matrix holder positioning spring bolt nut 48A3, turn machine carefully until centring pin seats in coned hole, see that the spring has correctly positioned itself in the groove in top of sliding frame and tighten nut.

To position the American matrix holder a49AA, perforate the paper ribbon to raise the pins H and 8, insert matrix holder, release the two screws b49A2 that hold the position spring a49A1, back off the adjusting screw 49A22 in end of holder, turn machine until centring pin seats in coned hole, adjust the screws 49A22 so that the position spring correctly engages in the nick in underside of sliding frame. Lock the spring and adjusting screw in position.

If the centring pin position is altered to obtain correct alignment, the position of the centring pin entering the coned hole must be checked and the matrix holder readjusted if necessary.

When commencing to cast display founts the quad must not be sized up before the wedges a11D1 and xb21D have been placed in the correct positions, given on chart of set sizes, otherwise the characters afterwards cast will not work out correct to figures on matrices.

DISPLAY MOULDS
(FOR PLATE SEE P. 290)

DISPLAY TYPE MOULDS are furnished with five interchangeable insets for casting type, high and low quads and spaces in 14, 18, 24, 30, and 36 points. Insets for casting special sizes can be supplied to suit customers' requirements.

Low spaces can be cast up to any width setwise, 2 points larger than their respective body sizes, *i.e.*, a 14-point inset will cast up to and including 16-point low spaces. High or low quads may also be cast for any of the smaller point sizes by adjusting the mould blade setwise to correspond to the body size required. For instance: a 36-point inset will cast 3 ems 12 point or 6 ems 6 point, and a 24-point inset will cast either 2 ems 12 point or 4 ems 6 point, etc.

Characters may be cast to any width as follows:

14- and 18-point body up to 30 points.

24- and 30-point body up to 42 points.

36-point body up to 48 points.

These moulds can be furnished with insets to compose type in justified lines in 14, 18 and 24 point.

The size of the mould is altered by removing the inset and substituting one of the point size required. To do this, proceed in the following manner:

1. Prepare a place covered with clean paper; have the hands clean and free from particles of metal.

2. Remove the crossblock.

3. Open the blades to approximately 18 point.

4. Swing the blade operating lever spring box (3152) out of contact with the lower blade lever.

5. Remove the two small screws (258) in the rear of the base and the two large ones (318) on top of inset.

The inset can now be removed by pushing it away from the back of the base in the direction formerly occupied by the crossblock at the same time holding it down on the base to prevent the blade operating levers (3150) from being bent.

M

When the inset is forward sufficiently to clear the aperture in the base which positions the inset, push end-wise to disengage the levers from the blades.

As the important sharp edges of the inset are unprotected when away from the base, extreme care must be taken that they are neither dulled nor damaged.

Blow the waterways clear, and wipe and oil thoroughly before placing it in its compartment in the mould box.

6. The required inset and the mould base must be thoroughly washed in clean naphtha, benzine or petrol, and dried with a clean white cloth; any small particle of type metal adhering to any part should be removed with a piece of type rule. In no circumstance must abrasives (such as emery cloth or oil stone) be used.

Smear a light coating of clean oil on the bottom of the inset and slide into position, engaging the blade levers by reversing the instructions contained in paragraph 5.

Insert the two small screws for holding the inset to the base and screw up firmly, then release and bring them just up to bearing. Insert the two large screws and screw down firmly, then release and bring them just up to bearing. Finally tighten the two small screws firmly; then the two large ones.

The crossblock must also be thoroughly washed before replacing and care taken that the jet blade (3159) is in its correct position, *i.e.*, the fluted end to the front. The crossblock must be thoroughly oiled before inserting, and it should work freely; if not, it indicates that the inset has been replaced with dirt between it and the base, in which case it must be taken out and cleaned. The oil hole on the end of the inset must be filled with warm oil before placing the mould on the casting machine. The mould oiler is regulated to give correct lubrication if kept between full and half-full of oil.

To cast low quads and spaces, swing the blade operating lever spring box out of contact with the lower blade lever into the reverse position, abutting on the stop fixed to the lubricator. It is not necessary to remove the bridge to make this adjustment. When casting low quads or spaces it is important that a blank matrix be inserted in the matrix-case, otherwise the pressure of the molten type metal will spring the blades apart.

CLEANING AND MAINTENANCE

It is not possible for operators to repair moulds, as they have neither the special tools nor the necessary experience. The moulds should never be taken apart as long as they produce good type; neither should a mould be altered in any detail.

If it is found necessary to take apart an inset proceed in the following manner: prepare a suitable place and bear in mind that success or failure to make a satisfactory job will depend entirely on scrupulous cleanliness and the preservation of the sharp edges of the insets.

1. Procure a steel punch of suitable size (this may be obtained from The Monotype Corporation Ltd.).

2. Plan a method whereby the tapered dowel pins (3197) are ensured of being replaced in the identical holes from which they are taken.

3. With the cover plate (3147) facing downward, place the inset on several thicknesses of cloth and release the pins with the punch by giving them a sharp tap with a small hammer.

4. Remove the four screws (263) holding the cover plate and take off the cover plate with the dowel pins still in their respective holes. Remove the blade back stop screw (325) in centre of intermediate plate.

5. In removing the blades they must be slid from front to rear. *Never lift the rear of the blades when passing them between the side blocks, nor try to force them over the nick pin,* as this would injure the blade or nick pin.

6. Clean carefully all parts which have been removed and insert blade. This is best done by placing the upper blade on the lower, and working backwards and forwards to make sure there is no dirt between them. Place the blades on the intermediate plate and hold them firmly down when sliding into position. These should also be worked backwards and forwards.

7. Before replacing the dowel pins pull a strip of clean cloth backwards and forwards through the holes in inset.

8. Replace cover plate and clean and insert dowel pins lightly; replace the four cover plate screws and bring them just up to bearing; tap the pins lightly and tighten screws a little; tap the pins home and screw up firmly.

The water passages of the mould must be kept clean, and whenever the mould is taken off the machine blow water out and blow oil through them.

If any defects occur in the mould that cannot be corrected by following these directions, it is usually advisable to return the complete mould with samples of the defective type and a memorandum giving particulars of the trouble.

CHANGING FROM COMPOSITION TO DISPLAY TYPE ATTACHMENT

TURN MACHINE APPROXIMATELY to zero position (between 360° and 10°). In this position the matrix jaws are just beginning to close and the centring pin lever is at its uppermost position.

Disconnect the air bar clamping lever connecting rod connecting hook 4G1.

Cut off water from mould.

Run down metal pot, making sure that the metal is completely molten, and swing it clear of mould.

REMOVE MOULD OILER AND UNLATCH CROSSBLOCK OILER. This cannot be used with display or large type composition moulds.

REMOVE MATRIX-CASE.—To do this, remove bridge lever link pin xa3A, withdraw fibre stop 7A, and disconnect the rear end of matrix-case from the cross slide g5cc. Slightly depress the bridge lever b2AA, keep the matrix-case towards the centre of the carrying frame c4AA, and withdraw the matrix-case.

REMOVE BRIDGE.—Remove the two screws a1A1, and lift the complete bridge off, taking care not to bend the sliding frame draw rod d9A1.

REMOVE MOULD.—Remove the mould blade operating rod fork pin c16c6, and the link connecting the mould crossblock to the type carrier. Remove the three screws from the mould base, then the two mould clamps a48E and a49E. Lift mould off carefully. Remove the two lubricating cups (if screwed pattern) from the mould, also the equalizing gear fulcrum block if mould below 20,000 is in use. Thoroughly clean mould, blow water out of the water course, oil the mould, and store away in proper box.

REMOVE NORMAL WEDGE.—To do this push forward the matrix jaws latch c7BB and turn the latch upward so that it will rest on the top of the matrix jaw. Hold the mould blade abutment slide forward by pressing the mould blade abutment slide spring post b14c8 towards the mould, and then withdraw the normal wedge from the left of the machine.

Withdraw line hook xa19F to galley mouth.

Turn the column pusher adjusting cam disc to the 12-point mark.

Remove galley cam driving pawl 14F1F.

Remove type channel blocks 50F and a51FF; to do this move machine forward so that type carrier advances sufficiently forward to clear.

Remove type carrier connecting rod forked eye pin 21B7 and place it in the two holes to suit type to be cast.

Insert transfer wedge shifter lever arm rod 57D4 into matrix centring pin lever, and lock it there by turning round the gag block from underneath normal wedge locking pin adjusting nut 14B1.

Remove rear justification wedge 11D.

Change position of mould blade cam lever compound lever locking screw a44E8.

Change nozzle on pump body.

Turn down the latch 57H1 on upper section of pumping mechanism.

Turn forward pump body spring rod stop block 63H1H or stop plates a63H1 if stop plates are on the machine.

Place on the two display type channel blocks to suit type to be cast, leaving the channel wide enough for the type to be cast next.

Insert the display justification wedge a11D1 and take both justification wedges to No. 8 positions.

Insert display normal wedge xb21D.

Change display type mould inset, and place mould on machine; tighten up side clamps. Screw mould to base of machine with three short screws. Insert mould blade operating rod fork pin c16c6. Connect mould crossblock to carrier. Lock low space mould blade forward.

Remove low space and character levers from bridge.

Place bridge on machine, leaving low space actuating cam disengaged to left.

Place on centring pin spring auxiliary spring xb36A.

Insert bridge lever link pin xa3A.

From perforations bring matrix jaws to central position, insert matrix-case, and turn machine carefully round to see that centring pin seats in matrix cone hole correctly. If so, turn machine to 360°, and disengage the locking bar operating rod hook a33E5 by lifting it up, and pushing the locking bar lever c34EE forward. Wind up metal pot, turn on water, put wedges in position, regulate gear, cast type, size up and line up.

CASTING FROM COMPOSITION MATRICES WITH DISPLAY TYPE NORMAL WEDGE IN USE

ON A 'MONOTYPE' Composition Caster and a 'Monotype' Display Machine, it is possible to cast from any composition matrix by using the display type normal wedge xb21D in conjunction with the two composition justification wedges 10D and 11D. This avoids the necessity for purchasing a special normal wedge for every set of matrices when casting type for case. A table is provided (p. 217) which gives the positions in which the wedges must be placed to produce the required type sizes.

To size up before commencing to cast type for case from composition matrices, first ascertain the size of a type body (preferably an 18-unit body) from the table of TYPE SIZES (p. 220), then find the equivalent to this (or nearest *larger* size), and position the three wedges as indicated in the table at the end of this book entitled: WEDGE POSITIONS FOR CASTING FROM COMPOSITION MATRICES (p. 216). After sizing, and providing the wedges are positioned as indicated for the different sizes required, all the various types will be cast to correct width or to within .00025″; this possible inaccuracy is negligible, but any discrepancy can be adjusted by manipulating the micrometer adjustment wedge.

As it is not possible to mark the wedge positions on composition matrices, the attendant should make out type sizing tables for the different composition founts which he has in stock.

The following is a sample table:

SERIES NO. 2.—10 point. 9¾ Set.

Units	Character	Normal Wedge Xb21D*	Justification Wedges		Width in Inches ‡	Increase beyond actual Size §
			10D†	11D†		
5	i l . , : ; ! ' '	6	7½	6	·0377	·00024
6	f j -) (..	6	8	6	·0452	·00025
7	r t s	7	7½	7	·0525	·00005
8	I z c e	7	8	7	·0600	·00006
9	g a o 1 2 3 4 5 6 7 8 9 0 £ ..	8	8	1	·0678	·00017
10	J S b y u n k q v p h d x fi fl	9	7½	2	·0752	·00027
11	C Z ff	9	8	2	·0827	·00028
12	P L F T æ	10	7½	3	·0900	·00009
13	A B E G O Q V w & ..	10	8	3	·0975	·00010
14	D R N U Y œ	11	7½	4½	·1053	·00040
15	H M K X m ffi ffl ..	11	8	4½	·1128	·00041
18	W Æ Œ	13	7½	6½	·1350	·00013

* The mould blade abutment screw packing piece 32c1 must be in position to obtain the sizes in this table.
† Use gauge a69D1 for positioning the justification wedges.
‡ These are actual sizes obtained from the position of wedges given in this table.
§ These minute differences can be rectified (if necessary) by adjusting the micrometer wedge a20D.

LEAD AND RULE CASTING AND CUTTING ATTACHMENT

(FOR PLATE SEE PP. 284–286)

THIS ATTACHMENT, which can be fitted to any 'Monotype' casting machine, enables printers to cast all their own leads and rules, and to cut the same automatically, while casting is proceeding, to any desired length from 6 ems to 150 ems of 12 point (1″ to 25″).

Any continuous length beyond this may be cast, in which case lead or rule of any measurement may be cut by hand.

The thickness of the lead or rule may range from 1½ point to 12 point.

The leads may be cast high for electrotyping, or low for ordinary work.

The object of this attachment (combined with the display type attachment) is to enable users of 'Monotype' machines to dispense with brass rule and to eliminate entirely the expense of distribution for all jobs containing type up to 36 point inclusive.

Formes containing type above 36 point simply have the large type lines lifted out, and the remainder is thrown into the metal bin.

TIE-UP STRIP MATERIAL

Suitable border rules or clumps may be cast with a groove along the entire length to allow for cord for tying-up purposes. This cord is not removed from the job or display advertisement, but is locked up in the forme. After printing or stereotyping, the job or advertisement is untied, and thrown complete into the metal bin. Should it be necessary to keep the type standing it is already tied up for future use.

ADJUSTMENTS FOR LEAD AND RULE STRIP MOULD OPERATING MECHANISM*

It is assumed the parts for lead and rule casting, including the mould, are in position, in accordance with instructions in article headed: CHANGING FROM TYPE CASTING TO LEAD AND RULE CASTING, p. 179.

MICROMETER WEDGE AND STAND x51B.—Object: To regulate the stroke of the mould blade.

If a $\frac{3}{4}''$ stroke is required for casting leads, use the left-hand hole (T) of the two at right-hand end of the stand (U) for the screw. If a $\frac{1}{2}''$ stroke is required for casting rules, use the right-hand hole (S) of the two at the right-hand end of the stand (U) for the screw.

A finer adjustment of the stroke (for example, to make the junction of the face of a rule coincide with the junction of the body) is obtained by raising or lowering the micrometer wedge (I) by means of its adjusting screw (H). This adjustment is made at the start of a cast after an examination of the product.

SPRING BOX x141E.—Object: To cause the mould blade to bear firmly against its stops at each end of its stroke.

With the nuts (A and D) backed off, turn the machine to 70°. Adjust the nut (A) on the left end of spring box spring rod (C) to give $\frac{1}{16}''$ compression on the spring. This compression is measured by the amount the spring abutment, against which the nut (A) abuts, is moved to the right by the nut (A); $\frac{1}{16}''$ compression will bring the face of the abutment about flush with the end of the spring box. Lock the nut (A) with its lock nut.

Turn the machine to 220° and adjust the nut (D) on right end of the spring box spring rod (C) to give $\frac{1}{16}''$ compression on the spring. This compression is measured by the amount the spring abutment, against which the nut (D) abuts, is moved to the left by the nut (D); $\frac{1}{16}''$ compression will bring the face of the abutment about flush with the end of the spring box. Lock the nut (D) with its lock nut.

If it is not possible to make these compressions $\frac{1}{16}''$, the auxiliary bracket clamp bolt (Y) and the adjusting screw (Z) will have to be adjusted to swing the bracket (B) slightly one way or the other to give the required compression. The bracket (B) should be kept as nearly horizontal as possible.

---

* All references in the following to 'front', 'rear', 'right', and 'left', assume the operator standing in front of and facing galley side of the machine. In this section the capital letters designating the parts refer to Fig. 1 of PLATE XIV, p. 284, unless otherwise noted.

When changing from $\frac{1}{2}''$ stroke to $\frac{3}{4}''$ stroke or *vice versa,* it is necessary to readjust the nut (D) on the right of the spring box, and when changing moulds the adjustment of the nuts on both ends should be tested.

CLAMPING SCREW CONNECTING ROD xa135E.—Object: To clamp the type blocks against the cast product while making the next cast and to release them for ejecting.

The rod a135E1 must be screwed into the connecting rod eye a135E9 so that its end is level with the bottom of slot in eye.

With a piece of product of the correct size inserted in the mould, connect the rod fork eye to the lever (P) on the mould and turn machine so that the centring pin lever is in its lowest position. Adjust the nuts at lower end of spring rod so that the length of the spring is $3\frac{3}{8}''$, and lock the nuts firmly in this position.

Adjust the nut (K) on the upper end of connecting rod so that there is $\frac{1}{16}''$ compression on its spring (L) when centring pin lever (E) is at the bottom of its stroke with the mould heated up and the machine running at 120 r.p.m. Watch this adjustment carefully, because if the clamping lever (P) works down, this compression will be lost.

The outer end of the clamping lever (P) on the front of the mould should be between the horizontal and $\frac{1}{8}''$ below horizontal when this setting is made. If it is not, note how much it needs to be turned in either direction to correct it. Turn the machine until the centring pin lever is at the top of its stroke, loosen the lock nut to free the clamping lever, and holding the clamping screw from turning, swing the clamping lever to the right or left as required and lock it with the lock nut. Now test again the clearance beneath the nut (K) on top of the clamping lever connecting rod as described above.

If through wear or loosening of this adjustment the compression on spring (L) becomes less than $\frac{1}{16}''$, readjust to make it $\frac{1}{16}''$. If the moving end of the lever (P) on the front of the mould works down so that at the bottom of its stroke (machine running at 120 r.p.m.) it is more than $\frac{1}{4}''$ below the horizontal, it must be readjusted.

ADJUSTMENTS OF THE LEAD AND RULE STRIP AUTOMATIC CUTTER MECHANISM*

THRUST BAR OPERATING ROD x129F—*Refer to Fig.* 2 *of* PLATE XIV p. 285.—Object: To ensure the proper engagement of thrust bar (P) by the cam lever (S).

If the adjustment of connecting rod x121F (*see next sub-heading but one*) *has not previously been made, remove pin* (U) *before proceeding.*

Trip the thrust bar (P), so that it is in its front position, by pulling

---

* All references in the following to 'front', 'rear', 'right', and 'left', assume the operator standing in front of and facing galley side of the machine. In this section the capital letters designating the parts refer to Fig. 2 of Plate XIV, p. 285, unless otherwise noted.

the shear blade shoe tube (E) to the right by hand. Loosen the operating lever screw a101f4. Turn the machine until the shear cam lever (S) has pushed the thrust bar (P) all the way down. *The machine is in this position for this and the next two adjustments.* Adjust the length of the thrust bar operating rod (N) by screwing it in or out of its eye (Q) so that the cam lever (S) rests in the bottom of the fillet of the thrust bar (P).

THRUST BAR x122F.—Object: To transfer leads or rules to the stacker plate (W).

Have the machine in the position previously described, with the thrust bar (P) tripped (in its front position) and the machine turned until the shear cam lever (S) has pushed the thrust bar (P) all the way down. Adjust the length of the thrust bar (P) by means of its two nuts (O), until the ends of the pushers (F) project $\frac{1}{16}''$ in front of the front face of the rear bar (B). Be sure that the thrust bar (P) is not jammed between the shear cam lever (S) and the shear bell crank (M); that is, see that the front end of the shear bell crank (M) can be pressed down to give clearance between the cam lever (S) and the thrust bar (P). If this clearance does not exist, the nuts (O) must be adjusted until there is a slight clearance; this may alter the position of the pushers (F) so that their ends are not $\frac{1}{16}''$ in front of the front face of the rear bar (B), as just described.

When tightening the lock nuts (O), be sure not to turn the thrust bar (P) about its vertical axis and thereby jam the operating rod (N) in its guide—or break it.

STACKER ROCK SHAFT CONNECTING ROD x121F.—Object: To stack leads or rules.

Remove the pin (U) from the upper eye (T) of the connecting rod (R). Have the machine with the thrust bar (P) tripped and the machine turned until the shear cam lever (S) has pushed the thrust bar (P) all the way down. Turn the stacker rock shaft (I) over towards the rear until its lug is up against its stop. Make the length of the connecting rod (R) such that its pin (U) can be inserted freely through the eye (T) with the parts in the position described.

Be sure that the pin (U) freely enters the eye (T) and the hole in the lug on the rock shaft (I); never force it in.

SHEAR BELL CRANK x108F.—Object: To prevent the shear blade interfering with the leads or rules entering the channel.

With the thrust bar (P) in its upper position adjust the shear bell crank (M) by means of its adjusting screw (L), so that, when the shear blade (K) is pushed forward with the fingers to take up all play, it just clears the rear side of the rule passage. With the parts in this position, make sure that the thrust bar (P) will pass under the shear cam lever (S). If the thrust bar will not pass under the shear cam lever readjust it until it will do so.

TRANSFER BARS xa96F (rear) and xa97F (front).—The transfer bars should be adjusted so as to open wide enough to clear the product as it comes from the mould, and to grip it tightly while transferring it to the stacker plate (W).

Trip the thrust bar so that it is in its front position, turn machine until the shear cam lever is in its lowest position. Adjust the transfer bar operating lever adjusting screw a101F4 so that transfer bar hanger 97F4F clears the transfer bar guard 176F1 by $\frac{1}{32}''$.

Turn machine until shear cam lever disengages from thrust bar. Adjust the transfer bar operating lever adjusting screw 102F1 so that the distance between the transfer bars is slightly greater than the size of leads or rules to be cast. This adjustment must be made for each change in point size of product.

GUIDE ROLLER x80F.—Objects: (a) To make leads or rules straight; (b) to make the ends of short lengths square.

To test whether the product is straight, cast two long lengths of the product for which the machine is adjusted. Lay them on the galley foot to foot. If the feet do not touch throughout their length the guide roller (N) (Fig. 1), which is on an eccentric, must be readjusted by means of the roller shaft handle (M) (Fig. 1). Continue comparing two lengths of the product and adjusting the roller (N) until the leads or rules are straight. This test should be made each time a mould is changed, and when casting long lengths of strip material this test should be made frequently.

To test whether the ends of short leads are square, stand two on end on a flat surface, foot to foot. If the feet do not touch throughout their length, readjust the guide roller, cast new pieces, and test again.

* CHANNEL BAR SUPPORT a77F3.—Object: To support long lengths of the product.

Adjust the support (D) so that the leads or rules will just slide over and be supported by its top face. This gives a support to the right end of the leads or rules, and prevents their bending from their own weight.

LENGTH OF LEAD OR RULE.—Object: To obtain any length of lead or rule from 6 ems to 150 ems of 12 point (1″ to 25″).

Loosen the clamp screw (H) and slide the collar (G) to the right or left on the tube (E) until the stop, against which the lead or rule strikes, is the required distance (as measured by a gauge) from the cutting edge of the shear blade. Tighten the clamp screw (H).

FINE ADJUSTMENT FOR LENGTH OF LEAD OR RULE.—After the shear gauge has been adjusted as described above, it can be adjusted to greater accuracy by rotating the shear gauge nut a88F5 to increase or decrease the length of product as required.

---

* Some of the earlier attachments did not have this support.

Always use the stop to the left of the collar except when the lead or rule is too long; then it is necessary to use the stop to the right of the collar.

When casting long leads or rules, be sure that when the lead or rule has pushed the stop as far to the right as possible there is at least $\frac{1}{32}''$ clearance between the stop and the right-hand guide (A) of the tube (E).

Never cut leads or rules any length less than twice the stroke of the mould blade. For example: if casting with a $\frac{3}{4}''$ stroke of the mould blade, and leads $1\frac{1}{4}''$ long are desired, the micrometer wedge must be changed to give length of stroke $\frac{1}{2}''$.

BOX FOR SHORT LENGTHS 76F1.—For leads or rules not long enough to stack, use the box furnished with the attachment. Remove galley x78F and stacker rock shaft connecting rod yoke pin 121F4. The box can then easily be placed into position.

GUIDE FOR TWO-POINT PRODUCT X79F.—Object: To prevent buckling of two-point product.

The guide plate (O) (Fig. 1) is provided for this purpose. It is positioned by hooking its left end over the friction block adjusting screw (Q) (Fig. 1) on the mould and resting its right end on the guide roller (N) (Fig. 1). Some of the earlier attachments did not have this guide plate, but, instead, had an adjusting screw and a guide spring. To adjust this guide spring, loosen the adjusting screw until the guide spring touches the lead or rule, screw in the adjusting screw until it touches the guide spring, then give it one-quarter of a turn more.

CHANGING FROM TYPE CASTING TO LEAD AND RULE CASTING*

WHEN CHANGING from type casting to lead and rule casting it is necessary to remove the following parts from the machine: bridge; both type channel blocks; type carrier complete; type pusher and guide; bridge lever connecting link piston; pump body; galley pan support complete. On a composing machine remove also pin jaw tongs spring complete and its links; disconnect the locking bar cam lever.

Having removed all the foregoing parts place the following in their correct position: The special pump body and its special nozzle should first be put in the melting pot to heat up. When they are hot, insert the piston (also hot). Two pistons are furnished with the attachment, one for $\frac{1}{2}''$ stroke with one metal inlet in stem end screw and used for

---

* All references in the following to 'front', 'rear', 'right', and 'left', assume the operator standing in front of and facing galley side of the machine. In this section, the capital letters designating the parts refer to Fig. 1 of PLATE XIV, p. 284, unless otherwise noted.

$1\frac{1}{2}$ to 4 point and the second $\frac{13}{16}''$ stroke with two metal inlets used for 6 to 12 point. The latter piston is identical to that used for composition and display type above 18 point. (These pistons are furnished specially with lead and rule casting and cutting attachment to ensure close-fitting pistons; use them only with this attachment.)

Swing the mould blade operating bar (V) (refer to Fig. 1, PLATE XIV, p. 284) from top of centring pin lever (E) (where placed when not in use) into operating position (as in Fig. 1), connecting the spring box lever link 144E1 to the lower left-hand hole in type carrier cam lever extension. On a composing machine, swing the front pin jaw tongs spring bell crank to the front, or remove it entirely, to clear these parts.*

Put the centring pin lever bracket (G) on the centring pin lever from beneath and tighten the clamps (F).†

The machine should now be turned to 15°. If attachment has not been adjusted, loosen the spring rod adjusting nuts (A and D) before attempting to put on the mould. Take the mould (R) in the right hand and pull its blade to the left as far as it will go, raise the right end of the mould blade operating bar (V) and put the lug on it into its hole in the mould blade; lower the mould (R) and the operating bar (V) into position. Attach the two mould clamps, the standard clamp being used at right-hand position and the special clamp 89E1 in the front. This special clamp, which is longer than the standard clamp, must be used to locate the mould securely against the face of rear pin block.

Use the three mould screws c50E1. These are identical to the short screw used under the crossblock position for securing the composition mould.‡

Turn the machine until the mould blade is at the right end of its stroke. Put the micrometer wedge stand (U) on the machine in place

---

* On machines where the spring box 141E1 is directly connected to the mould blade operating bar, screw the mould blade operating bar on to its extension in the spring box and lock it with its lock nut so that the lug on the right end of the bar will be to the front. Put these parts in position on the machine with the cam lever extension (X), on the spring box, in the end of the type carrier cam lever where the regular extension was. Screw the regular extension adjusting bolt into the lower end of the new extension to draw the new extension down so that its shoulder is solid on the top of the cam lever, and lock the adjusting screw with its lock nut. Tighten the cam lever extension clamp bolt (W), taking care that the extension is not swung sideways so as to spring the mould blade operating bar out of place.

† For machines equipped with the older style of centring pin lever bracket for use with the older style moulds having the short clamping lever on the front of the mould, put the bracket on the centring pin lever from underneath, slipping it on to the centring pin lever stud. Swing the bracket eye bolt up into the slot in the right end of the centring pin lever and tighten its wing nut. Put the rear bracket clamp in position so that tightening its nut clamps the rear arm of the centring pin lever (be sure the countersink in the front end of this clamp fits over its bearing, or the clamp will bind).

‡ On machines where the spring box is directly connected to the mould blade operating bar, have the machine turned so that the mould blade operating bar spring box is about midway of its stroke, pull the mould blade to the left as far as it will go, and continue as above.

of the type carrier shoes. In the right of the stand (U) are two screw holes—use the right-hand one (as shown in Fig. 1) for the $\frac{1}{2}''$ stroke of the mould blade for casting rules and the left-hand one for $\frac{3}{4}''$ stroke for casting leads; the screw holes in the left end of the stand (U) allow of this movement of the stand. The fine adjustment of the stroke of the mould blade is obtained by means of the micrometer screw (H).

The clamp connecting rod (J) should now be connected to the lever (P) on the front of the mould. The adjustment of the nuts on the upper end of this rod (J) should never be broken—if it is, it should carefully be readjusted.

If the attachment has not previously been adjusted, as per article headed: ADJUSTMENTS FOR LEAD AND RULE STRIP MOULD OPERATING MECHANISM, *p. 175, adjust at this point.*

Throw in the latch 57H1 to compress the piston spring and release it suddenly, as for display type. All the other settings of the pump are to be the same as for running on composition.

For the larger sizes of strip material, improved results are obtained by means of the pump body operating rod stop plates, which can be placed in the path of the operating stop nut in order to vary the stroke of the piston for the different sizes. For 12-point leads and rules 2 plates should be used and for 6 point 1 plate.

Set the speed-regulating attachment to give the required speed. (*Refer to sub-paragraph headed:* SPEEDS AND TEMPERATURES, p. 190.)

The water should now be turned on and regulated to give a maximum amount through the mould with very little through the main stand of the casting machine.

Now turn the machine by hand (with pump out of action) to see that everything is working correctly.

After first placing the pump in action turn the machine once or twice by hand to see that everything is working correctly before throwing over the starting lever.

The setting of the mould blade micrometer wedge (I) is now tested by breaking some of the rule to see if the junction of the face coincides with the junction of the top of the body. If this is not correct, adjust the micrometer wedge (I) by means of its adjusting screw (H) to bring the junctions of the rule in the desired relation.

In drilling the special nozzle for the rule mould use the same drills as for composition nozzle. That is, No. 50 drill from the top and No. 30 drill from the bottom. The upper end of the hole in the nozzle is tapered —do not drill up far enough to destroy this taper; the No. 30 drill should go in $1\frac{7}{8}''$ only.

When changing back to composition or to display type casting take out the pump used for rule casting and replace it with the regular pump.

The nozzle is in a different position on the pump used for rule casting from that on the standard pump.

SHORT LEAD AND RULE MOULD
(FOR PLATE SEE P. 289)

PREPARING THE MACHINE

To enable this mould to be used on the composition caster, remove the lever a20b11 (for type clamp) from type carrier and replace with the lever b20b11. This new lever need not be removed when reverting to composition matter.

Remove the type carrier shoe plate c24b2 and replace with the plate d24b2. The new plate delays and restricts the opening of the type clamp and must be removed when reverting to composition matter.

The stroke of the type carrier must be readjusted so that the two lines on the top of the mould crossblock register with the line on the inset, when carrier is in the forward and backward positions. This ensures the jet being in the centre of the mould blade when crossblock is in casting position.

The type carrier connecting rod yoke pin 21b7 must be connected to the holes in connecting rod yoke and cam lever extension as for composition moulds.

The lead and rule nozzle a14h4 must be used.

Adjust the piston spring pressure to the minimum consistent with good results.

If rules wider than 12 points are to be cast, the machine must be fitted with the mould blade cam lever compound lever b44e7 and distance piece d44e9 to give the wider opening for the blade.

Speed-reducing gears or pulleys will be required also, to obtain the necessary speed for casting.

The type channel block h51ff must be used. This channel block has no projecting centre rib to restrict the delivery of the short leads or rules.

A satisfactory method of delivering this product is to lock the galley mechanism by means of the trip lever retainer so that it is always in operation; this will deliver the leads or rules to the galley every seventh revolution.

Speed of machine: 3–12 point opening 110 r.p.m.
13–24 point opening 90 r.p.m.
Over 24 point opening 80 r.p.m

Lubricate the mould with castor oil.

CHANGING BLADES AND MATRICES

Remove cover plate (11602) complete with matrix stop (11483), remove blade stop (11058); loosen knurled nut (13453) and screw (11066) on top of mould but do not loosen the bridge in which they operate; withdraw blade and matrix.

Carefully clean the required blade and matrix, smear blade with castor oil and insert between side blocks. Turn machine so that crossblock is in casting position, place matrix in position with 'stepped' end to the front and press in contact with crossblock. Replace cover plate so that it is in contact with both side blocks. Press matrix back to the matrix stop and gradually tighten knurled screw whilst carefully moving the blade backward and forward to see that it is quite free in matrix. Secure with knurled lock nut.

QUAD AND SPACE MOULD
(FOR PLATE SEE P. 288)

TO CHANGE BODY SIZE
1. Remove crossblock.
2. Loosen nut (1053) and hollow screw (11581) in end of mould.
3. Remove blade stop (11524) and support (11527).
4. Remove cover plate (13917) and clamping bar (13641).
5. Withdraw blade, keeping it down on the intermediate plate (13590) whilst doing so in order not to damage the nick or nick recess.
6. Insert a few thicknesses of paper between the side blocks in place of the mould blade and remove the side blocks by canting them towards the blade opening.

This is as far as it is safe for a mould to be taken apart by the operator. The eccentric dowels (3575) which position the side blocks must not be interfered with in any way. If the dowels are moved the slightest amount the side blocks will not go back in correct alignment.

Wash all parts thoroughly in clean benzine, taking care not to damage the important corners of side blocks and blade. On no account attempt to polish the parts with oil stones or other abrasives, the effect of which would be to destroy the sharp corners which are so essential if clean, burrless product is to be cast.

Reassemble the mould in the following order:
1. Place screw side block (11516) in position (also distance plate (11521) for 8 point and under).
2. Place nick side block (11517) in position.
3. Insert mould blade of required point size exercising the same care as when withdrawing the blade to avoid damage to the nick or nick recess.

NOTE.—*In order that the blade should open to its fullest extent, it is essential that the distance pieces (3580, 11523) should be located in the rear ends of their recesses in the blade. To ensure this, advance the blade to a position slightly in advance of the side blocks by a continuous forward movement. If the blade is pushed too far forward the distance pieces will also be carried too far, so that when the blade is pulled back to a position slightly in advance of the side blocks, the distance pieces will be left some-*

where in the middle of the recesses and the movement of the blade will be restricted accordingly.

4. Advance the hollow screw in end of mould until the distance pieces are held between the side blocks.

5. Secure the clamping bar in position making sure that its front edge is located against the spring block (6322) and screw block (6320).

6. Replace cover plate and screw down firmly.

7. Tighten hollow screw, applying no more pressure than can be exerted by hand without undue strain. Tighten lock nut.

NOTE.—*To maintain accurate body size the spring block must be held securely in position, and all holding down screws firmly tightened.*

8. Replace blade stop and support.

9. Oil the mould thoroughly and replace the crossblock.

NOTE.—*Refer to composition mould instructions for adjustment of new style crossblock*, pp. 161, 162.

ARABIC COMPOSITION MOULD

THIS MOULD IS for type or high spaces only, the mechanism normally used for low spaces being used for operating the auxiliary blade. To dismantle and reassemble an inset proceed as for display mould.

CARE AND CLEANING OF LEAD AND RULE MOULD

MOULD BLADE STROKE.—Products for which a matrix is used must be cast with $\frac{1}{2}''$ stroke of the mould blade. Any more or any less than $\frac{1}{2}''$ will throw the blade out from register with the matrix, and in addition to giving an imperfect product may injure the mould.

Product for which a cap and cap support are used are cast with a $\frac{3}{4}''$ stroke of the mould blade. The stroke must never be made greater than this under any circumstances, but if necessary may be shortened, but never below $\frac{1}{2}''$. When the stroke is shortened, the cap and cap support must be moved to the right the amount by which the stroke is shortened, so that the blade and cap will register.

MOULD NOT TO BE TAKEN APART UNLESS NECESSARY.—It is not necessary to take the mould apart to change mould blades. If the mould shows signs of hanging up, stop the machine and thoroughly oil all moving parts of the mould so that it is properly lubricated. This will usually free a mould if the blade or vent pusher is hanging up. If the product being cast has become jammed, proceed as follows (refer to

PLATE XIX, p. 291), lock out the pump, remove the shield (6622), matrix clamp (4377), and matrix, also the right tie bar (6627) from the top of the mould. From the rule being cast, cut some pieces about two picas long, turn the machine until the mould blade is at the left of its stroke, drop one piece of the rule into the mould blade opening, and turn the machine so as to push the rule out. Repeat until the mould is free from the rule which is binding. If the rule does not move when the machine is turned, it will be necessary to take the mould apart as described on page 186; in which case thoroughly clean the vent pusher slot with a piece of wooden reglet or brass rule.

LUBRICATION.—Use castor oil (order 'Rule Mould Oil'). Standard 'Monotype' oil such as that used on other moulds and casting machine parts will *not* work satisfactorily on the lead and rule mould: Keep the oil hole in the left tie bar (6626) over the mould blade constantly filled with this lubricant; also put a little on the end of the operating bar where it joins the mould blade and on the end of the clamping screw (12024) where it touches the lead clamp screw distance piece (14106). This clamping screw must be removed completely and oiled its full length before the mould is put on the machine, and on long runs this must be done once a day.

WHEN CHANGING PRODUCT (as, for example, changing matrices to get a different face or changing from rules to leads) always save a piece about 4″ long of the product just cast (see next paragraph). In the case of taking off a matrix, wrap this piece with the matrix; in the case of low leads, wrap it with the mould blade cap.

BEFORE STARTING TO CAST, insert between the type blocks a piece of the product for which the mould is then adjusted, and push this piece in far enough to touch the end of the mould blade. Loosen the knurled screw (6263) on the friction block to clamp this product sufficiently to prevent the incoming metal from blowing it out. NOTE.—When a new matrix is received without a piece of the product, proceed as follows: insert between the type blocks, in the same manner as described above, a piece of lead or leads (either 'Monotype' or foundry) to equal the point size to be cast. Before putting on the shield (6622), cover the mould blade opening between the matrix and the right tie bar (6627) with common soap that is soft enough not to crumble and also force a little down into the opening. Put on the shield (6622). Throw the latch 57H1 (operated by the piston operating rod crosshead) out of action and turn the machine by hand for several casts until the new product is properly started; then throw the latch in again.

FIRST CAST.—Before starting to cast, turn the machine once by hand with the pump locked out, then release the pump and turn the machine again by hand to make the first cast. This is to see that the mould and machine are working correctly before starting under power.

TEMPERATURE.—For product from 2 to 6 point inclusive the temperature should not exceed 700°; for 12-point product it should not exceed 675°. These temperatures are for standard 'Monotype' metal. For other metals, special care must be used to obtain the correct temperatures by trial. For example: linotype metal, frequently used in non-distribution newspaper offices, casts at lower temperature.

WATER REGULATION.—Use just sufficient water to give a perfect product. Too much will give imperfect faces and prevent perfect fusion of the joints; too little will cause blistered body.

PUTTING ON A MOULD.—Never attempt to put on a mould with the casting machine at any other than the 15° position. Also be particular to have the base of the mould and its seat on the machine perfectly clean and free from particles of metal.

ALTERATIONS.—Never attempt to lap any part of the mould or alter its shape. These parts are made by experienced workmen trained for this special work and supplied with the finest gauges and measuring instruments.

TAKING APART.—Never remove from the mould any other parts than those directed in the following under the heading TAKING THE LEAD AND RULE MOULD APART.

SPEED.—The speed for a given point size is the same for all products; that is, rules and high and low leads including the longer stroke for low leads.

TAKING THE LEAD AND RULE MOULD APART
(FOR PLATE SEE P. 291)

PREPARE A SUITABLE PLACE for taking the mould apart. Spread down a clean sheet of paper, and as the parts are taken off the mould put them on it.

Refer to PLATE XIX.—Before taking off any part, loosen clamp screw (12024) two or three turns, using lever (5088) to turn it.

Remove, in the order here given, shield (6622), matrix clamp screw (231), matrix clamp (4377), matrix, upper mould blade shoe (6620), mould blade stop (6623), mould blade (*do not drop vent pusher*), and two tie bars (6626 and 6627).

Take out one screw (680) (PLATE XIX) and its washer from the bottom of the mould. Then from the front remove five screws that hold the front type blocks (6240 and 6241) to the rear type block (6239)—these are all at the left end, three near the top and two near the bottom—the lower right one and the upper right two are reached through holes in mould base. Slide the type blocks (6240 and 6241) out toward the left, and remove the two-point blocks (6625 and 4356) (PLATE XIX). (Note their positions when taking them off so that they will be replaced correctly; their corners are made to correspond with those of the type blocks.)

Remove the six short screws and the one long screw from the type blocks, and take the type blocks (6240 and 6241) apart.

CLEANING

Clean all parts thoroughly with a dry cloth free from lint. Never use waste, and be particularly careful to have the vent pusher slot in the type block clean.

ASSEMBLING

Put the type blocks (6240 and 6241) together, insert the six short screws and one long screw and bring them up to bearing. Get the left ends of the type blocks exactly even; try them with a straight edge or feel with the finger nail across the end, and tap one or the other lightly with a block of wood to bring the type blocks into position, then tighten the screws and test again.

Then slide the type blocks (6240 and 6241) into position, putting a slight downward pressure on them so as to remove any dirt from their bearings. Remove the type blocks, wipe them off and repeat, this time leaving them in position. NOTE.—*It is absolutely necessary to have the type blocks and their bearings in the mould perfectly clean; even the slightest particle of dirt will hold the type blocks out from position.*

Move the type blocks (6240 and 6241) forward a little, slide in the mould blade, and press the type blocks back against the mould blade. Insert the upper point block (6625) with the bevelled corner coinciding with the bevelled corners of the type blocks, press it down lightly with the thumb nail to take up all lost motion in the mould blade, and insert and bring just up to bearing its three screws, but do not tighten these screws. Turn the mould bottom up and insert and bring just up to bearing the screw (680). Insert the lower point block (4356) with its bevelled corner coinciding with the bevelled corners of the type blocks, push it in until it is flush or below the surface of the type blocks and then insert and bring just up to bearing its two screws. Turn the mould right side up again and test the position of the upper point block by seeing that there is no up-and-down play in the mould blade. Then go over the six screws, tightening each a little until all are brought up solid. Again test the mould blade to see that there is no up-and-down play in it.

Pull out mould blade. With the mould standing on its front side, and the left toward you, put in the vent-pusher with the sharp edge up and the lug on the end toward you.

Slide in the mould blade again gently until the square recess in the blade engages the lug on the end of the pusher, and push both gently in together, swinging the blade a little, if necessary, to enter its end in its slot. If the blade and pusher do not go in readily, remove them and try again. *Never* force the blade.

Put on the upper mould blade shoe (6620) with its two screws, and also the mould blade stop (6623).

Put on the two tie bars (6626 and 6627) and bring them toward each other so that the shield (6622) will just slide easily into position between them.

Put on the desired matrix, matrix clamp (4377), matrix clamp screw (231), and shield (6622).

FRICTION BLOCK.—This does not need to be taken off when cleaning the mould, but must be adjusted when changing from one point size to another. Remove the two screws holding the trimmer, shown just to the left of screw (6263) (PLATE XIX), and take off the trimmer and its packing plate. Hold the clamp (6614) to the rear and remove the screw (6263) with its washer; then remove the clamp (6614) and its spring. Remove the two screws (293) and take off the friction block. To replace the friction block proceed as follows: insert a piece of lead or rule (cast by this mould) into the opening from which it was ejected and push it in until it touches the end of the mould blade. Turn the lever (5088) over until the lead or rule just inserted is clamped tightly. Press the friction block against its two bearing surfaces and slide it forward until it touches the lead or rule which is projecting from the mould; then insert and set up very tightly its two screws (293). Remove the piece of lead or rule from the mould, insert the spring behind the clamp (6614), put this clamp in position, and hold it to the rear while inserting and tightening the release screw (6263). Be sure the washer is on the screw. Put in position the trimmer with its packing plate, and insert and tighten its two screws shown just to the left of the screw (6263) (PLATE XIX). Be sure the packing piece is inserted right side up so that its upper edge comes about flush with the top of the friction block. Loosen the release screw (6263) until it is just free. This screw is adjusted by screwing it in until the shoulder on it comes flush with the rear face of the friction block.

Screw into bearing the clamp screw (12024), turning it by the lever (5088). *Be sure a piece of the product is left in the mould.*

CHANGING FROM RULES TO LOW LEADS

TO CHANGE FROM RULES to low leads proceed as follows:

Take off the shield (6622), matrix clamp (4377), and matrix. Take off the mould blade stop (6623). Pull out the mould blade, taking care not to drop the vent pusher which is drawn out with it.

Clean thoroughly the slot for the mould blade and vent pusher.

Turn the mould on its front side and put in the vent pusher and mould blade.

Put on the mould blade stop and tighten its screws.

Put on the mould blade cap with its support. The mould blade cap goes in the mould blade opening with its open side up and its notched end to the left; push the lug on its left end in under the point block until the vertical face of the notch comes up solid against the side of the point block, and then replace the matrix clamp (4377) and shield (6622).

CHANGING FROM LOW LEADS TO RULES

To CHANGE FROM LOW LEADS to rules, proceed in a similar manner to that described under the heading CHANGING FROM RULES TO LOW LEADS. Substitute the high blade for the low blade, and a matrix for the mould blade cap and its support. Be sure to have the open end of the matrix to the right.

HINTS ON LEAD AND RULE CASTING

IF SHORT LENGTHS of lead or rule are required apply the special box for this, 76F1. Remove galley x78F and stacker rock shaft connecting rod yoke pin 121F4. The box can then easily be placed into position.

For cutting shorter than 6-em pica in length remove thrust bar bell crank spring 126F1 and run machine on $\frac{1}{2}''$ stroke.

To centre the nozzle do not strip a mould, but use the gauge made and supplied for that purpose. Best results are obtained by using a special nozzle for each lead and rule mould, as more accurate seating is thus obtained.

For casting leads or rules from 6 point upwards use latch 57H1. If not already fitted it should be purchased.

Should the mould blade hang up, such as after a long run, clean vent blade race with a little graphite, using the vent piece to remove carbonization.

When casting 6- to 12-point rule make sure that the matrix is correctly positioned. To test, after casting, take off the matrix, and it will be possible to see exactly if the joint is correct. With the 6-point and 12-point rule it is difficult to test this point by breaking the strip.

SPEEDS AND TEMPERATURES.—The temperature at which efficient casting may be made depends mainly upon the quality of metal in use.

The following table indicates the speeds and temperatures for casting 'Monotype' leads and rules from standard 'Monotype' metal:

Size		$1\frac{1}{2}$ pt.	2 pt.	3 pt.	4 pt.	6 pt.	12 pt.
Revolutions per min.	..	128	110	91·	80	49	23
Gear Positions	.. ..	3CE	2CE	1CE	3BE	3AE	1CD
Temperature (Fahr.)	· ..	725°	700°	700°	680°	680°	650°
Temperature (Cent.)	..	385°	371°	371°	360°	360°	343°

These speeds and temperatures are approximate and apply only when the mould is thoroughly warmed up.

ADJUSTMENT OF NOZZLE.—Always test the adjustment of the nozzle, especially in regard to its fitting into the mould, before starting to cast.

ACTION OF CLAMP SCREW.—When the machine is running at 120 r.p.m. the moving end of lever (5088) should be between horizontal and $\frac{1}{8}''$ below the horizontal, when the centring pin lever is at the bottom of its stroke and the type blocks locked together in casting position. If the moving end of the lever (5088) works down so that at the bottom of its stroke (machine running at 120 r.p.m.) it is more than $\frac{3}{8}''$ below the horizontal it must be readjusted. Be sure that proper spring compression is on the connecting rod to this lever (5088) when making this test. (*Refer to* PLATE XIX, p. 291.)

EACH TIME A MOULD IS PUT ON THE MACHINE OR ONE MATRIX IS CHANGED FOR ANOTHER, test the product by laying two long lengths foot to foot on the galley. If they do not touch throughout their length, adjust the guide roller to straighten them, and the channel plate support to suit. (*See p.* 178.)

'MONOTYPE' CASTING SPEEDS*

Body Size		SET POINTS										
		4	6	8	10	12	14	15	18	24	30	36
12 point	..	140	140	140	140	110	—	—	—	—	—	—
14 point	..	140	140	140	128	110	91	—	—	—	—	—
18 point	..	140	140	140	91	91	68	68	49	—	—	—
24 point	..	140	128	91	68	68	49	49	36	27	—	—
30 point	..	140	91	80	57	49	36	36	27	20	14	—
36 point	..	128	80	68	49	43	32	32	23	17	12	9

* Where the matrix marking indicates half-way between two speeds on the speed plate of the casting machine always take the *slower* speed. Example: A 24-point matrix is marked *8–8; the speed taken should be *9–4 (68 revs.) and not *8–4 (80 revs.).

All types below 4 points in set in any size from 36 point downwards may be cast at 140 or more per minute. Where body point and set point are equal the type body is perfectly square in section. Casting speed is governed by cubic content of type body and by hardness of metal, hard metal requiring higher casting temperatures than soft metal. Average composition speeds: 5, 6, and 7 point, 180 per minute; 8, 9, and 10 point, 160 per minute; 11 and 12 point, 150 per minute; 14 point, 100 per minute; 18 point, 60 to 80 per minute; 24 point, 50 to 60 per minute. Spaces may be cast rather faster than type.

Weight of Type and Number of Letters Cast per Hour on a 'Monotype' Display Machine, based on a maximum (non-stop) speed of 140 revolutions per minute

6 pt. 7·28 lb. 8,400	7 pt. 9·92 lb. 8,400	8 pt. 12·96 lb. 8,400	9 pt. 16·23 lb. 8,400
10 pt. 20·27 lb. 8,400	11 pt. 24·51 lb. 8,400	12 pt. 29·16 lb. 8,400	14 pt. 39·71 lb. 8,400
18 pt. 51·56 lb. 6,600	24 pt. 56·6 lb. 4,080	30 pt. 46·97 lb. 2,160	36 pt. 43·12 lb. 1,380

The number of types cast per hour from 14 point upwards are assumed to be of an en quad thickness. Should the maximum speed be increased above 140 revs. per minute the output figures will be correspondingly increased. Output is decided by cubic content of type body and quality of metal.

DISPLAY MATRIX MARKING

DISPLAY MATRICES are marked with the face series number and the point size of the type to be cast from them; also with the set measurement in points. Thus, 199–18 towards one end of the matrix means that the face series is No. 199, and the body size is 18 point. At the other end of the same edge of the matrix is a number indicating the 'set' size in points to which type must be cast from that matrix, such as 16¾, indicating that the sizing wedges must be adjusted to 16¾ points.

The 'set' size, taken into consideration with the body size of the type, is an indication of the speed at which the type must be cast. A chart is provided from which the speed of casting may be obtained from any matrix marking.

There are also in circulation a number of display matrices which are marked with the face series number, the point size, and wedge positions indicating the set size, thus 159–24–*9–6 or 159–24–9–6. This indicates 159 series of face, 24 point; with the asterisk it means $9\frac{3}{4}$ points in set, and without the asterisk $26\frac{3}{4}$ points. Omission of the asterisk implies an addition of 17 points. On these matrices the final 2 indicates $\frac{1}{4}$ point, 4 indicates $\frac{1}{2}$ point, and 6 indicates $\frac{3}{4}$ point.

When a correct type size has been obtained by the method described under DISPLAY TYPE SIZING, pp. 167–169, it is possible—with moulds of the square nick pattern and certain moulds of the round nick pattern converted to a larger opening—to cast types in all sizes from $2\frac{1}{4}$ points to 48 points setwise. There are, however, a number of round nick moulds in which the maximum blade opening is not sufficient to allow the body of certain of the characters in the many extended faces to be cast in one piece. With these it is necessary to cast the body with the character overhanging, and then to cast a high space to support the overhang.

Only the $1'' \times 1''$ display matrices are used for these founts, and the particular characters which are outside the range of the mould are—in the case of matrices with new style marking—indicated on the matrix by the set size being greater than the body size. For example: if a character of $39\frac{1}{2}$ points set is to be cast on a mould with a maximum opening of, say, 38 points, a high space must be cast to support the overhang of the character. Place the wedges in position for 34 points and cast the type; subtract 34 points from the set size of the character to find the thickness of the high space—in this example it is $5\frac{1}{2}$ points— place the wedges and 17 point packing piece in position for this size, change the matrix and cast again.

When using matrices with the old style marking, the characters which have to be dealt with in this way are marked with two asterisks (**) in addition to figures indicating the wedge positions. The asterisks indicate that the wedges should be at 16–8 without the 17 point packing piece when casting the character; the figures indicate the wedge positions for the high space. For this the packing piece should be in position.

This method has been adopted as the one calculated to give the greatest degree of uniformity in wedge positioning, but in some instances it is possible to prevent the disadvantage of too great an overhang by departing from the above instructions; for by increasing the size of the body cast and decreasing the size of the supporting space the same final result is obtained, so long as the thickness of the space is decreased by exactly the same amount as the type body is increased. The design of the face in many cases demands that certain characters must overhang, therefore great care must be taken that the final dimensions of the type plus the space are correct.

PERFORATION TABLE

Units																			
5	I	*l*	*i*	*j*	'	*j*	'	i	□	l	,	.	**i**	**l**	**j**	,	.	**1**	17
6	J	*¹f*	*t*	(	)	-	f	t	□	**f**	**t**	'	'	**!**	**-**	**(**	**)**	**2**	18
7	s	·	;	*I*	*r*	*s*	I	r	s	:	;	**!**	**r**	**s**	**;**	**:**	⁵⅄	**3**	19
8	·F	E	*J*	*q*	*z*	*v*	*c*	e	e	c	z	J	**e**	**c**	**v**	**z**	**?**	**4**	20
9	B	T	*y*	*o*	3	6	9	*a*	□	x	**o**	**p**	**q**	**b**	**9**	**6**	**3**	**5**	21
9	L	*d*	*g*	*n*	7	4	1	0	g	y	**h**	**g**	**y**	**0**	**1**	**4**	**7**	**6**	22
9	P	*b*	*p*	*h*	2	5	8	*u*	a	v	**a**	**n**	**u**	**d**	**8**	**5**	**2**	**7**	23
10	X	Y	R	C	A	o	*x*	d	p	b	q	k	S	?	**J**	**£**	**k**	**8**	24
10	z	Q	v	*fi*	*fl*	*?*	*k*	u	o	h	n	fi	fl	£	**x**	**fi**	**fl**	**9**	25
11	K	D	G	H	N	⁶*ff*	U	⁷*F*	*S*	⁷*T*	*L*	*P*	ff	P	**ff**	**S**	**F**	**10**	26
12	M	*Z*	*B*	*E*	*w*	Z	F	T	E	L	B	**w**	**E**	**T**	**L**	**P**	**B**	**11**	27
13	*K*	⁷*V*	*C*	*G*	*R*	*A*	V	C	w	**A**	**R**	**C**	**V**	**Y**	**K**	**X**	**Z**	**12**	28
14	⁷*X*	⁷*Y*	*N*	*O*	*U*	*m*	Q	A	O	R	X	Y	**m**	**U**	**N**	**D**	**G**	**13**	29
15	w	*Q*	*D*	*H*	K	D	ffi	ffl	m	U	N	G	H	&	**O**	**H**	**Q**	**14**	30
18	Œ	²W	Æ	²M	%	²Æ	Œ	²M	**Æ**	²W	**Œ**	⁹M	**—**	⁹**W**	**.**	**.**	²	□	15

23   23   11 12   23   9 10   9 10   9 10   2 3

NI NL A B C D E F G H I J K L M N O

16 15 14 12 11 9 8 7 6 5 4 3 2 1   31 = .0005″   Just. Wedge

13 = .0075″   10 = Space
Just. Wedge   Trans. Wedge

By means of the letters at the base and large figures on right-hand side of the above table, any letter may be obtained from the holes in air tower. Thus, the cap. 'M' will be indicated by F15, and 'b' by H8. Number 10 hole leads to the transfer wedge shifter lever arm rod, and brings the space transfer wedge into operation. Numbers 13 and 31 lead to the justification wedge lever arm rods operating the coarse (.0075″) and the fine (.0005″) wedges respectively. The figures on right-hand side indicate the stop pin that will be in operation on 'B' pin block and the capital characters at the base indicate the required stop pin on 'C' pin block.

The small figures against certain of the characters in the above layout refer to notes in the printed Matrix Case Arrangement.

PERFORATION CODE

16	15	14	12	11	9	8	7	6	5	4	3	2	1	0	= sequence of pipes in caster air tower
A	B	C	D	E	F	G	H	I	J	K	L	M	N	O	= set rows of matrix-case

1	2	3	4	5	6	7	8	9	10	11	12	13	14	15	= unit rows of matrix-case
17	18	19	20	21	22	23	24	25	26	27	28	29	30	0	= sequence of pipes in caster air tower

Space Transfer Wedge, No. 10. Justification Wedges: 10D (.0075″) No. 13; 11D (.0005″) No. 31.

The first extended row on rear pin block is obtained by using the combination of N and L perforations, 1 and 3 air pipes on air tower; the second row by N and I perforations, 1 and 6 air pipes on air tower.

When the caster air tower is fitted with paper perforation indicator, the selection of matrices is simplified, as the marking on the indicator corresponds with the marking on the punch guide index plate on the keyboard.

The centre rows of characters and figures are used by the keyboard operator to indicate the matrix positions in the matrix-case. The top and bottom rows of figures indicate the sequence of the air pipes on the caster air tower, counting from left to right. Thus: G–13 indicates caster air tower pipes 8 and 29.

JUSTIFICATION WEDGE POSITIONS FOR CASTING THIN SPACES

POSITIONS OF JUSTIFICATION WEDGES to produce spaces one-fourth, one-fifth and one-sixth of the em quad of any set. These are to be perforated for in conjunction with the 'S' perforation, and cast from the 5-unit space position of matrix-case. In each case it is assumed that the type has first been sized up correctly. The 18-unit, 9-unit and 6-unit spaces are cast from their respective positions in the matrix-case, without the use of the 'S' perforation.

Set	Con-stant	One-fourth	One-fifth	One-sixth
6	2–5	3–3	2–10	2–4
$6\frac{1}{4}$	2–4	3–3	2–10	2–4
$6\frac{1}{2}$	2–3	3–3	2–9	2–3
$6\frac{3}{4}$	2–2	3–3	2–9	2–2
7	2–1	3–3	2–8	2–2
$7\frac{1}{4}$	2–1	3–2	2–7	2–1
$7\frac{1}{2}$	1–15	3–2	2–7	1–15
$7\frac{3}{4}$	1–14	3–2	2–6	1–14
8	1–13	3–2	2–6	1–14
$8\frac{1}{4}$	1–13	3–2	2–5	1–13
$8\frac{1}{2}$	1–12	3–1	2–5	1–12
$8\frac{3}{4}$	1–11	3–1	2–4	1–11
9	1–10	3–1	2–4	1–10
$9\frac{1}{4}$	1–10	3–1	2–3	1–10
$9\frac{1}{2}$	1–9	3–1	2–3	1–9
$9\frac{3}{4}$	1–8	3–1	2–2	1–8
10	1–7	2–15	2–2	1–7
$10\frac{1}{4}$	1–6	2–15	2–1	1–7
$10\frac{1}{2}$	1–6	2–15	2–1	1–6
$10\frac{3}{4}$	1–5	2–15	1–15	1–5
11	1–4	2–15	1–14	1–4
$11\frac{1}{4}$	1–3	2–15	1–14	1–4
$11\frac{1}{2}$	1–3	2–14	1–13	1–3
$11\frac{3}{4}$	1–2	2–14	1–13	1–2
12	1–1	2–14	1–12	1–1

TIMING OF CAMS

IF ALL CASTER ADJUSTMENTS are made as intended by the timing of the driving cams the machine will function correctly, the conditions due to wear and dirt excepted. Upon new machines the following are the times at which all the main movements take place:

PIN JAWS.—105° reach limit of opening; 200° start closing; 306° meet over air pin; 5° start opening.

MATRIX JAWS.—105° meet over stop rack head; 200° start opening; 306° reach limit of opening; 5° start closing.

MATRIX-CASE.—12° reaches highest position; 160° starts descending; 210° seats on mould; 332° starts leaving mould.

CENTRING PIN.—12° reaches highest position; 160° starts descending; 195° starts entering matrix; 208° reaches base of cone hole; 330° starts returning and leaving base of cone hole.

NORMAL WEDGE LOCKING PIN.—12° reaches highest position; 160° starts descending; 168° starts entering wedge; 178° reaches base of wedge teeth; 353° starts leaving wedge; 2° is clear of wedge teeth.

MATRIX JAW STOP RACK LOCKING BARS.—195° start leaving base of teeth of stop racks; 207° clear teeth of stop racks; 215° fully back; 354° start going towards stop racks; 355° reach teeth of stop racks; 5° reach base of teeth of stop racks.

TRANSFER WEDGES.—60° reach end of outward stroke (operating spring starts compressing); 80° start returning towards micrometer wedge; 159° reach micrometer wedge (operating spring starts compressing); 342° start returning.

JUSTIFICATION WEDGES.—12° fully lifted; 160° start descending; 182° seated on fixed tooth (wedge lever arm nut a15D1, starts to leave centring pin lever); 350° start rising (centring pin lever reaches wedge lever arm nut a15D1).

MOULD BLADE.—70° bell crank lever commences to move forward; 90° type ejected (type ejecting spring starts compressing); 136° ejecting spring free; 188° bell crank picks up collar (starts sizing); 210° finishes sizing, spring compressed; 305° sizing spring starts to be released; 319° bell crank clears 16c3 (12-set 18-unit position); 330° mould blade bell crank stops in normal position for setting wedges.

TYPE CARRIER.—200° comes to rest in casting position; 340° starts receding to cut off tang at foot of type; 356° tang cut off, and carrier starts to move forward; 30° tang starts to be ejected from mould; 43° tang ejected into melting pot; 80° starts receiving type from mould, and carrier starts moving back to casting position.

TYPE PUSHER.—185° starts moving forward to push type into type channel; 285° end of forward stroke (type behind latches) and start of return stroke; 355° reaches end of return stroke.

PUMP.—140° pump cam lever starts going back, lifting piston operating rod 19H; 215° pump cam lever pauses as nozzle reaches mould; 220° start of piston stroke; 260° end of piston stroke and start of pause after the piston has acted; 280° start of piston return stroke; 350° start of pause of cam lever during piston return stroke to permit pump trip tube collar b49D1, to be moved forward when the pump is to be automatically cut off, such as during the setting of justification wedges; 10° pump cam lever starts to continue piston return stroke; 75° piston return ends. (Pump lock becomes disengaged when trip tube collar has been advanced.)

AIR TOWER.—4° operating rod 54E, starts rising; 10° air valve closed; 13° air bar lifted; 18° locking pawl seated; 25° feeding pawl lifted; 48° pawl ring finishes rotating (right hand); 90° feeding pawl seated; 100° locking pawl lifted; 138° pawl ring finishes rotating (left hand); 140° air bar seated; 148° air valve opened.

METALS FOR USE ON 'MONOTYPE' MACHINES

SINCE THE VERY early days of printing, alloys of lead, tin and antimony have been used as type metals. Over the years, the compositions appropriate for specific purposes have been more closely defined and the standards of purity have been raised.

Scientific study of the alloys has lagged behind their practical application but in recent times there has been a good deal of research on the constitution of the alloys and on those properties of importance in printing. Such work not only offers a valuable supplement to experience in the investigation of practical problems; it also provides a picture of the behaviour of the alloys on melting and casting which can be of great assistance to anyone engaged in their handling.

REQUIREMENTS OF A TYPE METAL

(1) A type metal should give sharp and true castings.

It should reproduce faithfully every minute detail of the matrix and give a casting correct in form and dimension when cold.

(2) It should give strong and sound castings.

Cast type should be as sound as possible and stand up well to printing wear and pressure.

(3) It should be easy to cast.

The melting temperature should be reasonably low. The molten metal should not attack the iron and steel from which composing machinery is made, nor clog the small apertures in mouthpieces or nozzles.

(4) It should be clean to melt.

   When molten, it should give as little dross as possible and losses on remelting should be low.

CONSTITUENTS OF TYPE METALS

Long experience has shown that alloys based on lead with additions of tin and antimony meet these requirements better than any other metal or alloy.

Lead. Lead, which forms the basis of all printing metals, melts at 621°F., and is exceptionally malleable and ductile. It is comparatively cheap, so that it is a suitable metal economically as well as metallurgically, but by itself it is very soft and does not give sharp castings.

Antimony. Antimony melts at 1166°F. It is a hard, brittle and highly crystalline metal, which supplies hardness to the alloy and promotes sharp reproduction of the mould.

Tin. Tin, which has a melting point of 450°F., is not much harder than lead but much tougher. In a printing metal it adds toughness and wear-resistance to the alloy, in addition to making it more fluid and easy-flowing.

MELTING PROPERTIES

Pure Lead. Pure lead has a sharp melting point at 621°F. This means that at temperatures above 621°F. it is always completely molten forming a homogeneous liquid, and that below 621°F. it is always completely solid.

A pot full of molten lead, cooled down slowly from say 700°F., will stay molten until the temperature has dropped to 621°F. At this point, the metal will solidify and the temperature remains constant until the whole contents of the pot are solid (which will take some time). Once the metal has completely solidified, the temperature will again fall steadily.

EFFECT OF ANTIMONY

Thus pure metal melts and solidifies in a simple manner at a single temperature. The solidification of alloys is not so simple. Only in special cases does an alloy solidify at a single temperature; most compositions solidify over a range of temperatures.

Consider an alloy containing 5 per cent of antimony, 95 per cent of lead. At a temperature of 700°F. the antimony will be completely dissolved in the molten lead, forming a homogeneous liquid, although the melting point of pure antimony is 1166°F.

When this alloy is cooled, nothing happens at 621°F. (the temperature at which pure lead solidifies) and the contents of the pot remain fully molten until the temperature has dropped to 555°F. Here small

SOLIDIFICATION OF ANTIMONY-LEAD ALLOYS

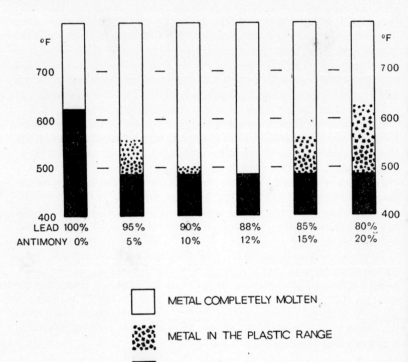

FIG. 1.—Diagram comparing the melting behaviour of various antimony-lead alloys

particles like 'grit' appear in the metal, showing that solidification has commenced, but the metal continues to cool, and becomes more pasty, until the temperature drops to 486°F.

Then, while the temperature remains constant, the remainder of the metal sets solid (which again takes some time). As soon as all the metal has solidified, cooling continues once again.

If the test is repeated with an alloy of 10 per cent antimony, 90 per cent lead, it will be found that the temperature falls to 500°F. before the grittiness appears which indicates the commencement of solidification. Again cooling continues to 486°F. and again the metal remains at that temperature until solidification is complete.

Thus, when antimony is alloyed with lead, the temperature of final solidification (which is called the 'solidus') is lowered to 486°F.; all alloys containing only antimony and lead finally solidify at this temperature. A second effect of initial antimony additions is to *lower* the temperature at which solidification commences (the 'liquidus'); 621° with no antimony; 555° with 5 per cent antimony; 500° with 10 per cent antimony (Figure 1). The alloy 12 per cent antimony, 88 per cent lead begins to solidify at 486°F. and remains at this temperature until it is a solid. In other words, this one composition behaves like a pure metal in having a single melting point or solidification temperature.

With alloys containing more than 12 per cent of antimony—and these are of the greatest interest to a 'Monotype' user—the liquidus temperature rises again. Thus in the alloy containing 15 per cent antimony, 85 per cent lead, gritty crystals appear on cooling at 558°F. Cooling continues and the metal becomes more pasty until the final solidification temperature of 486°F. is reached.

For the 20 per cent antimony, 80 per cent lead alloy the liquidus temperature is still higher—626°F., though the final, solidus temperature remains at 486°F.

When the alloy contains over 12 per cent antimony, then, the liquidus temperature rises as the antimony content of the alloy is increased. Since the final solidification temperature is constant, it follows that increasing the antimony content over 12 per cent increases the length of the solidification or pasty range. This fact has an important bearing on the choice of an alloy for casting type, since alloys with a long solidification range are more difficult to handle.

MICROSTRUCTURE OF ALLOYS

All metals are composed of crystals which can be clearly seen if a piece of metal is sectioned, ground flat, polished and examined under a microscope.

Solidification of metals can be regarded as a process of crystallization. Thus in pure lead, the crystals form at 621°F. to combine into an assembly of close-fitting grains.

Consider again the alloy containing 5 per cent antimony, 95 per cent lead. The first sign of solidification as the alloy cools was described above as the appearance of small particles like 'grit' in the molten metal. These particles consist of crystals of lead which, at the commencement of solidification are very small, but grow as cooling proceeds. The crystals are, in effect, extracting lead from the liquid metal which therefore gets progressively richer in antimony. Crystal growth continues until the metal which still remains liquid contains 12 per cent of antimony, 88 per cent of lead, by which time the temperature has fallen to 486°F.

Similarly when the alloy containing 15 per cent antimony, 85 per cent lead cools, the crystals which appear are of pure antimony. These crystals grow until the metal still liquid contains only 12 per cent of antimony.

It is possible now to see the significance of the special composition 12 per cent of antimony, 88 per cent of lead. When an alloy cools, it sheds whichever metal is in excess, as solid crystals. Ultimately the liquid remaining always contains 12 per cent antimony and as we have seen, this always solidifies at 486°F.

This composition is called the 'eutectic' which means easy melting. The name is given

(1) to the alloy itself containing 12 per cent antimony, 88 per cent lead and solidifying at the single fixed temperature of 486°F.

(2) to the constituent in other lead-antimony alloys which remains after the crystals, either lead or antimony (whichever is in excess), have formed and which likewise solidifies at 486°F.

Thus an alloy of 15 per cent antimony, 85 per cent lead is seen, under the microscope, to contain isolated crystals of pure antimony surrounded by the eutectic constituent. The latter is in fact a very fine network of interlaced lead and antimony.

EFFECT OF TIN

Tin in printing metals can be considered as modifying, but not altering in principle, the features observed in lead-antimony alloys.

The two changes which are of importance in consideration of 'Monotype' metal are:

(1) some tin enters the eutectic, which in type metals has the composition 4 per cent tin, 12 per cent antimony, 84 per cent lead. This melts at the single definite temperature of 464°F.

(2) excess tin and antimony over and above the eutectic composition form tin-antimony crystals, instead of the antimony crystals which are present in plain lead-antimony alloys.

MICROSTRUCTURE OF TYPE METALS

Figures 2-4 are microphotographs of some type metals. Figure 2 shows the eutectic alloy. The dark material is lead, the fine white lines are tin-antimony. The constituents are very intimately mixed.

This alloy, which incidentally is very close to the composition of slug casting metal, is rather soft and lacking in wear resistance for direct printing. A dual purpose 'Monotype' metal is shown in the next photograph. The white cubic crystals are tin-antimony, which being hard themselves, confer on the alloy improved resistance to wear. Surrounding these crystals is the eutectic constituent.

In the display metal (Figure 4) there are many more of the hard tin-antimony crystals.

FIG. 2.—Lead-tin-antimony eutectic: 4 per cent tin, 12 per cent antimony, 84 per cent lead. Melts sharply at 464°F. Note characteristic laminated structure

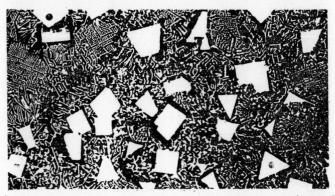

FIG. 3.—Alloy for composition work: 10 per cent tin, 16 per cent antimony, 74 per cent lead. White cubic tin-antimony crystals set in a groundmass of eutectic

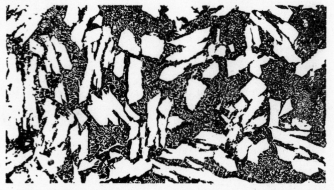

FIG. 4.—Alloy for display type: 12 per cent tin, 24 per cent antimony, 64 per cent lead. Note higher proportion of the hard crystals in comparison with Fig. 3

O

The size of the crystals in the metal depends on the rate of solidification. If this is very slow, the crystals have time to grow large. Rapid solidification on the other hand produces a very fine structure. It is very advisable that the crystals in metal fed into the machine pot should have a fine structure, so that they dissolve rapidly when the metal is added.

In type, the tin-antimony crystals may be only one ten-thousandth of an inch across.

The tin-antimony crystals are very hard in comparison with the lead-rich eutectic and it is desirable to have a high proportion present in the alloy for good wear resistance. But as the proportion of tin-antimony crystals is increased, to secure greater hardness, so the melting temperature goes up.

The same effect was observed in lead-antimony alloys containing more than 12 per cent of antimony. If we consider the addition of tin alone, we may find that it lowers the melting point; thus an alloy containing 6 per cent tin, 15 per cent antimony, 79 per cent lead not only has a lower melting point than the plain 15 per cent antimony, 85 per cent lead alloy, but it is also much harder. There is, however, a limit to the amount of tin which can usefully be added in this way, apart from economic considerations. Broadly speaking, the best results are obtained by increasing both tin and antimony together, and—to repeat —when this is done, the hardness is increased but the final melting temperature rises also.

PRACTICAL DISADVANTAGES OF HIGH-MELTING-POINT ALLOYS

The speed of casting normally demanded limits the range of alloys which can be used. It may be assumed that the metal enters the mould when it is only just completely liquid and that the type is ejected very soon after it has solidified. Consider two rather extreme alloys: 6 per cent tin, 15 per cent antimony, 79 per cent lead for composition work, and 18 per cent tin, 27 per cent antimony, 55 per cent lead, a very hard metal for display type.

	6/15	18/27
Completely liquid at ..	502°F.	646°F.
Completely solid at ..	464°F.	464°F.
Solidification range ..	38°F.	182°F.

The 'solidification range' for the hard metal is vastly greater. In comparable conditions of casting, therefore, the hard metal takes a much longer time to solidify. The cooling could of course be accelerated by extra water cooling, but even so, reduction in the speed of casting would be necessary to maintain satisfactory production of sound type.

The comparison is an extreme one but even within the range of alloys normally used, there are alloys having widely different melting points. Since there is a maximum casting temperature above which the metal would not solidify rapidly enough to maintain the speed of the machine, it is clear that the margin between this working temperature and the first freezing point of the alloy is much narrower with hard metals. There is a narrower permissible range of temperature with hard metal and closer attention to temperature control is necessary.

A further disadvantage of hard metals is their greater erosive effect on matrices.

CHOICE OF METAL COMPOSITION

To some extent, therefore, the composition of the alloy must represent a compromise between hardness and ease of casting. The final choice is dictated by the service to which the type will be put.

There is, however, one most important point which must be borne in mind. The resistance of type to wear depends not only on its hardness but also on its soundness and, particularly, the solidity of the printing surface. With the harder alloys more care and preferably a slower rate of casting are necessary to secure solidity. If high speeds of casting are to be maintained, then it is unwise to aim for hardness at the expense of solidity. A somewhat softer alloy which will in routine casting yield solid type will in the end be more reliable.

The foregoing may explain why metal compositions are not more rigidly standardized. Conditions of casting and use vary and it is for the individual user to select the composition which most nearly meets his requirements.

COMPOSITIONS AND PROPERTIES OF ALLOYS

6 per cent tin, 15 per cent antimony, 79 per cent lead

Completely liquid at	..	..	502°F.
Completely solid at	..	..	464°F.
Brinell Hardness Number	..	23·0

The alloy containing 6 or 7 per cent of tin with 15 per cent of antimony is most widely used for composition work. It has the lowest melting point of the alloys normally cast on a 'Monotype' machine and is easy to handle, giving sound type at high casting speeds. The type is naturally softer than that produced from the higher melting point alloys but has adequate wear resistance for the general run of composition work.

10 per cent tin, 16 per cent antimony, 74 per cent lead

Completely liquid at	..	..	524°F.
Completely solid at	..	..	464°F.
Brinell Hardness Number	..	27·0

Containing a higher proportion of tin-antimony crystals, this is considerably harder than the preceding alloy, although the liquidus temperature is not very much higher. It has excellent fluidity, thanks to the relatively high tin content. This is the recommended alloy for the dual purposes of composition and case type, for which it is well suited by reason of its good combination of wear resistance and ease of handling.

9 per cent tin, 19 per cent antimony, 72 per cent lead

Completely liquid at	.. ..	546°F.
Completely solid at	.. ..	464°F.
Brinell Hardness Number	..	28·5

This formula was once very popular but it has lost ground as a dual purpose metal to the 10/16 alloy. The reason lies in the higher liquidus temperature, for although it is slightly harder intrinsically than 10/16, and in favourable conditions gives excellent results, there is greater difficulty in maintaining output of solid type in routine production.

The difference shows up sharply in the casting of rule. Particular care is required with the 9/19 alloy to secure a clean face and good welds. By contrast, the 10/16 alloy, with its high ratio of tin to antimony, flows and welds more easily.

13 per cent tin, 17 per cent antimony, 70 per cent lead

Completely liquid at	.. ..	542°F.
Completely solid at	.. .:	464°F.
Brinell Hardness Number	..	29·5

This alloy illustrates the virtues of a high tin content. It is particularly tough as well as free flowing. Easy to cast, it yields beautifully clean, hard-wearing type.

A particular application is in the setting of jobs such as catalogues or timetables which will be reprinted with corrections or additions. When a metal less resistant to wear is used, alterations will show up after a comparatively short run even though the old type is still printing clearly.

12 per cent tin, 24 per cent antimony, 64 per cent lead

Completely liquid at	.. ..	626°F.
Completely solid at	.. ..	464°F.
Brinell Hardness Number	..	33·0

This is the recommended composition for display type. The hardest metal normally cast on a 'Monotype' caster, it contains, as Figure 4 shows, a very high proportion of the hard tin-antimony crystals.

The liquidus temperature is a good deal higher than any considered above; this means that special care is required in casting to maintain a homogeneous metal in the pot and to prevent blockage of nozzles.

HANDLING OF MOLTEN PRINTING METALS

FROM THE EXAMINATION of metals under the microscope, it is possible to deduce a good deal about their behaviour on melting and casting.

We have seen that a normal metal for 'Monotype' composition, properly melted and maintained throughout at a temperature of say 700°F., is a completely uniform and homogeneous liquid. The tin and antimony are dissolved in the lead, and so long as the temperature is maintained, they will stay dissolved. No separation will occur, for even though tin and antimony are lighter than lead, they cannot separate because they are in solution.

The temperature of 700°F. is well above the temperature at which the alloy commences to solidify. The superheat is necessary to allow for the cooling which occurs on the passage of the metal through the pump and nozzle, so that when it enters the mould it is still sufficiently fluid to fill out all the detail.

Unfortunately, practical factors tend to disturb the uniformity. The temperature in a caster pot is not absolutely the same at all points. Conduction away of heat by pump parts lowers the temperature of surrounding metal. Fresh metal added has a cooling effect. A current of cold air passing over the pot will tend to chill the metal on the surface. The ejected jet pieces both chill and aerate the metal where they fall. Thus the temperature generally may remain satisfactory but the metal may be chilled locally to such an extent that the temperature falls below its upper melting point. It is this condition which gives rise to separation in the pot.

SEPARATION OF CRYSTALS

The alloy 10 per cent tin, 16 per cent antimony, 74 per cent lead, as an example, commences to solidify at 524°F. When the temperature drops below this, tin-antimony crystals form. If cooling continues, more and more tin-antimony crystallizes out. If, however, the temperature remains constant at a few degrees below the liquidus, say at 515°, crystal formation is arrested: the crystals which have formed remain suspended in metal still molten.

The tin-antimony crystals are, however, much lighter than the remainder of the metal and hence they tend to float to the surface where they form a scum. If the pot is skimmed in this condition, a proportion of the valuable hardening constituents will be removed and the quality of the metal will fall.

If separation of the rich constituents does take place, as evidenced by the presence on the surface of the metal of a thick scum, do not skim this material off. Steps must be taken to redissolve the crystals as soon as possible, for if they become oxidized on the surface, they may be drawn into the dross and lost. The temperature should be raised well above normal for a brief period and the metal thoroughly stirred.

If the metal is always raised to 730°F. before skimming, loss of hard crystals will be kept to a minimum.

The metal should always be stirred well after it has been melted from cold in the mornings and at frequent intervals during the day, particularly after the addition of cold metal. This helps to even out the temperature and to redissolve crystals which may have formed.

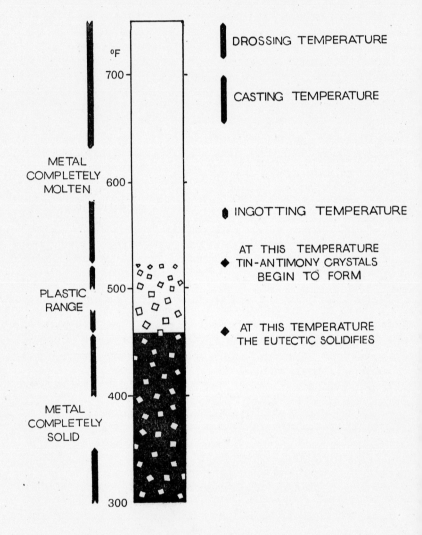

FIG. 5.—Solidification and treatment temperatures for the alloy containing 10 per cent tin, 16 per cent antimony, 74 per cent lead

FEEDING THE POT

It is advisable to add metal to the pot regularly as required, one ingot at a time. If a lot of metal is added at once, the pot is chilled: separation is likely to occur and the temperature will fluctuate widely. A single nugget melts quickly and produces less disturbance of the general temperature.

Though there is not the same need on the caster for an automatic Ingot Feeder Attachment as on the super-caster, this is the ideal method of supplying make-up metal. The level in the pot remains constant and steady feeding of small quantities of pre-heated metal provides the best conditions for precise control of the temperature.

SPEED OF MELTING

Printing metals should always be melted quickly, and there should always be adequate input of heat for this purpose. With a slow rate of heating between the first melting of the eutectic and the final melting of the tin-antimony crystals, the latter will be free to separate to the surface into a concentrated crust which is only redissolved with difficulty. Similarly, when the caster is working, the reduced heat supply may be inadequate to give the required quick response after the pot has been chilled by the addition of fresh metal. Reductions in the supply voltage are a frequent cause of slow heating, and furthermore, they are most likely to occur in cold weather, at just the time when extra heat is needed in the metal pot to make up for losses due to the colder machine and atmosphere.

EFFECT OF SEPARATION ON THE CASTING OPERATION

Possible loss of hardening constituents is not the only consequence of separation. The operation of the caster may be affected.

If separation has occurred, there will be solid grit-like crystals floating around in the metal. They will tend to settle out on cooler surfaces. As the metal flows from the pump to the mould, it loses heat. The crystals may settle out in the metal channels and in particular, in the nozzle. A build-up occurs, which gradually reduces the effective area of the nozzle, thus contributing towards hollow type. Ultimately, the nozzle becomes so blocked that casting is stopped.

This hazard is clearly more serious with the higher melting point metals and it can readily be seen that these require greater care to keep the metal channels free and thus to maintain production of solid type.

MELTING LOSS AND DEPRECIATION

Printing metals when molten form dross which contains slightly higher proportions of tin and antimony than the molten metal. If the same metal is used over and over again, the result is a gradual depreciation which ultimately throws the composition out of balance and results in type of inferior quality.

The depreciation can be ascribed to two separate causes.

Firstly, when type metal is molten and in contact with air, oxidation takes place. All three constituents of the alloy suffer, but tin, and to a lesser degree antimony, oxidize rather more rapidly than lead.

The second cause of depreciation arises from the separation of the tin-antimony crystals which occurs when the metal is chilled.

REDUCING THE MELTING LOSS

The formation of dross by oxidation of the metal is inescapable: little can be done to reduce the amount apart from the exercise of reasonable precautions in the remelting of type. Oxidation takes place more rapidly at high temperatures; if metal is overheated and then vigorously stirred for a long time so that a fresh surface is continually exposed to the air, then a heavy dross will be formed. Losses of this kind are avoided by working at the correct temperature.

Losses due to the separation of tin-antimony crystals, while they can be much more serious, are kept low if care is taken in the handling of metal whenever it is molten or melting.

The greater part of the loss is likely to occur during re-melting but loss in the machines *can* be considerable in unfavourable conditions: the precautions necessary to limit the loss from this cause have already been described: melt the metal quickly; maintain it at the correct temperature; do not skim when it is cold.

DEPRECIATION AND HOW IT IS MADE GOOD

However carefully type metals are handled, some depreciation will occur. The joint effects of oxidation and separation produce a gradual reduction in the tin and antimony contents of the metal which, if not corrected, will soon be evident in the quality of the type.

The regular addition of new metal to the old stock helps partially to maintain the quality but it is rarely easy to ensure uniformity in this way. Since some of the metal in printing works is locked up for long periods, while other metal is used again and again, the quality of the stock is liable to become irregular.

Satisfactory results in the composing room depend on a uniform supply of metal. Perfect uniformity can only be achieved if every potful of type, as it is re-melted, is brought up to the standard of new metal.

This ideal can be approached very closely by the regular use of reviving alloy.

Experience has shown the average loss of tin and antimony occurring each time an alloy is used, i.e. cast into type and subsequently re-melted. On the basis of these figures, reviving alloys have been designed containing high proportions of tin and antimony so adjusted that the addition of the correct proportion of the alloy at each re-melting will restore the tin and antimony wastage. Since most of the wastage occurs in re-melting, the effect is to correct the loss as soon as it has occurred.

This procedure is recommended in preference to the occasional addition of a substantial quantity of reviving alloy, which costs just as much but only improves part of the stock.

RE-MELTING TYPE

The importance of careful re-melting of type can hardly be over-stressed. Poor metal, which has become contaminated or impoverished produces bad type wastes time in all departments and does a poor job in the end. Careful re-melting—which does not mean expensive re-melting—saves money at every stage of production.

EQUIPMENT FOR RE-MELTING

The melting pot should hold at least 3 cwt. and preferably 5 cwt., so that the metal is melted in batches of reasonable size and is thus kept uniform. The pot can be efficiently heated by gas or electricity. Gas is cheaper both in first cost and in operation, electricity is cleaner and simpler to control but whereas electrical heating of composing machines has enormous advantages, there is not the same need of it for re-melting.

The pot should preferably have a bottom pouring valve. This saves labour and ensures that only the clean metal below is poured.

The pot should be hooded and the outlet conveyed out of doors, in order to take away fumes and, if gas heating is used, the products of combustion. The fumes from the pot arise mostly from the ink and from floor sweepings and also from the use of flux, which cannot be avoided. All these fumes are harmless but unpleasant. No fumes are given off by the metal but a certain amount of dusting from the dross is inevitable and such dust is of course obnoxious.

The best position for the re-melting pot is near a wall for simplicity of providing gas or electricity supply and as near the flue as possible.

Other equipment required is: Ingot moulds—for large outputs, water-cooled moulds are desirable but for normal work, heavy cast iron moulds are satisfactory; at least six should be available. A ladle, which can be used for stirring; a perforated ladle for removing the dross. Dross container to keep the dross under cover. Mould skimmer to remove the 'froth' from the ingots after they are poured. Thermometer to test the temperature of the metal.

KEEPING GRADES OF METAL SEPARATE

Type should be kept apart from slugs or stereos since a few pounds of these in a melting pot may affect the composition appreciably.

Founders' leads and furniture should be kept out of the pot for the same reason.

Founders' type should not be re-melted with 'Monotype' metal since it is likely to contain quite a high percentage of copper which will lead to trouble in casting.

Any 'foreign' metals should therefore be carefully picked out before type is put into the melting pot.

MELTING AND CLEANING THE METAL

Metal should be melted quickly because, as already described, slow melting leads to separation of the tin-antimony crystals with probable loss of some of these valuable hardening constituents in the dross.

The correct temperature to which the metal should be raised for cleaning is 700-750°F., the higher temperature being necessary for harder metals.

Regular use of a thermometer will avoid under- or over-heating, both possible sources of loss through extra dross formation.

When the metal has been raised to the cleaning temperature and thoroughly stirred, the dross on the surface will be rather thick and contain a high proportion of metal in addition to metal oxides and dirt.

A flux should then be used to clean the metal from oxides and non-metallic matter and to produce a dross which contains as little valuable metal as possible. The flux should not have any corrosive action which might affect pot or machine parts. The flux is added to the molten metal, well stirred into the dross and, if it is of the burning type, the fumes should be ignited and allowed to burn out. The dross should then be fine and powdery, showing that the bulk of the metal has been released into the bath.

This dross is then taken off in a perforated ladle. The ladle is shaken each time to allow the good metal to drain away.

Dross should be immediately dumped into a suitable container so that it is kept under cover.

REVIVING OR REJUVENATING THE METAL

It has already been pointed out that the best way to maintain the standard of the metal is to add reviving alloy to every pot full of metal re-melted.

The recommended quantity of reviver is $\frac{1}{2}$ lb. to every 1 cwt. After the metal has been skimmed free from dross, the reviver should be added and well mixed in for several minutes.

INGOTTING THE METAL

The temperature required for cleaning the metal is comparatively high to provide the right conditions for separating metal from dross. It is advisable to lower the temperature for pouring the ingots. A high pouring temperature results in slow cooling of the ingots; this is undesirable as it produces a coarse-grained structure which may lead to trouble in the machine.

Ingots should be skimmed as they are poured to remove any froth and scum from the surface.

IMPURITIES IN TYPE METALS

Molten printing alloys will attack and dissolve many other metals. The resulting contamination nearly always has a detrimental effect on the working properties, hence the need for care in handling of type to keep out any 'foreign' metals which might give rise to trouble.

Zinc is the most harmful impurity. In the form of zincos, this metal is quite readily dissolved if it remains in contact with molten printing metal for some time. Brass rule, another source of zinc, is rather more resistant, but even here the molten metal will exert a solvent action. When only a few thousandths of one per cent of zinc is present, the effect is immediately noticeable on the surface of the molten metal. The freshly-skimmed surface of properly melted metal should be bright and mirror-like. Metal contaminated with zinc, however, will not skim cleanly; there will be a strong thick film which immediately re-forms as the skimmer is drawn through the surface.

This strong film tends to enclose droplets of metal and thus greatly increases the amount of dross. Furthermore, the film retards the flow of the metal and restrains its entry into fine detail in the mould, thus spoiling the sharpness of the type.

Aluminium has rather a similar effect to zinc. Fortunately it is not readily dissolved by the molten metal. If any aluminium is accidentally charged into the pot with type, it usually rises to the surface and is skimmed off with the dross.

Copper is not quite so harmful an impurity and a certain quantity can be tolerated in the metal without detriment to the casting properties. The exact amount depends on the composition of the alloy, being higher with the harder metals.

Copper in excess of this safe limit forms crystals with antimony which have a relatively high melting point. The crystals readily separate from the molten metal and deposit on cooler surfaces of the pump assembly. As the metal flows through the nozzle the copper-rich crystals tend to build up in the orifice, restricting and ultimately blocking the flow.

Nickel in very small proportions has the same effect in causing blocking of nozzles. Nickel quite frequently occurs as an impurity through the accidental inclusion of plated stereos with type for re-melting: this should be carefully guarded against.

Iron. Printing metals are melted and cast in iron pots so that it might be expected that they would gradually absorb iron. Fortunately there is very little corrosive attack of the metal on iron and steel. The amount of iron absorbed in normal working is very small and has no practical influence on the behaviour of the metal.

ANALYSIS OF METAL

FROM TIME TO time, metal should be analysed to check the quality and the effectiveness of the reviving procedure. In the average jobbing works a check analysis once every six months is adequate.

For the analysis to be of value it must be reasonably representative of the metal in circulation. Samples should be selected with this point in mind. It is recommended that a few stamps should be taken from each machine on two or three separate days to form a composite sample which is sent for analysis.

CHANGE SPEED GEAR TABLE

36 point (and below) Display Matrices

Set Points	Matrix Marking	36 point	30 point	24 point	18 point	14 point	12 point
36	18–8	1AD (9)	2AD (11)	1BD (14)	1CD (23)	3CD (32)	1AE (36)
32	14–8	2AD (11)	3AD (12)	2BD (17)	2CD (27)	1AE (36)	2AE (43)
29	11–8	3AD (12)	1BD (14)	3BD (20)	2CD (27)	1AE (36)	2AE (43)
26	8–8	1BD (14)	2BD (17)	1CD (23)	3CD (32)	2AE (43)	3AE (49)
23	5–8	2BD (17)	3BD (20)	2CD (27)	1AE (36)	3AE (49)	1BE (57)
20	2–8	3BD (20)	1CD (23)	3CD (32)	2AE (43)	1BE (57)	2BE (68)
18	*17–8	1CD (23)	2CD (27)	1AE (36)	3AE (49)	2BE (68)	3BE (80)
16	*15–8	2CD (27)	3CD (32)	2AE (43)	1BE (57)	3BE (80)	1CE (91)
14	*13–8	3CD (32)	1AE (36)	3AE (49)	2BE (68)	1CE (91)	1CE (91)
12¾	*12–6	1AE (36)	2AE (43)	1BE (57)	3BE (80)	1CE (91)	3CE (110)
10¾	*10–6	2AE (43)	3AE (49)	2BE (68)	1CE (91)	2CE (110)	3CE (128)
9½	*9–4	3AE (49)	1BE (57)	2BE (68)	1CE (91)	3CE (128)	4 (140)
8½	*8–4	1BE (57)	2BE (68)	3BE (80)	2CE (110)	4 (140)	
7	*6–8	2BE (68)	3BE (80)	1CE (91)	4 (140)		
6	*5–8	3BE (80)	1CE (91)	3CE (128)			
5½	*5–4	1CE (91)	2CE (110)	4 (140)			
4½	*4–4	2CE (110)	3CE (128)				
4	*3–8	3CE (128)	4 (140)				
3½	*3–4	4 (140)					

Tumbler = 1–2–3
Section Lever = A–B–C
Back Gear = D–E
4 = Top gear of 140 r.p.m.

The above table gives the positions for the Tumbler Section Lever and Back Gear on Display Type Attachment change speed gear; also the markings on Display Matrices (12 point to 36 point). The figures in parentheses indicate the speeds obtained.

Where the matrix marking indicates half-way between two speeds on the speed plate of the casting machine always take the *slower* speed. *Example:* A 24-point matrix is marked *8–8; the speed taken should be *9–4 (68 revs.), and not *8–4 (80 revs.).

The speeds indicated are maximum and should not be exceeded.

AIR COMPRESSOR AND POWER TABLE

Table showing requisite number of revolutions per minute for air compressors for given number of 'Monotype' casters and standard keyboards, also Horse Power required by each with total.

FLAT BELT DRIVE TO COMPRESSOR

Size of Compressor	Speed	Casters	Keyboards	Power taken by Compressor	Power taken by Casters	Total
				H.P.	H.P.	H.P.
'Monotype' 5 cub. ft. ...	160	1	1	¾	⅜	1⅛
" ...	240	1	2	¾	⅜	1⅛
" ...	325	2	2	¾	¾	1½
LH YB 1 ...	190	2	3	1½	¾	2¼
" ...	190	3	3	1½	1⅛	2⅝
" ...	190	3	4	1½	1⅛	2⅝
" ...	220	4	4	1½	1½	3
" ...	240	4	5	1½	1½	3
" ...	270	5	5	1½	1⅞	3⅜
" ...	290	5	6	1½	1⅞	3⅜
" ...	315	6	6	1½	2¼	3¾
LH YB 2 ...	190	6	7	2½	2¼	4¾
" ...	190	7	7	2½	2⅝	5⅛
" ...	200	7	8	2½	2⅝	5⅛
" ...	210	8	8	2½	3	5½
" ...	222	8	9	2½	3	5½
" ...	237	9	9	2½	3⅜	5⅞
" ...	250	9	10	2½	3⅜	5⅞
" ...	262	10	10	2½	3¾	6¼
" ...	275	10	11	2½	3¾	6¼
" ...	285	11	11	2½	4⅛	6⅝
" ...	300	11	12	2½	4⅛	6⅝
LH YB 3 ...	190	12	12	3½	4½	8
" ...	198	12	13	3½	4½	8
" ...	205	13	13	3½	4⅞	8⅜
" ...	212	13	14	3½	4⅞	8⅜
" ...	220	14	14	3½	5¼	8¾
" ...	228	14	15	3½	5¼	8¾
" ...	237	15	15	5	5⅝	10⅝
" ...	244	15	16	5	5⅝	10⅝
" ...	256	16	16	5	6	11
" ...	263	16	17	5	6	11
" ...	270	17	17	5	6⅜	11⅜
" ...	278	17	18	5	6⅜	11⅜
" ...	285	18	18	5	6¾	11¾
" ...	296	18	19	5	6¾	11¾
" ...	300	19	19	5	7⅛	12⅛
" ...	310	19	20	5	7⅛	12⅛
" ...	320	20	20	5	7½	12½

AIR COMPRESSOR AND POWER TABLE

Table showing requisite number of revolutions per minute for air compressors for given number of 'Monotype' casters and standard keyboards, also Horse Power required by each with total.

V BELT DRIVE TO COMPRESSOR

Size of Compressor	Speed	Casters	Keyboards	Power taken by Compressor	Power taken by Casters	Total
				H.P.	H.P.	H.P.
'Monotype' 5 cub. ft. ...	160	1	1	3/4	3/8	1 1/8
,, ...	195	1	2	3/4	3/8	1 1/8
,, ...	240	2	2	3/4	3/4	1 1/2
LH YB 1 ...	178	2	3	1 1/2	3/4	2 1/4
,, ...	178	3	3	1 1/2	1 1/8	2 5/8
,, ...	194	3	4	1 1/2	1 1/8	2 5/8
,, ...	210	4	4	1 1/2	1 1/2	3
,, ...	245	4	5	1 1/2	1 1/2	3
,, ...	255	5	5	1 1/2	1 7/8	3 3/8
,, ...	280	5	6	1 1/2	1 7/8	3 3/8
,, ...	305	6	6	1 1/2	2 1/4	3 3/4
LH YB 2 ...	178	6	7	2 1/4	2 1/4	4 1/2
,, ...	194	7	7	2 1/4	2 5/8	5 1/8
,, ...	194	7	8	2 1/4	2 5/8	5 1/8
,, ...	210	8	8	2 1/4	3	5 1/4
,, ...	225	8	9	2 1/4	3	5 1/4
,, ...	245	9	9	2 1/4	3 3/8	5 7/8
,, ...	245	9	10	2 1/4	3 3/8	5 7/8
,, ...	255	10	10	2 1/4	3 3/8	6 1/4
LH YB 3 ...	188	10	11	3 3/4	3 3/4	7 1/4
,, ...	188	11	11	3 1/4	4 1/8	7 7/8
,, ...	188	11	12	3 1/4	4 1/8	7 7/8
,, ...	188	12	12	3 1/4	4 1/2	8
,, ...	202	12	13	3 1/2	4 1/2	8
,, ...	215	13	13	3 1/4	4 7/8	8 7/8
,, ...	215	13	14	3 1/4	4 7/8	8 7/8
,, ...	215	14	14	3 1/4	5 1/4	8 3/4
,, ...	230	14	15	5	5 1/4	10 1/4
,, ...	240	15	15	5	5 5/8	10 5/8
,, ...	240	15	16	5	5 5/8	10 5/8
,, ...	255	16	16	5	6	11
LH YB 4 ...	160	16	17	5	6	11
,, ...	160	17	17	5	6 3/8	11 3/8
,, ...	160	17	18	5	6 3/8	11 3/8
,, ...	160	18	18	5	6 3/4	11 3/4
,, ...	170	18	19	5	6 3/4	11 3/4
,, ...	170	19	19	5	7 1/4	12 1/4
,, ...	170	19	20	5	7 7/8	12 1/4
,, ...	180	20	20	5	7 1/2	12 1/2

LH YB 4 may be speeded up to 250 r.p.m. to give 76 cub. ft. per minute. 6 h.p. required to drive.

'MONOTYPE' DISPLAY MACHINE

WEDGE POSITIONS FOR CASTING FROM COMPOSITION MATRICES

Width in Inches	Normal Wedge (Xc21D)	Front Just. Wedge (10D)	Rear Just. Wedge (a11D1)	Width in Inches	Normal Wedge (Xc21D)	Front Just. Wedge (10D)	Rear Just. Wedge (a11D1)	Width in Inches	Normal Wedge (Xc21D)	Front Just. Wedge (10D)	Rear Just. Wedge (a11D1)	Width in Inches	Normal Wedge (Xc21D)	Front Just. Wedge (10D)	Rear Just. Wedge (a11D1)	Width in Inches	Normal Wedge (Xc21D)	Front Just. Wedge (10D)	Rear Just. Wedge (a11D1)
.0193	5	7½	1½	.0500	7	7½	4½	.0807	9	7½	7½	.1113	11	8	3	.1420	13	8	6
.0198	5	7½	2	.0505	7	7½	5	.0812	9	7½	8	.1118	11	8	3½	.1425	13	8	6½
.0203	5	7½	2½	.0510	7	7½	5½	.0817	9	8	1	.1123	11	8	4	.1430	13	8	7
.0208	5	7½	3	.0515	7	7½	6	.0822	9	8	1½	.1128	11	8	4½	.1435	13	8	7½
.0213	5	7½	3½	.0520	7	7½	6½	.0827	9	8	2	.1133	11	8	5	.1440	13	8	8
.0218	5	7½	4	.0525	7	7½	7	.0832	9	8	2½	.1138	11	8	5½	.1443	14	7½	2
.0223	5	7½	4½	.0530	7	7½	7½	.0837	9	8	3	.1143	11	8	6	.1448	14	7½	2½
.0228	5	7½	5	.0535	7	7½	8	.0842	9	8	3½	.1148	11	8	6½	.1453	14	7½	3
.0233	5	7½	5½	.0540	7	8	1	.0847	9	8	4	.1153	11	8	7	.1458	14	7½	3½
.0238	5	7½	6	.0545	7	8	1½	.0852	9	8	4½	.1158	11	8	7½	.1463	14	7½	4
.0243	5	7½	6½	.0550	7	8	2	.0857	9	8	5	.1163	11	8	8	.1468	14	7½	4½
.0248	5	7½	7	.0555	7	8	2½	.0862	9	8	5½	.1167	12	7½	2	.1473	14	7½	5
.0253	5	7½	7½	.0560	7	8	3	.0867	9	8	6	.1172	12	7½	2½	.1478	14	7½	5½
.0258	5	7½	8	.0565	7	8	3½	.0872	9	8	6½	.1177	12	7½	3	.1483	14	7½	6
.0263	5	8	1	.0570	7	8	4	.0877	9	8	7	.1182	12	7½	3½	.1488	14	7½	6½
.0268	5	8	1½	.0575	7	8	4½	.0882	9	8	7½	.1187	12	7½	4	.1493	14	7½	7
.0273	5	8	2	.0580	7	8	5	.0887	9	8	8	.1192	12	7½	4½	.1498	14	7½	7½
.0278	5	8	2½	.0585	7	8	5½	.0890	10	7½	2	.1197	12	7½	5	.1503	14	7½	8
.0283	5	8	3	.0590	7	8	6	.0895	10	7½	2½	.1202	12	7½	5½	.1508	14	8	1
.0288	5	8	3½	.0595	7	8	6½	.0900	10	7½	3	.1207	12	7½	6	.1513	14	8	1½
.0293	5	8	4	.0600	7	8	7	.0905	10	7½	3½	.1212	12	7½	6½	.1518	14	8	2
.0298	5	8	4½	.0605	7	8	7½	.0910	10	7½	4	.1217	12	7½	7	.1523	14	8	2½
.0303	5	8	5	.0610	7	8	8	.0915	10	7½	4½	.1222	12	7½	7½	.1528	14	8	3
.0308	5	8	5½	.0613	8	7½	2	.0920	10	7½	5	.1227	12	7½	8	.1533	14	8	3½
.0313	5	8	6	.0618	8	7½	2½	.0925	10	7½	5½	.1232	12	8	1	.1538	14	8	4
.0318	5	8	6½	.0623	8	7½	3	.0930	10	7½	6	.1237	12	8	1½	.1543	14	8	4½
.0323	5	8	7	.0628	8	7½	3½	.0935	10	7½	6½	.1242	12	8	2	.1548	14	8	5
.0328	5	8	7½	.0633	8	7½	4	.0940	10	7½	7	.1247	12	8	2½	.1553	14	8	5½
.0333	5	8	8	.0638	8	7½	4½	.0945	10	7½	7½	.1252	12	8	3	.1558	14	8	6
.0337	6	7½	2	.0643	8	7½	5	.0950	10	7½	8	.1257	12	8	3½	.1563	14	8	6½
.0342	6	7½	2½	.0648	8	7½	5½	.0955	10	8	1	.1262	12	8	4	.1568	14	8	7
.0347	6	7½	3	.0653	8	7½	6	.0960	10	8	1½	.1267	12	8	4½	.1573	14	8	7½
.0352	6	7½	3½	.0658	8	7½	6½	.0965	10	8	2	.1272	12	8	5	.1578	14	8	8
.0357	6	7½	4	.0663	8	7½	7	.0970	10	8	2½	.1277	12	8	5½	.1582	15	7½	2
.0362	6	7½	4½	.0668	8	7½	7½	.0975	10	8	3	.1282	12	8	6	.1587	15	7½	2½
.0367	6	7½	5	.0673	8	7½	8	.0980	10	8	3½	.1287	12	8	6½	.1592	15	7½	3
.0372	6	7½	5½	.0678	8	8	1	.0985	10	8	4	.1292	12	8	7	.1597	15	7½	3½
.0377	6	7½	6	.0683	8	8	1½	.0990	10	8	4½	.1297	12	8	7½	.1602	15	7½	4
0382	6	7½	6½	.0688	8	8	2	.0995	10	8	5	.1302	12	8	8	.1607	15	7½	4½
.0387	6	7½	7	.0693	8	8	2½	.1000	10	8	5½	.1305	13	7½	2	.1612	15	7½	5
.0392	6	7½	7½	.0698	8	8	3	.1005	10	8	6	.1310	13	7½	2½	.1617	15	7½	5½
.0397	6	7½	8	.0703	8	8	3½	.1010	10	8	6½	.1315	13	7½	3	.1622	15	7½	6
.0402	6	8	1	.0708	8	8	4	.1015	10	8	7	.1320	13	7½	3½	.1627	15	7½	6½
.0407	6	8	1½	.0713	8	8	4½	.1020	10	8	7½	.1325	13	7½	4	.1632	15	7½	7
.0412	6	8	2	.0718	8	8	5	.1025	10	8	8	.1330	13	7½	4½	.1637	15	7½	7½
.0417	6	8	2½	.0723	8	8	5½	.1028	11	7½	2	.1335	13	7½	5	.1642	15	7½	8
.0422	6	8	3	.0728	8	8	6	.1033	11	7½	2½	.1340	13	7½	5½	.1647	15	8	1
.0427	6	8	3½	.0733	8	8	6½	.1038	11	7½	3	.1345	13	7½	6	.1652	15	8	1½
.0432	6	8	4	.0738	8	8	7	.1043	11	7½	3½	.1350	13	7½	6½	.1657	15	8	2
.0437	6	8	4½	.0743	8	8	7½	.1048	11	7½	4	.1355	13	7½	7	.1662	15	8	2½
.0442	6	8	5	.0748	8	8	8	.1053	11	7½	4½	.1360	13	7½	7½	.1667	15	8	3
.0447	6	8	5½	.0752	9	7½	2	.1058	11	7½	5	.1365	13	7½	8	.1672	15	8	3½
.0452	6	8	6	.0757	9	7½	2½	.1063	11	7½	5½	.1370	13	8	1	.1677	15	8	4
.0457	6	8	6½	.0762	9	7½	3	.1068	11	7½	6	.1375	13	8	1½	.1682	15	8	4½
.0462	6	8	7	.0767	9	7½	3½	.1073	11	7½	6½	.1380	13	8	2	.1687	15	8	5
.0467	6	8	7½	.0772	9	7½	4	.1078	11	7½	7	.1385	13	8	2½	.1692	15	8	5½
.0472	6	8	8	.0777	9	7½	4½	.1083	11	7½	7½	.1390	13	8	3	.1697	15	8	6
.0475	7	7½	2	.0782	9	7½	5	.1088	11	7½	8	.1395	13	8	3½	.1702	15	8	6½
.0480	7	7½	2½	.0787	9	7½	5½	.1093	11	8	1	.1400	13	8	4	.1707	15	8	7
.0485	7	7½	3	.0792	9	7½	6	.1098	11	8	1½	.1405	13	8	4½	.1712	15	8	7½
.0490	7	7½	3½	.0797	9	7½	6½	.1103	11	8	2	.1410	13	8	5	.1717	15	8	8
.0495	7	7½	4	.0802	9	7½	7	.1108	11	8	2½	.1415	13	8	5½	.1720	16	7½	2

The abutment screw packing piece 32c1 must be in position on top of the mould blade operating fork to obtain the sizes in this table.

Table of wedge positions for casting sorts from composition matrices in all measurements from 5 units of 5 set to 18 units of 12½ set. For some sizes the mould blade abutment screw must be adjusted. The type body must never be *smaller* than the measurement for which it was designed. Fractional differences less than .0005″ can be obtained by micrometer wedge adjustment.

POSITIONS OF DISPLAY TYPE WEDGES FOR CASTING TYPE BODIES UP TO 36 POINT FROM 2¼ TO 36 POINTS IN WIDTH

Width in Points	Width in Inches	Wedge Xb21D Position	Wedge a11D1 Position	Width in Inches	Width in Points
* 2¼	.0311	2	2	.2663	19¼
* 2½	.0346	2	4	.2698	19½
* 2¾	.0380	2	6	.2732	19¾
* 3	.0415	2	8	.2767	20
* 3¼	.0450	3	2	.2801	20¼
* 3½	.0484	3	4	.2836	20½
* 3¾	.0519	3	6	.2870	20¾
* 4	.0553	3	8	.2905	21
* 4¼	.0588	4	2	.2940	21¼
* 4½	.0623	4	4	.2974	21½
* 4¾	.0657	4	6	.3009	21¾
* 5	.0692	4	8	.3043	22
* 5¼	.0726	5	2	.3078	22¼
* 5½	.0761	5	4	.3113	22½
* 5¾	.0795	5	6	.3147	22¾
* 6	.0830	5	8	.3182	23
* 6¼	.0865	6	2	.3216	23¼
* 6½	.0899	6	4	.3251	23½
* 6¾	.0934	6	6	.3285	23¾
* 7	.0968	6	8	.3320	24
* 7¼	.1003	7	2	.3355	24¼
* 7½	.1038	7	4	.3389	24½
* 7¾	.1072	7	6	.3424	24¾
* 8	.1107	7	8	.3458	25
* 8¼	.1141	8	2	.3493	25¼
* 8½	.1176	8	4	.3528	25½
* 8¾	.1210	8	6	.3562	25¾
* 9	.1245	8	8	.3597	26
* 9¼	.1280	9	2	.3631	26¼
* 9½	.1314	9	4	.3666	26½
* 9¾	.1349	9	6	.3700	26¾
*10	.1383	9	8	.3735	27
*10¼	.1418	10	2	.3770	27¼
*10½	.1453	10	4	.3804	27½

Width in Points	Width in Inches	Wedge Xb21D Position	Wedge a11D1 Position	Width in Inches	Width in Points
*10¾	.1487	10	6	.3839	27¾
*11	.1522	10	8	.3873	28
*11¼	.1556	11	2	.3908	28¼
*11½	.1591	11	4	.3943	28½
*11¾	.1625	11	6	.3977	28¾
*12	.1660	11	8	.4012	29
*12¼	.1695	12	2	.4046	29¼
*12½	.1729	12	4	.4081	29½
*12¾	.1764	12	6	.4115	29¾
*13	.1798	12	8	.4150	30
*13¼	.1833	13	2	.4185	30¼
*13½	.1868	13	4	.4219	30½
*13¾	.1902	13	6	.4254	30¾
*14	.1937	13	8	.4288	31
*14¼	.1971	14	2	.4323	31¼
*14½	.2006	14	4	.4358	31½
*14¾	.2040	14	6	.4392	31¾
*15	.2075	14	8	.4427	32
*15¼	.2110	15	2	.4461	32¼
*15½	.2144	15	4	.4496	32½
*15¾	.2179	15	6	.4530	32¾
*16	.2213	15	8	.4565	33
*16¼	.2248	16	2	.4600	33¼
*16½	.2283	16	4	.4634	33½
*16¾	.2317	16	6	.4669	33¾
*17	.2352	16	8	.4703	34
*17¼	.2386	17	2	.4738	34¼
*17½	.2421	17	4	.4773	34½
*17¾	.2455	17	6	.4807	34¾
*18	.2490	17	8	.4842	35
*18¼	.2525	18	2	.4876	35¼
*18½	.2559	18	4	.4911	35½
*18¾	.2594	18	6	.4945	35¾
*19	.2628	18	8	.4980	36

* The abutment screw packing piece 32c1 must be in position on top of the mould blade operating fork to obtain this set size.

Removing the packing piece 32c1 increases the set size 17 points. To avoid duplicating the central columns giving wedge positions, the sizes produced with the packing piece in place are given to the left of the wedge positions, and the sizes without the packing piece to the right.

NOTE.—To obtain the width in inches of any eighth point size, subtract .0017 from the next larger quarter point size. To obtain the setting of the wedges for any eighth point size, take the setting for the next larger quarter point size and subtract one from the position of the wedge a11D1. Thus the wedge position for two and seven-eighths points is 2–7.

JUSTIFICATION ADDED BY EVERY ADJUSTMENT OF JUSTIFICATION WEDGES

Fractions	Wedge moves	+ 3-8
.0005	0-1	3-9
.0010	0-2	3-10
.0015	0-3	3-11
.0020	0-4	3-12
.0025	0-5	3-13
.0030	0-6	3-14
.0035	0-7	3-15
.0040	0-8	4-1
.0045	0-9	4-2
.0050	0-10	4-3
.0055	0-11	4-4
.0060	0-12	4-5
.0065	0-13	4-6
.0070	0-14	4-7
.0075	0-15	4-8
.0080	1-1	4-9
.0085	1-2	4-10
.0090	1-3	4-11
.0095	1-4	4-12
.0100	1-5	4-13
.0105	1-6	4-14
.0110	1-7	4-15
.0115	1-8	5-1
.0120	1-9	5-2
.0125	1-10	5-3
.0130	1-11	5-4
.0135	1-12	5-5
.0140	1-13	5-6
.0145	1-14	5-7
.0150	1-15	5-8
.0155	2-1	5-9
.0160	2-2	5-10
.0165	2-3	5-11
.0170	2-4	5-12
.0175	2-5	5-13
.0180	2-6	5-14
.0185	2-7	5-15
.0190	2-8	6-1
.0195	2-9	6-2
.0200	2-10	6-3
.0205	2-11	6-4
.0210	2-12	6-5
.0215	2-13	6-6
.0220	2-14	6-7
.0225	2-15	6-8
.0230	3-1	6-9
.0235	3-2	6-10
.0240	3-3	6-11
.0245	3-4	6-12
.0250	3-5	6-13
.0255	3-6	6-14
.0260	3-7	6-15
.0265	3-8	7-1
.0270	3-9	7-2
.0275	3-10	7-3
.0280	3-11	7-4
.0285	3-12	7-5
.0290	3-13	7-6
.0295	3-14	7-7
.0300	3-15	7-8
.0305	4-1	7-9
.0310	4-2	7-10
.0315	4-3	7-11
.0320	4-4	7-12
.0325	4-5	7-13
.0330	4-6	7-14
.0335	4-7	7-15
.0340	4-8	8-1
.0345	4-9	8-2
.0350	4-10	8-3
.0355	4-11	8-4
.0360	4-12	8-5
.0365	4-13	8-6
.0370	4-14	8-7
.0375	4-15	8-8
.0380	5-1	8-9
.0385	5-2	8-10
.0390	5-3	8-11
.0395	5-4	8-12
.0400	5-5	8-13
.0405	5-6	8-14
.0410	5-7	8-15
.0415	5-8	9-1
.0420	5-9	9-2
.0425	5-10	9-3
.0430	5-11	9-4
.0435	5-12	9-5
.0440	5-13	9-6
.0445	5-14	9-7
.0450	5-15	9-8
.0455	6-1	9-9
.0460	6-2	9-10
.0465	6-3	9-11
.0470	6-4	9-12
.0475	6-5	9-13
.0480	6-6	9-14
.0485	6-7	9-15
.0490	6-8	10-1
.0495	6-9	10-2
.0500	6-10	10-3
.0505	6-11	10-4
.0510	6-12	10-5
.0515	6-13	10-6
.0520	6-14	10-7
.0525	6-15	10-8
.0530	7-1	10-9
.0535	7-2	10-10
.0540	7-3	10-11
.0545	7-4	10-12
.0550	7-5	10-13
.0555	7-6	10-14
.0560	7-7	10-15
.0565	7-8	11-1
.0570	7-9	11-2
.0575	7-10	11-3
.0580	7-11	11-4
.0585	7-12	11-5
.0590	7-13	11-6
.0595	7-14	11-7
.0600	7-15	11-8
.0605	8-1	11-9
.0610	8-2	11-10
.0615	8-3	11-11
.0620	8-4	11-12
.0625	8-5	11-13
.0630	8-6	11-14
.0635	8-7	11-15
.0640	8-8	12-1
.0645	8-9	12-2
.0650	8-10	12-3
.0655	8-11	12-4
.0660	8-12	12-5
.0665	8-13	12-6
.0670	8-14	12-7
.0675	8-15	12-8
.0680	9-1	12-9
.0685	9-2	12-10
.0690	9-3	12-11
.0695	9-4	12-12
.0700	9-5	12-13
.0705	9-6	12-14
.0710	9-7	12-15
.0715	9-8	13-1
.0720	9-9	13-2
.0725	9-10	13-3
.0730	9-11	13-4
.0735	9-12	13-5
.0740	9-13	13-6
.0745	9-14	13-7
.0750	9-15	13-8
.0755	10-1	13-9
.0760	10-2	13-10
.0765	10-3	13-11
.0770	10-4	13-12
.0775	10-5	13-13
.0780	10-6	13-14
.0785	10-7	13-15
.0790	10-8	14-1
.0795	10-9	14-2
.0800	10-10	14-3
.0805	10-11	14-4
.0810	10-12	14-5
.0815	10-13	14-6
.0820	10-14	14-7
.0825	10-15	14-8
.0830	11-1	14-9
.0835	11-2	14-10
.0840	11-3	14-11
.0845	11-4	14-12
.0850	11-5	14-13
.0855	11-6	14-14
.0860	11-7	14-15
.0865	11-8	15-1
.0870	11-9	15-2
.0875	11-10	15-3
.0880	11-11	15-4
.0885	11-12	15-5
.0890	11-13	15-6
.0895	11-14	15-7
.0900	11-15	15-8
.0905	12-1	15-9
.0910	12-2	15-10
.0915	12-3	15-11
.0920	12-4	15-12
.0925	12-5	15-13
.0930	12-6	15-14
.0935	12-7	15-15
.0940	12-8	
.0945	12-9	
.0950	12-10	
.0955	12-11	
.0960	12-12	
.0965	12-13	
.0970	12-14	
.0975	12-15	
.0980	13-1	
.0985	13-2	
.0990	13-3	
.0995	13-4	
.1000	13-5	
.1005	13-6	
.1010	13-7	
.1015	13-8	
.1020	13-9	
.1025	13-10	
.1030	13-11	
.1035	13-12	
.1040	13-13	
.1045	13-14	
.1050	13-15	
.1055	14-1	
.1060	14-2	
.1065	14-3	
.1070	14-4	
.1075	14-5	
.1080	14-6	
.1085	14-7	
.1090	14-8	
.1095	14-9	
.1100	14-10	
.1105	14-11	
.1110	14-12	
.1115	14-13	
.1120	14-14	

This table shows amount of justification to be added to (or to a limited extent subtracted from) 3—8 for the purpose of increasing (or reducing) width of type bodies.

Example: Casting machine is occupied casting 8 point, 8½ set, and a quantity of 8 point, 9 set, figures is urgently needed. The difference between 9 units of 8½ set and of 9 set = .0034″ so by adjusting the justification wedges to 3-15 (3-8+0-7 = 3-15), and bringing the space transfer wedge into operation the figures may be cast without disturbing the adjustment of mould blade. The margin of error is only 1/10,000″ per character. If 9 set was being cast and 8½ set figures were needed the justification wedge adjustment would be 3-1 (3-8−0-7 = 3-1).

The figures in the second column of each section of the above table show the wedge moves from any given positions of the justification wedges to obtain the increase in space or type thickness indicated by the measurements in the first column. The maximum movement of the justification wedges from 1-1 is 14-14. The figures in the third column of each section indicate the actual positions of the justification wedges to increase the type bodies by the amount indicated in the first column.

JUSTIFICATION WEDGE POSITIONS FOR ADDING COMPLETE UNITS

	UNITS																		Limit*		
Set	1	2	3	4	5	6	7	8	9	10	11	12	13	14	15	16	17	18	Units	Inches	Set
6	4–2	4–11	5–6	5–15	6–9	7–3	7–13	8–7	9–1	9–10	10–4	10–14	11–8	12–2	12–11	13–6	13–15	14–9	33	.1522	**6**
6¼	4–3	4–12	5–7	6–1	6–11	7–6	7–15	8–10	9–4	9–14	10–9	11–3	11–13	12–7	13–2	13–12	14–6	15–1	32	.1536	**6¼**
6½	4–3	4–13	5–8	6–3	6–13	7–8	8–3	8–13	9–8	10–3	10–13	11–8	12–3	12–13	13–8	14–3	14–13	15–8	31	.1550	**6½**
6¾	4–3	4–14	5–9	6–4	6–15	7–10	8–6	9–1	9–11	10–7	11–2	11–12	12–8	13–3	13–14	14–9	15–4	15–15	30	.1557	**6¾**
7	4–4	4–15	5–10	6–6	7–2	7–13	8–8	9–4	9–15	10–11	11–6	12–2	12–13	13–9	14–4	14–15	15–11	—	29	.1560	**7**
7¼	4–4	4–15	5–11	6–8	7–4	7–15	8–11	9–7	10–3	10–14	11–11	12–7	13–3	13–14	14–10	15–6	—	—	28	.1559	**7¼**
7½	4–5	5–1	5–13	6–9	7–6	8–2	8–14	9–10	10–7	11–3	11–15	12–11	13–8	14–4	15–1	15–12	—	—	27	.1555	**7½**
7¾	4–5	5–2	5–14	6–11	7–8	8–4	9–1	9–13	10–10	11–7	12–4	13–1	13–13	14–10	15–7	—	—	—	26	.1549	**7¾**
8	4–5	5–3	5–15	6–12	7–9	8–7	9–4	10–1	10–14	11–11	12–8	13–6	14–3	14–15	15–12	—	—	—	25	.1537	**8**
8¼	4–6	5–3	6–1	6–14	7–11	8–9	9–7	10–4	11–2	11–15	12–12	13–10	14–8	15–6	—	—	—	—	24	.1521	**8¼**
8½	4–6	5–4	6–2	6–15	7–13	8–11	9–9	10–8	11–6	12–4	13–2	13–15	14–13	15–11	—	—	—	—	24	.1567	**8½**
8¾	4–6	5–5	6–3	7–2	7–15	8–14	9–12	10–11	11–9	12–8	13–6	14–4	15–3	—	—	—	—	—	23	.1545	**8¾**
9	4–7	5–6	6–4	7–3	8–2	9–1	9–15	10–14	11–12	12–11	13–10	14–9	15–8	—	—	—	—	—	22	.1522	**9**
9¼	4–7	5–6	6–6	7–5	8–4	9–3	10–3	11–2	12–1	12–15	13–14	14–14	15–13	—	—	—	—	—	22	.1564	**9¼**
9½	4–8	5–7	6–7	7–6	8–6	9–6	10–5	11–5	12–4	13–4	14–4	15–3	—	—	—	—	—	—	21	.1533	**9½**
9¾†	4–8	5–8	6–8	7–8	8–8	9–8	10–8	11–8	12–8	13–8	14–8	15–8	—	—	—	—	—	—	20	.1499	**9¾†**
10	4–8	5–9	6–9	7–9	8–10	9–10	10–11	11–11	12–11	13–12	14–12	—	—	—	—	—	—	—	20	.1537	**10**
10¼	4–9	5–10	6–10	7–11	8–12	9–13	10–13	11–14	12–15	14–1	15–1	—	—	—	—	—	—	—	19	.1497	**10¼**
10½	4–9	5–10	6–11	7–13	8–14	9–15	11–1	12–2	13–3	14–4	15–6	—	—	—	—	—	—	—	19	.1533	**10½**
10¾	4–10	5–11	6–13	7–14	9–1	10–2	11–4	12–5	13–7	14–8	15–10	—	—	—	—	—	—	—	18	.1487	**10¾**
11	4–10	5–12	6–14	8–1	9–3	10–4	11–6	12–8	13–10	14–12	15–14	—	—	—	—	—	—	—	18	.1522	**11**
11¼	4–10	5–13	6–15	8–2	9–4	10–7	11–9	12–11	13–14	15–1	—	—	—	—	—	—	—	—	18	.1556	**11¼**
11½	4–11	5–13	7–1	8–4	9–6	10–9	11–12	12–14	14–2	15–5	—	—	—	—	—	—	—	—	17	.1502	**11½**
11¾	4–11	5–14	7–2	8–5	9–8	10–11	11–14	13–2	14–6	15–9	—	—	—	—	—	—	—	—	17	.1535	**11¾**
12‡	4–11	5–15	7–3	8–7	9–10	10–14	12–2	13–6	14–9	15–12	—	—	—	—	—	—	—	—	18	.1660	**12‡**

* The two limits of type expansion by letter-spacing are: (1) The limit of justification wedge adjustment, which is 15–15; (2) the safe limit of the .2″ × .2″ matrix width which may be presented to the mould orifice so as to effect a metal-tight covering.

† Note that in 9¾ set one move on 10D wedge equals 1 unit of set, and one move of 11D wedge equals 1/15th unit of set.

‡ Characters of 12-point matrices are punched .025″ from side of matrix-body; in founts smaller than 12 point this measurement is .035″.

This table shows the justification to be made so that characters, placed in the matrix-case in rows of different unit value from that for which they are cut, may be cast to the intended increased width. When using ordinary composition matrices (.2″ × .2″) it is not safe to attempt to cast type wider than .156″, except from 12-point matrices. The limit of *addition* to type units by justification wedge adjustment is 12–7 (3–8 + 12–7 = 15–15); 12–7 = .0935″. The limit of type *reduction* is 2–7 (3–8 — 2–7 = 1–1); 2–7 = .0185″. To find the amount added, deduct 3–8 from the figures given in the table (thus: 2 units 12 set = 5–15 — 3–8 = 2–7 = .0185″). In the last two columns are indicated the limit in units and inch measurements to which any set size may be expanded. Thus: in 8 set the limit is 25 units, which may be obtained by increasing an 18-unit character 7 units, a 15-unit character 10 units, and so on; but characters in 8 set *below* 11 units in width cannot in composition be expanded to the casting limit of the matrix width on account of the limit of justification wedge adjustment (thus 9 units + 12–7 justification = .1488″).

TYPE SIZES FOR USE WITH NORMAL WEDGES. (Based on 12 Point = .166)

Set	Unit	2	3	4	5	6	7	8	9	10	11	12	13	14	15	16	17	18	19	20	21	22	Set
5	.00384	.0077	.0115	.0154	.0192	.0231	.0269	.0307	.0346	.0384	.0423	.0461	.0500	.0538	.0576	.0615	.0653	.0692	.0730	.0769	.0807	.0845	5
5¼	.00403	.0081	.0121	.0161	.0202	.0242	.0282	.0323	.0363	.0403	.0444	.0484	.0525	.0565	.0605	.0646	.0686	.0726	.0767	.0807	.0847	.0888	5¼
5½	.00423	.0085	.0127	.0169	.0211	.0254	.0296	.0338	.0380	.0423	.0465	.0507	.0549	.0592	.0634	.0676	.0719	.0761	.0803	.0845	.0888	.0930	5½
5¾	.00442	.0088	.0133	.0177	.0221	.0265	.0309	.0354	.0398	.0442	.0486	.0530	.0574	.0619	.0663	.0707	.0751	.0795	.0840	.0884	.0928	.0972	5¾
6	.00461	.0092	.0138	.0184	.0231	.0277	.0323	.0369	.0415	.0461	.0507	.0553	.0599	.0646	.0692	.0738	.0784	.0830	.0876	.0922	.0968	.1014	6
6¼	.00480	.0096	.0144	.0192	.0240	.0288	.0336	.0384	.0432	.0480	.0528	.0576	.0624	.0672	.0720	.0769	.0817	.0865	.0913	.0961	.1009	.1057	6¼
6½	.00500	.0100	.0150	.0200	.0250	.0300	.0350	.0400	.0450	.0500	.0549	.0599	.0649	.0699	.0749	.0799	.0849	.0899	.0949	.0999	.1049	.1099	6½
6¾	.00519	.0104	.0156	.0207	.0259	.0311	.0363	.0415	.0467	.0519	.0571	.0622	.0674	.0726	.0778	.0830	.0882	.0934	.0986	.1037	.1089	.1141	6¾
7	.00538	.0108	.0161	.0215	.0269	.0323	.0377	.0430	.0484	.0538	.0592	.0646	.0699	.0753	.0807	.0861	.0915	.0968	.1022	.1076	.1130	.1184	7
7¼	.00557	.0111	.0167	.0223	.0279	.0334	.0390	.0446	.0501	.0557	.0613	.0669	.0724	.0780	.0836	.0892	.0947	.1003	.1059	.1114	.1170	.1226	7¼
7½	.00576	.0115	.0173	.0231	.0288	.0346	.0403	.0461	.0519	.0576	.0634	.0692	.0749	.0807	.0865	.0922	.0980	.1038	.1095	.1153	.1210	.1268	7½
7¾	.00596	.0119	.0179	.0238	.0298	.0357	.0417	.0476	.0536	.0596	.0655	.0715	.0774	.0834	.0893	.0953	.1013	.1072	.1132	.1191	.1251	.1310	7¾
8	.00615	.0123	.0184	.0246	.0307	.0369	.0430	.0492	.0553	.0615	.0676	.0738	.0799	.0861	.0922	.0984	.1045	.1107	.1168	.1230	.1291	.1353	8
8¼	.00634	.0127	.0190	.0254	.0317	.0380	.0444	.0507	.0571	.0634	.0697	.0761	.0824	.0888	.0951	.1014	.1078	.1141	.1205	.1268	.1331	.1395	8¼
8½	.00653	.0131	.0196	.0261	.0327	.0392	.0457	.0523	.0588	.0653	.0719	.0784	.0849	.0915	.0980	.1045	.1111	.1176	.1241	.1307	.1372	.1437	8½
8¾	.00672	.0134	.0202	.0269	.0336	.0403	.0471	.0538	.0605	.0672	.0740	.0807	.0874	.0941	.1009	.1076	.1143	.1210	.1278	.1345	.1412	.1479	8¾
9	.00692	.0138	.0207	.0277	.0346	.0415	.0484	.0553	.0622	.0692	.0761	.0830	.0899	.0968	.1037	.1107	.1176	.1245	.1314	.1383	.1452	.1522	9
9¼	.00711	.0142	.0213	.0284	.0355	.0427	.0498	.0569	.0640	.0711	.0782	.0853	.0924	.0995	.1066	.1137	.1208	.1280	.1351	.1422	.1493	.1564	9¼
9½	.00730	.0146	.0219	.0292	.0365	.0438	.0511	.0584	.0657	.0730	.0803	.0876	.0949	.1022	.1095	.1168	.1241	.1314	.1387	.1460	.1533	.1606	9½
9¾	.00749	.0150	.0225	.0300	.0374	.0450	.0525	.0599	.0674	.0749	.0824	.0899	.0974	.1049	.1124	.1199	.1274	.1349	.1424	.1499	.1574	.1648	9¾
10	.00769	.0154	.0231	.0307	.0384	.0461	.0538	.0615	.0692	.0769	.0845	.0922	.0999	.1076	.1153	.1230	.1306	.1383	.1460	.1537	.1614	.1691	10
10¼	.00788	.0158	.0236	.0315	.0394	.0473	.0551	.0630	.0709	.0788	.0867	.0945	.1024	.1103	.1182	.1260	.1339	.1418	.1497	.1576	.1654	.1733	10¼
10½	.00807	.0161	.0242	.0323	.0403	.0484	.0565	.0646	.0726	.0807	.0888	.0968	.1049	.1130	.1210	.1291	.1372	.1453	.1533	.1614	.1695	.1775	10½
10¾	.00826	.0165	.0248	.0330	.0413	.0496	.0578	.0661	.0744	.0826	.0909	.0991	.1074	.1157	.1239	.1322	.1404	.1487	.1570	.1652	.1735	.1818	10¾
11	.00845	.0169	.0254	.0338	.0423	.0507	.0592	.0676	.0761	.0845	.0930	.1014	.1099	.1184	.1268	.1353	.1437	.1522	.1606	.1691	.1775	.1860	11
11¼	.00865	.0173	.0259	.0346	.0432	.0519	.0605	.0692	.0778	.0865	.0951	.1037	.1124	.1210	.1297	.1383	.1470	.1556	.1643	.1729	.1816	.1902	11¼
11½	.00884	.0177	.0265	.0354	.0442	.0530	.0619	.0707	.0795	.0884	.0972	.1061	.1149	.1237	.1326	.1414	.1502	.1591	.1679	.1768	.1856	.1944	11½
11¾	.00903	.0181	.0271	.0361	.0452	.0542	.0632	.0722	.0813	.0903	.0993	.1084	.1174	.1264	.1355	.1445	.1535	.1625	.1716	.1806	.1896	.1987	11¾
12	.00922	.0184	.0277	.0369	.0461	.0553	.0646	.0738	.0830	.0922	.1014	.1107	.1199	.1291	.1383	.1476	.1568	.1660	.1752	.1844	.1937	.2029	12
12¼	.00941	.0188	.0282	.0377	.0471	.0565	.0659	.0753	.0847	.0941	.1036	.1130	.1224	.1318	.1412	.1506	.1600	.1695	.1789	.1883	.1977	.2071	12¼
12½	.00961	.0192	.0288	.0384	.0480	.0576	.0672	.0769	.0865	.0961	.1057	.1153	.1249	.1345	.1441	.1537	.1633	.1729	.1825	.1921	.2017	.2113	12½
12¾	.00980	.0196	.0294	.0392	.0490	.0588	.0686	.0784	.0882	.0980	.1078	.1176	.1274	.1372	.1470	.1568	.1666	.1764	.1862	.1960	.2058	.2156	12¾

TYPE SIZES FOR USE WITH NORMAL WEDGES. (Based on 12 Point=.166)

Set	Unit	2	3	4	5	6	7	8	9	10	11	12	13	14	15	16	17	18	19	20	21	22	Set
13	.00999	.0200	.0300	.0400	.0500	.0599	.0699	.0799	**.0899**	.0999	.1099	.1199	.1299	.1399	.1499	.1598	.1698	**.1798**	.1898	.1998	.2098	.2198	**13**
13¼	.01018	.0204	.0305	.0407	.0509	.0611	.0713	.0815	**.0916**	.1018	.1120	.1222	.1324	.1426	.1527	.1629	.1731	**.1833**	.1935	.2037	.2138	.2240	**13¼**
13½	.01038	.0207	.0311	.0415	.0519	.0622	.0726	.0830	**.0934**	.1037	.1141	.1245	.1349	.1452	.1556	.1660	.1764	**.1867**	.1971	.2075	.2179	.2282	**13½**
13¾	.01057	.0211	.0317	.0423	.0528	.0634	.0740	.0845	**.0951**	.1057	.1162	.1268	.1374	.1479	.1585	.1691	.1796	**.1902**	.2008	.2113	.2219	.2325	**13¾**
14	.01076	.0215	.0323	.0430	.0538	.0646	.0753	.0861	**.0968**	.1076	.1184	.1291	.1399	.1506	.1614	.1722	.1829	**.1937**	.2044	.2152	.2259	.2367	**14**
14¼	.01095	.0219	.0329	.0438	.0548	.0657	.0767	.0876	**.0986**	.1095	.1205	.1314	.1424	.1533	.1643	.1752	.1862	**.1971**	.2081	.2190	.2300	.2409	**14¼**
14½	.01114	.0223	.0334	.0446	.0557	.0669	.0780	.0891	**.1003**	.1114	.1226	.1337	.1449	.1560	.1671	.1783	.1894	**.2006**	.2117	.2229	.2340	.2452	**14½**
14¾	.01134	.0227	.0340	.0454	.0567	.0680	.0793	.0907	**.1020**	.1134	.1247	.1360	.1474	.1587	.1700	.1814	.1927	**.2040**	.2154	.2267	.2380	.2494	**14¾**
15	.01153	.0231	.0346	.0461	.0576	.0692	.0807	.0922	**.1038**	.1153	.1268	.1383	.1499	.1614	.1729	.1844	.1960	**.2075**	.2190	.2306	.2421	.2536	**15**
15¼	.01172	.0234	.0352	.0469	.0586	.0703	.0820	.0938	**.1055**	.1172	.1289	.1406	.1524	.1641	.1758	.1875	.1992	**.2110**	.2227	.2344	.2461	.2578	**15¼**
15½	.01191	.0238	.0357	.0476	.0596	.0715	.0834	.0953	**.1072**	.1191	.1310	.1429	.1549	.1668	.1787	.1906	.2025	**.2144**	.2263	.2382	.2501	.2621	**15½**
15¾	.01210	.0242	.0363	.0484	.0605	.0726	.0847	.0968	**.1089**	.1210	.1331	.1452	.1574	.1695	.1816	.1937	.2058	**.2179**	.2300	.2421	.2542	.2663	**15¾**
16	.01230	.0246	.0369	.0492	.0615	.0738	.0861	.0984	**.1107**	.1230	.1353	.1476	.1599	.1721	.1844	.1967	.2090	**.2213**	.2336	.2460	.2582	.2705	**16**
16½	.01268	.0254	.0380	.0507	.0634	.0761	.0888	.1014	**.1141**	.1268	.1395	.1522	.1648	.1775	.1902	.2029	.2156	**.2282**	.2409	.2536	.2663	.2790	**16½**
17	.01306	.0261	.0392	.0523	.0653	.0784	.0915	.1045	**.1176**	.1307	.1437	.1568	.1698	.1829	.1960	.2090	.2221	**.2352**	.2482	.2613	.2744	.2874	**17**
17½	.01345	.0269	.0403	.0538	.0672	.0807	.0941	.1076	**.1210**	.1345	.1479	.1614	.1748	.1883	.2017	.2152	.2286	**.2421**	.2555	.2690	.2824	.2959	**17½**
18	.01383	.0277	.0415	.0553	.0692	.0830	.0968	.1107	**.1245**	.1383	.1522	.1660	.1798	.1937	.2075	.2213	.2352	**.2490**	.2628	.2767	.2905	.3043	**18**
18½	.01422	.0284	.0427	.0569	.0711	.0853	.0995	.1137	**.1280**	.1422	.1564	.1706	.1848	.1990	.2133	.2275	.2417	**.2559**	.2701	.2844	.2986	.3128	**18½**
19	.01460	.0292	.0438	.0584	.0730	.0876	.1022	.1168	**.1314**	.1460	.1606	.1752	.1898	.2044	.2190	.2336	.2482	**.2628**	.2774	.2920	.3066	.3212	**19**
19½	.01499	.0300	.0450	.0599	.0749	.0899	.1049	.1199	**.1349**	.1499	.1648	.1798	.1948	.2098	.2248	.2398	.2548	**.2697**	.2847	.2997	.3147	.3297	**19½**
20	.01537	.0307	.0461	.0615	.0769	.0922	.1076	.1230	**.1383**	.1537	.1691	.1844	.1998	.2152	.2306	.2460	.2613	**.2767**	.2920	.3074	.3228	.3381	**20**
20½	.01575	.0315	.0473	.0630	.0788	.0945	.1103	.1260	**.1418**	.1576	.1733	.1891	.2048	.2206	.2363	.2521	.2678	**.2836**	.2993	.3151	.3308	.3466	**20½**
21	.01614	.0323	.0484	.0646	.0807	.0968	.1130	.1291	**.1453**	.1614	.1775	.1937	.2098	.2259	.2421	.2582	.2744	**.2905**	.3066	.3228	.3389	.3551	**21**
21½	.01652	.0330	.0496	.0661	.0826	.0991	.1157	.1322	**.1487**	.1652	.1818	.1983	.2148	.2313	.2478	.2644	.2809	**.2974**	.3139	.3305	.3470	.3635	**21½**
22	.01691	.0338	.0507	.0676	.0845	.1014	.1184	.1353	**.1522**	.1691	.1860	.2029	.2198	.2367	.2536	.2705	.2874	**.3043**	.3212	.3382	.3551	.3720	**22**
22½	.01729	.0346	.0519	.0692	.0865	.1037	.1210	.1383	**.1556**	.1729	.1902	.2075	.2248	.2421	.2594	.2767	.2940	**.3113**	.3285	.3458	.3631	.3804	**22½**
23	.01768	.0354	.0530	.0707	.0884	.1061	.1237	.1414	**.1591**	.1768	.1944	.2121	.2298	.2475	.2651	.2828	.3005	**.3182**	.3358	.3535	.3712	.3889	**23**
23½	.01806	.0361	.0542	.0722	.0903	.1084	.1264	.1445	**.1625**	.1806	.1987	.2167	.2348	.2528	.2709	.2890	.3070	**.3251**	.3431	.3612	.3793	.3973	**23½**
24	.01844	.0369	.0553	.0738	.0922	.1107	.1291	.1476	**.1660**	.1844	.2029	.2213	.2398	.2582	.2767	.2951	.3136	**.3320**	.3504	.3689	.3873	.4058	**24**
24½	.01883	.0377	.0565	.0753	.0941	.1130	.1318	.1506	**.1695**	.1883	.2071	.2259	.2448	.2636	.2824	.3013	.3201	**.3389**	.3577	.3766	.3954	.4142	**24½**
25	.01921	.0384	.0576	.0769	.0961	.1153	.1345	.1537	**.1729**	.1921	.2113	.2306	.2498	.2690	.2882	.3074	.3266	**.3458**	.3650	.3843	.4035	.4227	**25**
25½	.01960	.0392	.0588	.0784	.0980	.1176	.1372	.1568	**.1764**	.1960	.2156	.2352	.2548	.2744	.2940	.3136	3332	**.3527**	.3723	.3919	.4115	.4311	**25½**
26	.01998	.0400	.0599	.0799	.0999	.1199	.1399	.1598	**.1798**	.1998	.2198	.2398	.2597	.2797	.2997	.3197	.3397	**.3597**	.3796	.3996	.4196	.4396	**26**

PICA EQUIVALENTS—1 Em to 26 Ems   5 Set to 12 Set

Pica Ems	5	5¼	5½	5¾	6	6¼	6½	6¾	7	7¼	7½	7¾	8	8¼	8½
	Set Keyboard Scale														
1	2–7	2–5	2–3	2–2	2–0	1½8	1½6	1½5	1½4	1½3	1½2	1½1	1½0	1–8	1–7
2	4½5	4½1	4–7	4–3	4–0	3½6	3½3	3½1	3–8	3–6	3–4	3–2	3–0	2½7	2½6
3	7–4	6½6	6½1	6–5	6–0	5½5	5½1	5–6	5–3	4½8	4½5	4½3	4½0	4–7	4–4
4	9½2	9–3	8½4	8–6	8–0	7½3	7–7	7–2	6½6	6½2	6–7	6–3	6–0	5½6	5½3
5	12–0	11–8	10½7	10–8	10–0	9½2	9–4	8½7	8½1	8–5	8–0	7½4	7½0	7–5	7–1
6	14–7	13½4	13–2	12½0	12–0	11½0	11–1	10½3	10–5	9½8	9½2	9–5	9–0	8½4	8–8
7	16½5	16–0	15–5	14½2	14–0	13–8	12½8	12–8	12–0	11½2	11–4	10½6	10½0	10–3	9½7
8	19–4	18–5	17–8	16½4	16–0	15–6	14½5	14–4	13½4	13–4	12½5	12–7	12–0	11½2	11–5
9	21½2	20½1	19½2	18½5	18–0	17–5	16½2	16–0	15–8	14½7	14–7	13½8	13½0	13–2	12½4
10	24–0	22½6	21½6	20½7	20–0	19–4	18–8	17½5	17–3	16½1	16–0	15½0	15–0	14½1	14–2
11	26–7	25–3	24–0	22½8	22–0	21–2	20–6	19½1	18½6	18–4	17½2	17–1	16½0	16–0	15½1
12	28½5	27–8	26–3	25–1	24–0	23–1	22–3	21–6	20½1	19½7	19–4	18½1	18–0	17–8	16½8
13	31–4	29½4	28–7	27–2	26–0	24½8	24–0	23–2	22–5	21½0	20½5	20–2	19½0	18½7	18–6
14	33½2	32–0	30½1	29–4	28–0	26½7	25½6	24½7	24–0	23–3	22–7	21½3	21–0	20–7	19½5
15	36–0	34–5	32½4	31–5	30–0	28½5	27½3	26½3	25½4	24½6	24–0	23–4	22½0	21½6	21–3
16	38–7	36½1	34½7	33–7	32–0	30½4	29½1	28–8	27–8	26½0	25½2	24½5	24–0	23–5	22½2
17	40½5	38½6	37–2	35½0	34–0	32½3	31–7	30–4	29–3	28–2	27–4	26–6	25½0	24½4	24–0
18	43–4	41–3	39–5	37½1	36–0	34½1	33–4	32–0	30½6	29½5	28½5	27½7	27–0	26–3	25–7
19	45½2	43–8	41–8	39½3	38–0	36½0	35–1	33½5	32½1	31–8	30–7	29–8	28½0	27½2	26½6
20	48–0	45½4	43½2	41½4	40–0	38–7	36½8	35½1	34–5	33–2	32–0	30½8	30–0	29–2	28–4
21	50–7	48–0	45½6	43½6	42–0	40–6	38½5	37–6	36–0	34½5	33½2	32½0	31½0	30½1	29½3
22	52½5	50–5	48–0	45½7	44–0	42–4	40½2	39–2	37½4	36–7	35–4	34–1	33–0	32–0	31–1
23	55–4	52½1	50–3	48–0	46–0	44–3	42–8	40½7	39–8	38–1	36½5	35½2	34½0	33–8	32–8
24	57½2	54½6	52–7	50–2	48–0	46–1	44–6	42½3	41–3	39½4	38–7	37–3	36–0	34½7	33½7
25	60–0	57–3	54½1	52–3	50–0	48 0	46–3	44–8	42½6	41–7	40–0	38½4	37½0	36–7	35–5
26	62–7	59–8	56½4	54–5	52–0	49½8	48–0	46–4	44½1	43–1	41½2	40–5	39–0	37½6	36½4
	5	**5¼**	**5½**	**5¾**	**6**	**6¼**	**6½**	**6¾**	**7**	**7¼**	**7½**	**7¾**	**8**	**8¼**	**8½**

Pica Ems	8¾	9	9¼	9½	9¾	10	10¼	10½	10¾	11	11¼	11½	11¾	12	Pica Ems
	Set Keyboard Scale														
1	1–7	1–6	1–5	1–5	1–4	1–4	1–3	1–3	1–2	1–2	1–1	1–1	1–0	1–0	**1**
2	2½4	2½3	2½2	2½0	2–8	2–7	2–6	2–5	2–4	2–3	2–2	2–2	2–1	2–0	**2**
3	4–2	4–0	3½7	3½5	3½3	3½2	3½0	3–8	3–6	3–5	3–4	3–2	3–1	3–0	**3**
4	5½0	5–6	5–4	5–1	4½8	4½5	4½3	4½1	4–8	4–7	4–5	4–3	4–2	4–0	**4**
5	6½6	6½3	6½0	6–6	6–3	6–0	5½6	5½4	5½1	5–8	5–6	5–4	5–2	5–0	**5**
6	8–4	8–0	7½5	7½1	7–7	7–4	7–0	6½6	6½4	6½1	6–7	6–5	6–2	6–0	**6**
7	9½2	9–6	9–1	8½6	8½2	8–7	8–4	8–0	7½6	7½2	7–8	7–5	7–3	7–0	**7**
8	10½8	10½3	10–7	10–2	9½6	9½2	9–7	9–3	8½8	8½4	8½1	8–6	8–3	8–0	**8**
9	12–6	12–0	11½3	11–7	11–1	10½5	10½1	10–5	10–1	9½6	9½2	9–7	9–3	9–0	**9**
10	13½4	13–6	13–0	12½2	12–6	12–0	11½4	11–8	11–3	10½7	10½3	10–8	10–4	10–0	**10**
11	15–2	14½3	14–5	13½7	13½1	13–4	12½7	12½1	12–5	12–0	11½4	11½0	11–4	11–0	**11**
12	16–8	16–0	15½1	15–3	14½5	14–7	14–1	13½4	13–7	13–2	12½5	12½0	12–5	12–0	**12**
13	17½6	17–6	16½7	16–8	16–0	15½2	15–4	14½6	14½0	14–3	13½7	13½1	13–5	13–0	**13**
14	19–4	18½3	18–3	17½3	17–4	16½5	16–7	16–0	15½2	15–5	14½8	14½2	14–5	14–0	**14**
15	20½1	20–0	19–8	18½8	18–8	18–0	17½1	17–3	16½4	16–7	16–0	15½3	15–6	15–0	**15**
16	21½8	21–6	20½5	20–4	19½3	19–4	18½4	18–5	17½6	17–8	17–1	16½4	16–6	16–0	**16**
17	23–6	22½3	22–1	21½0	20½8	20–7	19½7	19–8	19–0	18½1	18–2	17½4	17–7	17–0	**17**
18	24½3	24–0	23–6	22½4	22–3	21½2	21–1	20½1	20–2	19½2	19–4	18½5	18–7	18–0	**18**
19	26–1	25–6	24½3	24–0	23–7	22½5	22–4	21½4	21–4	20½4	20–5	19½6	19–7	19–0	**19**
20	27–8	26½3	25½8	25–5	24½2	24–0	23–7	22½6	22–6	21½6	21–6	20½7	20–8	20–0	**20**
21	28½5	28–0	27–4	26½0	25½6	25–4	24½2	24–0	23–8	22½7	22–7	21½7	21–8	21–0	**21**
22	30–3	29–6	28½1	27½5	27–1	26–7	25½5	25–3	24½1	24–0	23–8	22½8	22–8	22–0	**22**
23	31½1	30½3	29½6	29–1	28–6	27½2	26½8	26–5	25½3	25–2	24½1	24–0	23½0	23–0	**23**
24	32½7	32–0	31–2	30–6	29½1	28½5	28–2	27–8	26½5	26–3	25½2	25–1	24½0	24–0	**24**
25	34–5	33–6	32–8	31½1	30½5	30–0	29–5	28½1	27½7	27–5	26½3	26–2	25½1	25–0	**25**
26	35½3	34½3	33½4	32½6	32–0	31–4	30–8	29½4	29–0	28–7	27½4	27–2	26½1	26–0	**26**
	8¾	**9**	**9¼**	**9½**	**9¾**	**10**	**10¼**	**10½**	**10¾**	**11**	**11¼**	**11½**	**11¾**	**12**	

PICA EQUIVALENTS—27 Ems to 52 Ems 5 Set to 12 Set

Pica Ems	5	5¼	5½	5¾	6	6¼	6½	6¾	7	7¼	7½	7¾	8	8¼	8½	Pica Ems
						Set Keyboard Scale										
27	64½5	61½4	58½7	56–6	54–0	51½6	49½6	48–0	46–5	44½3	43–4	41½6	40½0	39–5	38–2	**27**
28	67–4	64–0	61–2	58–8	56–0	53½5	51½3	49½5	48–0	46–6	44½5	43–6	42–0	40½4	39½1	**28**
29	69½2	66–5	63–5	60½0	58–0	55½3	53½1	51½1	49½4	48–0	46–7	44½7	43½0	42–3	40½8	**29**
30	72–0	68½1	65–8	62½2	60–0	57½2	55–7	53–6	51–8	49½3	48–0	46–8	45–0	43½2	42–6	**30**
31	74–7	70½6	67½2	64½4	62–0	59½0	57–4	55–2	53–3	51–6	49½2	48–0	46½0	45–2	43½5	**31**
32	76½5	73–3	69½6	66½5	64–0	61–8	59–1	56½7	54½6	52½8	51–4	49½1	48–0	46½1	45–3	**32**
33	79–4	75–8	72–0	68½7	66–0	63–6	60½8	58½3	56½1	54½2	52½5	51–2	49½0	48–0	46½2	**33**
34	81½2	77½4	74–3	70½8	68–0	65–5	62½5	60–8	58–5	56–5	54–7	52½3	51–0	49–8	48–0	**34**
35	84–0	80–0	76–7	73–1	70–0	67–4	64½2	62–4	60–0	57½8	56–0	54–3	52½0	50½7	49–7	**35**
36	86–7	82–5	78½1	75–2	72–0	69–2	66–8	64–0	61½4	59½2	57½2	55½4	54–0	52–7	50½6	**36**
37	88½5	84½1	80½4	77–4	74–0	71–1	68–6	65½5	63–8	61–4	59–4	57–5	55½0	53½6	52–4	**37**
38	91–4	86½6	82½7	79–5	76–0	72½8	70–3	67½1	65–3	62½7	60½5	58½6	57–0	55–5	53½3	**38**
39	93½2	89–3	85–2	81–7	78–0	74½7	72–0	69–6	66½6	64½1	62–7	60–7	58½0	56½4	55–1	**39**
40	96–0	91–8	87–5	83½0	80–0	76½5	73½6	71–2	68½1	66–4	64–0	61½8	60–0	58–3	56–8	**40**
41	98–7	93½4	89–8	85½1	82–0	78½4	75½3	72½7	70–5	67½7	65½2	63½0	61½0	59½2	57½7	**41**
42	100½5	96–0	91½2	87½3	84–0	80½3	77½1	74½3	72–0	69½0	67–4	65–1	63–0	61–2	59–5	**42**
43	103–4	98–5	93½6	89½4	86–0	82½1	79–7	76–8	73½4	71–3	68½5	66½1	64½0	62½1	60½4	**43**
44	105½2	100½1	96–0	91½6	88–0	84½0	81–4	78–4	75–8	72½6	70–7	68–2	66–0	64–0	62–2	**44**
45	108–0	102½6	98–3	93½7	90–0	86–7	83–1	80–0	77–3	74½0	72–0	69½3	67½0	65–8	63½1	**45**
46	110–7	105–3	100–7	96–0	92–0	88–6	84½8	81½5	78½6	76–2	73½2	71–4	69–0	66½7	64½8	**46**
47	112½5	107–8	102½1	98–2	94–0	90–4	86½5	83½1	80½1	77½5	75–4	72½5	70½0	68–7	66–6	**47**
48	115–4	109½4	104½4	100–3	96–0	92–3	88½2	85–6	82–5	79–8	76½5	74–6	72–0	69½6	67½5	**48**
49	117½2	112–0	106½7	102–5	98–0	94–1	90–8	87–2	84–0	81–2	78–7	75½7	73½0	71–5	69–3	**49**
50	120–0	114–5	109–2	104–6	100–0	96–0	92–6	88½7	85½4	82½5	80–0	77–8	75–0	72½4	70½2	**50**
51	122–7	116½1	111–5	106–8	102–0	97½8	94–3	90½3	87–8	84–7	81½2	78½8	76½0	74–3	72–0	**51**
52	124½5	118½6	113–8	108½0	104–0	99½6	96–0	92–8	89–3	86–1	83–4	80½0	78–0	75½2	73–7	**52**
	5	**5¼**	**5½**	**5¾**	**6**	**6¼**	**6½**	**6¾**	**7**	**7¼**	**7½**	**7¾**	**8**	**8¼**	**8½**	

Pica Ems	8¾	9	9¼	9½	9¾	10	10¼	10½	10¾	11	11¼	11½	11¾	12	Pica Ems
						Set Keyboard Scale									
27	37–1	36–0	35–1	34–2	33–4	32–7	31½2	30½6	30–3	29–8	28½5	28–3	27½1	27–0	**27**
28	38–7	37–6	36–6	35–7	34–8	33½2	32½5	32–0	31–5	30½1	29½7	29–4	28½2	28–0	**28**
29	39½5	38½3	37½2	36½2	35½3	34½5	33½8	33–3	32–7	31½2	30½8	30–5	29½2	29–0	**29**
30	41–3	40–0	38½8	37½7	36½8	36–0	35–2	34–5	33½0	32½4	32–0	31–5	30½2	30–0	**30**
31	42½0	41–6	40–4	39–3	38–3	37–4	36–5	35–8	34½2	33½6	33–1	32–6	31½3	31–0	**31**
32	43½7	42½3	41½0	40–8	39–7	38–7	37–8	36½1	35½4	34½7	34–2	33–7	32½3	32–0	**32**
33	45–5	44–0	42½6	41½3	40½2	39½2	38½2	37½4	36½6	36–0	35–4	34–8	33½4	33–0	**33**
34	46½2	45–6	44–2	42½8	41½6	40½5	39½5	38½6	37½8	37–2	36–5	35½0	34½4	34–0	**34**
35	48–0	46½3	45–7	44–4	43–1	42–0	41–0	40–0	39–1	38–3	37–6	36½0	35½4	35–0	**35**
36	49–7	48–0	46½4	45½0	44–6	43–4	42–3	41–3	40–3	39–5	38–7	37½1	36½5	36–0	**36**
37	50½4	49–6	48–0	46½4	45½1	44–7	43–6	42–5	41–5	40–7	39–8	38½2	37½5	37–0	**37**
38	52–2	50½3	49–5	48–0	46½5	45½2	44½0	43–8	42–8	41–8	40½1	39½3	38½6	38–0	**38**
39	53½0	52–0	50½2	49–5	48–0	46½5	45½3	44½1	43½1	42½1	41½2	40½4	39½6	39–0	**39**
40	54½6	53–6	51½7	50½0	49–4	48–0	46½6	45½4	44½3	43½2	42½3	41½4	40½6	40–0	**40**
41	56–4	54½3	53–3	51½5	50–8	49–4	48–0	46½6	45½5	44½4	43½4	42½5	41½7	41–0	**41**
42	57½2	56–0	54½0	53–1	51½3	50–7	49–3	48–0	46½7	45½6	44½5	43½6	42½7	42–0	**42**
43	58½8	57–6	55½5	54–6	52½8	51½2	50–6	49–3	48–0	46½7	45½7	44½7	43½7	43–0	**43**
44	60–6	58½3	57–1	55½1	54–3	52½5	51½0	50–5	49–2	48–0	46½8	45½7	44½8	44–0	**44**
45	61½4	60–0	58–7	56½6	55–7	54–0	52½3	51–8	50–4	49–2	48–0	46½8	45½8	45–0	**45**
46	63–2	61–6	59½3	58–2	56½2	55–4	53½6	52½1	51–6	50–3	49–1	48–0	47–0	46–0	**46**
47	64–8	62½3	61–0	59–7	57½6	56–7	55–0	53½4	52–8	51–5	50–2	49–1	48–0	47–0	**47**
48	65½6	64–0	62–5	60½2	59–1	57½2	56–4	54½6	53½1	52–7	51–4	50–2	49–0	48–0	**48**
49	67–4	65–6	63½1	61½7	60–6	58½5	57–7	56–0	54½4	53–8	52–5	51–2	50–1	49–0	**49**
50	68½1	66½3	64½7	63–3	61½1	60–0	58½1	57–3	55½6	54½1	53–6	52–3	51–1	50–0	**50**
51	69½8	68–0	66–3	64–8	62½5	61–4	59½4	58–5	56½8	55½2	54–7	53–4	52–2	51–0	**51**
52	71–6	69–6	67–8	65½3	64–0	62–7	60½7	59–8	58–1	56½4	55–8	54–5	53–2	52–0	**52**
	8¾	**9**	**9¼**	**9½**	**9¾**	**10**	**10¼**	**10½**	**10¾**	**11**	**11¼**	**11½**	**11¾**	**12**	

STANDARD FOUNT SCHEMES

(Based on lower-case founts of 1,000, 500 and 250 characters)

Lower-case

	a	b	c	d	e	f	g	h	i	j	k	l	m	n	o	p	q	r	s	t	u	v	w	x	y	z	&	Total
1 Strength (Body)	74	18	34	42	118	24	18	50	74	6	8	42	26	66	66	20	6	58	66	84	38	12	20	6	20	4	8	1,000
1 Strength (Jobbing)	74	18	34	42	118	24	18	50	74	6	8	42	26	66	66	20	6	58	66	84	38	12	20	6	20	4	8	1,000
½ Strength (Jobbing)	36	10	16	20	58	12	10	24	36	4	6	20	14	32	32	12	4	26	32	40	18	8	10	6	10	4	6	500
¼ Strength (Jobbing)	18	6	8	10	28	6	6	12	16	4	4	10	6	14	14	8	4	12	14	18	8	4	6	4	6	4	4	250

Capitals

	A	B	C	D	E	F	G	H	I	J	K	L	M	N	O	P	Q	R	S	T	U	V	W	X	Y	Z
1 Strength (Body)	8	8	8	8	12	6	6	8	10	6	4	8	8	8	8	8	4	8	8	12	6	4	8	4	4	4
1 Strength (Jobbing)	28	10	14	16	44	10	10	20	28	6	6	18	14	24	24	10	4	22	26	32	14	6	10	4	6	4
½ Strength (Jobbing)	16	6	8	10	26	6	6	12	16	4	4	10	8	14	14	6	4	14	16	20	8	4	6	4	4	4
¼ Strength (Jobbing)	10	4	6	6	16	4	4	8	10	4	4	6	6	10	10	4	4	10	10	12	6	4	4	4	4	4

Figures, etc.

	1	2	3	4	5	6	7	8	9	0
1 Strength (Body)	6	6	4	5	5	7	8	8	9	8
1 Strength (Jobbing)	20	12	10	8	8	8	8	12	18	18
½ Strength (Jobbing)	16	10	8	8	8	8	8	10	10	10
¼ Strength (Jobbing)	10	6	6	6	6	6	6	8	8	8

Ligatures

	Æ	Œ	æ	œ	ff	fi	fl	ffi	ffl
1 Strength (Body)	4	4	2	2	6	8	4	3	3
1 Strength (Jobbing)	4	4	4	4	4	8	6	3	3
½ Strength (Jobbing)	4	—	4	—	6	8	6	6	6
¼ Strength (Jobbing)	4	—	4	—	6	6	4	6	6

Spaces

	Ems	Ens	Thick	Mid.	Thin	Hair
1 Strength	100	50	200	100	100	50
1 Strength	100	50	200	100	100	50
½ Strength	75	40	100	80	80	40
¼ Strength	50	30	60	40	40	20

Accents

á	à	â	ä	é	è	ê	ë	í	ì	î	ï	ó	ò	ô	ö	ú	ù	û	ü	ç	ç	ñ
2	2	2	2	2	2	2	2	2	2	2	2	2	2	2	2	2	2	2	2	2	2	2

Small Caps

A	B	C	D	E	F	G	H	I	J	K	L	M	N	O	P	Q	R	S	T	U	V	W	X	Y	Z
8	3	4	5	13	3	3	6	8	2	2	5	6	8	8	3	2	7	8	10	4	2	3	2	3	2

Signs

*	†	‡	§	¶	@	℔	-	…	$	%	‰	/	+	-	×	÷	=	=
6	4	2	2	2	2	2	12	8	2	4	6	2	2	2	2	2	2	2

The proportions of the 'body' founts are based upon the average recurrence of the various characters in average English literature. The proportions of the capital letters of the 'jobbing' founts relative to the lower-case characters provide for the greater use of capital letter composition when using jobbing founts. An all-capital fount should equal the strength of a 'body' lower-case and capital fount combined. Em quads should be ordered separately; the quantity required should depend upon the nature of the composition. The number of em quads given above applies to the ems used in the composition apart from those required for short or white lines. The proportions of the body fount (upper- and lower-case combined) serve as a basis for the capitals required for jobbing founts. As there is a great demand upon the capitals of jobbing founts, which becomes increased as the strength of the fount decreases, the following rule has been laid down for deciding the proportions of the jobbing capitals. For capitals required for a full strength jobbing fount: Add body fount lower-case and caps. together, and divide by 3; for half-strength jobbing founts, divide by 5; for quarter-strength founts, divide by 8. Keep to the nearest even number, and the minimum number of any capital letter should never be less than 4. The basis of the small capital fount is the adding together of the lower-case and caps. of the full strength fount and dividing the result by 10. Thus $A = \overline{74 + 8} \div 10 = 8$.

DRAWINGS

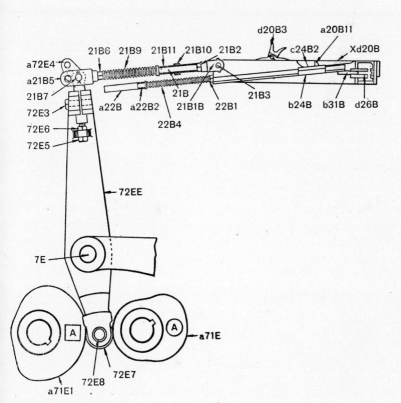

FIG. 1

Cams, cam lever and connections for operating and controlling the type carrier xd20B. The spring 21B9 keeps the cam lever roller in contact with the surface of cam a71E when the carrier is at the end of the forward stroke (whilst the type is being ejected from the mould), and the spring 22B4 keeps the cam lever roller in contact with the cam a71E1 when the carrier is at the end of the backward stroke (whilst a type is being cast and whilst the last type previously cast is being pushed between the type channel blocks 50F and a51FF). The type carrier is thus rigidly held during these two important operations.

Plate I—TYPE CARRIER

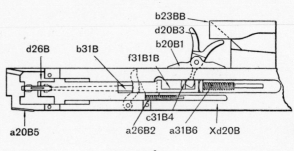

FIG. 2

View of rear side of type carrier xd20B at the end of its forward stroke, showing the type clamp d26B held back and the type support spring b31B in position ready to support the type as it is ejected from the mould into the type carrier (note position of type support spring lever d20B3). The drawing shows the type clamp shoe c27B removed.

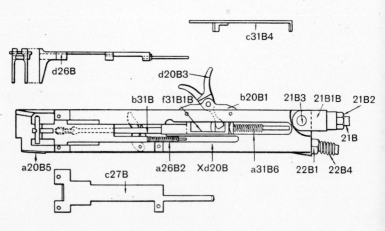

FIG. 3

View of rear side of type carrier xd20B at the end of its backward stroke, showing the type clamp d26B holding the type. The type support spring b31B has been withdrawn (note position of type support spring lever d20B3), leaving a clear path for the type to be pushed between the type channel blocks 50F and a51FF. The drawing shows the type clamp shoe c27B removed.

Plate I continued—Type Carrier

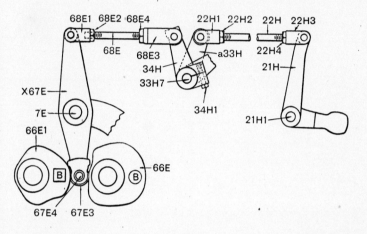

FIG. 1

Shows pump cams 66E and 66E1, pump cam lever X67E, and connecting mechanism. As the cams rock the cam lever X67E the pump operating lever 34H is rocked. If the pump rocker arm latch a33H1 (not shown) is disengaged, no action on the pump takes place; but if the rocker arm latch is connected to the pump operating lever 34H the pump and piston are brought into action, and casting then takes place. The connecting rod 68E is adjusted so that when the upper end of the cam lever X67E is at the end of its right-hand stroke (100°) there will be no compression on the pump rocker arm plunger spring a33H6 (see Fig. 3).

Plate II—PUMP

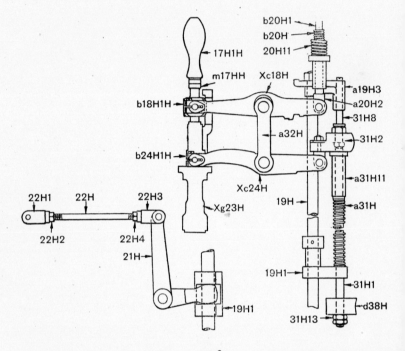

FIG. 2

View of pump operating mechanism after the pump body spring rod stop nuts 31H13 have reached their abutment (at 218°), thus checking any further upward movement of the pump body crosshead 31H2. By this time the nozzle will have seated in the mould. The further rise of the piston crosshead a19H3 forces the piston down into the pump body, ejecting the metal through the nozzle into the mould. When the mould is full of metal any further rise of the piston operating rod 19H is absorbed by the piston spring. In the lower left-hand corner of this block is shown a side view of the pump bell crank 21H which operates the piston operating rod 19H through the crosshead 19H1.

Plate II continued—Pump

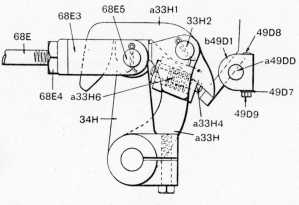

FIG. 3

Pump rocker arm latch a33H1 engaged with the operating lever 34H, thus bringing the complete pumping mechanism into action. This condition is maintained so long as the pump trip tube collar b49D1 is clear of the path of the lower projection of the pump rocker arm latch a33H1, and a casting thus takes place during each revolution of the machine.

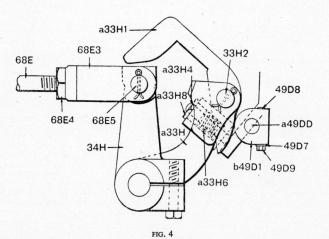

FIG. 4

In this drawing the pump trip tube collar b49D1 is supposed to have been moved forward into the path of the pump rocker arm latch a33H1, causing it to be lifted out of contact with the operating lever 34H, permitting the latter to reciprocate without producing any movement of the pump rocker arm a33H; no casting can therefore take place. The pump trip tube collar is moved into the path of the pump rocker arm latch (as shown) when the justification wedge lever arm rods 15D3 are engaged in the centring pin lever g16EE (during the adjustment of the justification wedges before each line is cast) or when the pump trip handle a35H12 is pulled forward by hand.

Plate II continued—Pump

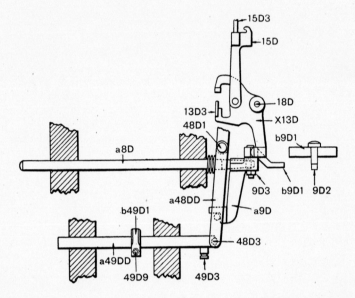

FIG. 5

Side view of mechanism operating the pump trip tube collar b49D1. When the air passes through a justification perforation in the paper ribbon a justification wedge lever arm rod 15D3 engages the centring pin lever g16EE, and as the latter rises it lifts the justification wedge lever x13D, or the justification wedge lever x14D (not seen in the above drawing). This action causes a justification wedge (not shown) to be lifted into the path of the matrix jaws c5B and b6B, and at the same time the galley trip rod a8D is pushed forward (causing the line just cast to be carried to the galley), and the pump trip tube is pushed forward, causing the collar b49D1 to be placed in the path of the pump rocker arm latch a33H1, and thereby disconnecting the pump mechanism (as explained under drawing of Fig. 4). This action occupies two revolutions of the machine; during the first revolution the ·0005″ justification wedge is adjusted, and during the second revolution the ·0075″ justification wedge is adjusted.

Plate II continued—Pump

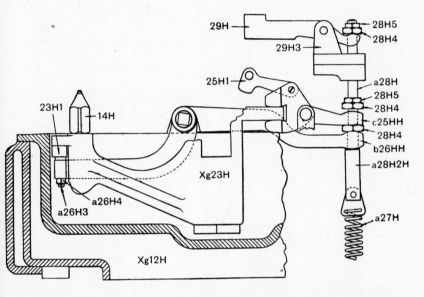

FIG. 6

Section through melting pot and melting pot casing. During the rise of the piston operating rod 19H (see Fig. 2) the pump body operating rod lever 29H is released, and the pump body lifting spring a27H causes the pump body Xg23H to rise until the nozzle 14H is seated in the mould. The metal is then pumped into the mould.

Plate II continued—Pump

Q

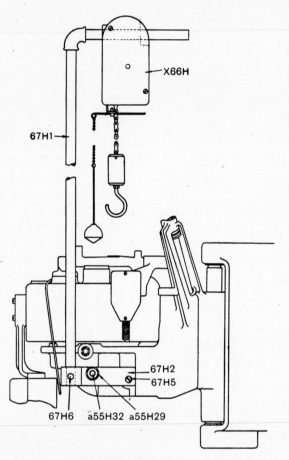

X66H

67H1

67H2
67H5

67H6   a55H32 a55H29

INGOT FEEDER ATTACHMENT

FIG. 6A

The mechanism consists of a sensitive escapement, actuated by an iron float in the molten metal. As the metal in the pot becomes lessened the float sinks a corresponding degree, causing the chain attached to it to release the escapement shoe, so that the ingot starts to descend, and instantly melts. As the molten metal becomes replenished the float rises, causing friction to be applied to the escapement brake disc, thus preventing any further descent of the ingot until the metal level is again lowered.

Plate II continued—Pump

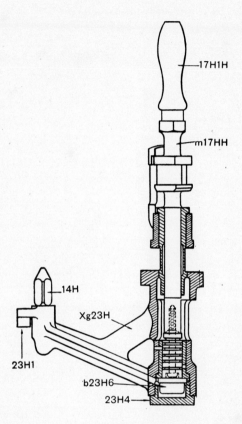

FIG. 7

Section through pump body showing piston at rest at the end of its upper stroke. After pumping, the piston is raised, and the pump body valve b23H6 becomes seated, preventing metal in the channel of pump body from following the piston. During the upstroke of the loose-ended piston the metal flows down the inside of piston, and past the lower fixed valve. During the down stroke the piston stem closes the upper metal inlet, maintaining full pressure below the piston.

Plate II continued—Pump

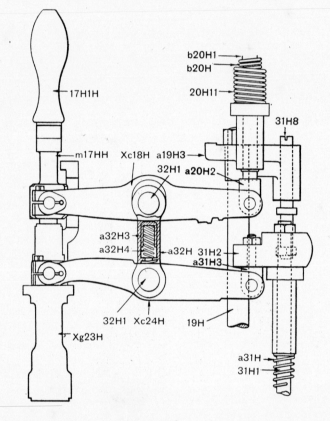

FIG. 8

This drawing shows the pump body lever xc24H and piston lever xc18H, and the manner in which they are connected. Immediately the nuts 31H13 (see Fig. 10) reach the swing frame post casting d38H the continued motion of the piston operating rod 19H—carrying with it the piston operating rod upper crosshead a19H3—rocks the piston lever xc18H, causing the piston m17HH to descend. Whilst this is taking place the upward pull upon the pump lever connecting link a32H causes the pump body lever xc24H to hold the nozzle firmly in the mould. At the end of the upper stroke of piston m17HH the pump lever connecting link plunger spring a32H4 supports the piston against its upper stop.

Plate II continued—Pump

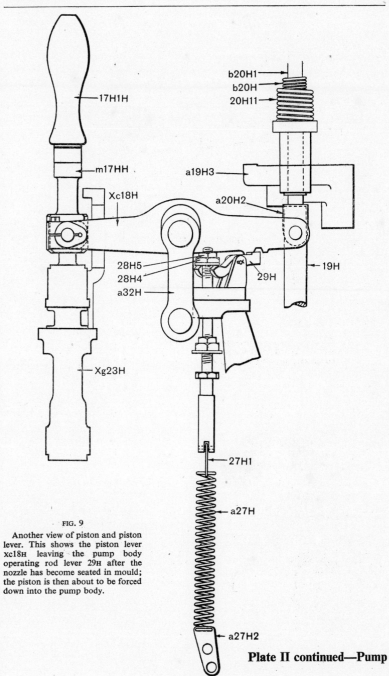

17H1H

m17HH

Xc18H

28H5
28H4
a32H

Xg23H

b20H1
b20H
20H11

a19H3

a20H2

29H

19H

27H1

a27H

a27H2

FIG. 9

Another view of piston and piston lever. This shows the piston lever xc18H leaving the pump body operating rod lever 29H after the nozzle has become seated in mould; the piston is then about to be forced down into the pump body.

Plate II continued—Pump

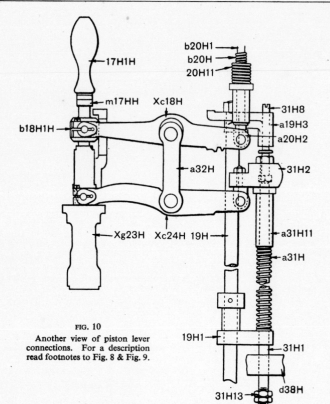

FIG. 10
Another view of piston lever
connections. For a description
read footnotes to Fig. 8 & Fig. 9.

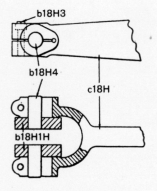

FIG. 11
The piston lever bearing blocks
b18H1H rock upon the piston lever
block bearing pins b18H4. The bearing blocks are easily changed when
worn.

Plate II continued—Pump

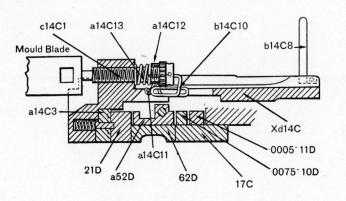

TYPE TRANSFER WEDGE IN OPERATION

FIG. 1

Section through the mould blade abutment slide, the transfer wedges, and the justification wedges, when the machine is assumed to be casting type. The mould blade is drawn against the mould blade abutment slide adjusting screw c14c1. The mould blade abutment is drawn against the normal wedge 21D, and this is drawn against the type transfer wedge 62D. The type transfer wedge is drawn against the normal wedge abutment 17C. It will be observed that the space transfer wedge a52D and the two justification wedges 10D and 11D are free, *i.e.*, out of action

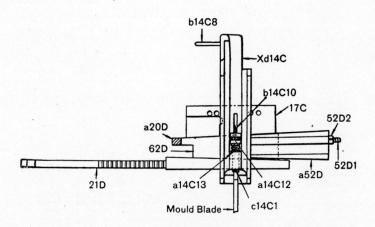

TYPE TRANSFER WEDGE IN OPERATION

FIG. 2

This is a plan view of Fig. 1, with the justification wedges removed to show how the type transfer wedge is drawn against its abutment 17c whilst the space transfer wedge a52D remains free.

Plate III—TRANSFER WEDGES

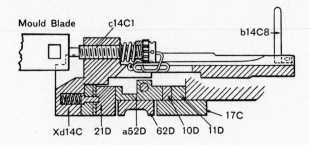

SPACE TRANSFER WEDGE IN OPERATION

FIG. 3

Section through the mould blade abutment slide, the transfer wedges, and the justification wedges when the machine is assumed to be casting spaces. The mould blade is drawn against the mould blade abutment slide adjusting screw c14C1. The mould blade abutment is drawn against the normal wedge 21D, and this is drawn against the space transfer wedge a52D. The space transfer wedge is drawn against the two justification wedges 10D and 11D, and these are drawn against their abutment on the air pin block j3C. It will be observed that the type transfer wedge 62D is free, *i.e.*, out of action.

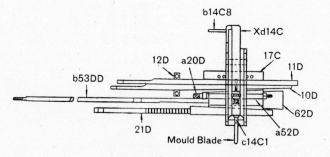

SPACE TRANSFER WEDGE IN OPERATION

FIG. 4

This is a plan view of Fig. 3, showing the space transfer wedge and the justification wedges in operation.

Plate III continued—Transfer Wedges

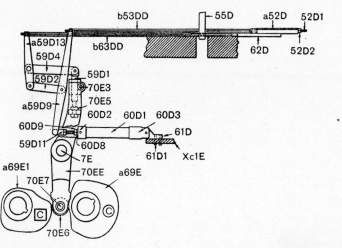

FIG. 5

Position of the transfer tongs when the type transfer wedge 62D is drawn against the micrometer wedge a20D (not shown). The space transfer wedge is locked forward (out of action) by the transfer wedge shifter 55D entering a slot in the upper edge of the space transfer wedge operating rod b53DD (this slot is plainly shown in Fig. 6).

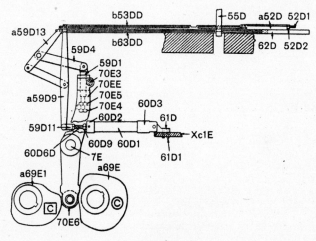

FIG. 6

Position of the transfer tongs when the space transfer wedge a52D is drawn against the micrometer wedge a20D (not shown). The type transfer wedge is locked forward (out of action) by the transfer wedge shifter 55D being lifted into a slot in the lower edge of the type transfer wedge operating rod b63DD; this action takes place when the transfer wedge shifter lever arm rod 57D4 is engaged in the centring pin lever g16EE, and the latter is at its extreme upper throw.

Plate III continued—Transfer Wedges

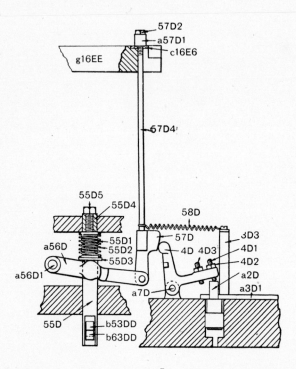

FIG. 7

This shows the action which takes place when compressed air passes through the space perforation (No. 10 from the left side) in the paper ribbon. The air pin a2D is raised, and this rocks the bell crank 4D, which in turn causes the transfer wedge shifter lever arm rod 57D4 to become engaged in a slot in the centring pin lever g16EE. As the centring pin lever rises, the transfer wedge shifter lever a56D is lifted, and the transfer wedge shifter 55D engages a slot in the lower edge of the type transfer wedge operating rod b63DD as the latter reaches the end of its forward stroke. The transfer tongs xa59D then pull the space transfer wedge into position against the micrometer wedge a20D. A type body (*i.e.*, space) is then cast, and its thickness is determined by the positions of the two justification wedges. If the next perforations in the paper ribbon represent a type the transfer wedge shifter lever arm rod 57D4 will not be pushed forward, and as the space transfer wedge operating rod b53DD reaches the end of its forward stroke the transfer wedge shifter springs 55D1 and 55D2 will cause the transfer wedge shifter 55D to release the type transfer wedge b63DD and to engage and lock forward the space transfer wedge b53DD.

Plate III continued—Transfer Wedges

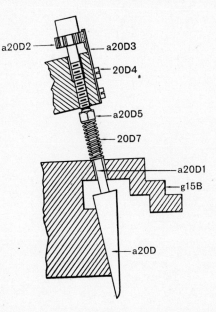

a20D2 — a20D3

— 20D4

— a20D5

— 20D7

— a20D1

— g15B

— a20D

FIG. 8

Micrometer wedge a20D, against which the space transfer wedge a52D and the type transfer wedge 62D are held during type casting. If the type bodies need enlarging or reducing in set thickness the micrometer wedge adjusting screw a20D2 is rotated as desired; the spring 20D7 keeps the micrometer wedge shank pressed against the adjusting screw. If the micrometer wedge is lowered it reduces the distance to which the transfer wedges are pulled back, and the type bodies will be cast thicker; if the micrometer wedge is raised the transfer wedges are pulled further back and the type bodies will be cast smaller.

Plate III continued—Transfer Wedges

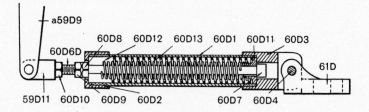

FIG. 9

Section through transfer wedge spring box. In adjusting the throw of the transfer tongs first see that the spring box rod adjusting nut 60D8 is taken firmly up to the outside spring abutment 60D11, but without compressing the spring in the spring box; then tighten the lock nut 60D9. If the adjusting nut is *not* taken up to the abutment the rod 60D6D will be loose lengthwise; if the adjusting nut is screwed too far after reaching the abutment the spring will be compressed, and it will be loose lengthwise in the spring box; in either case the full length of throw upon the transfer tongs will not be obtainable. After making the foregoing adjustment the spring box rod 60D6D must be screwed into the transfer tong space wedge lever eye 59D11 to such a distance that at each end of the stroke of the cam lever the compression on the spring in the spring box will be equal. When testing this adjustment the micrometer wedge a20D should be at its highest position and the transfer rods b53DD and b63DD should be correctly connected to the transfer tongs. Tighten the lock nut 60D10. The throw on the transfer tongs is regulated by raising or lowering the transfer tongs cam lever extension 59D1.

Plate III continued—Transfer Wedges

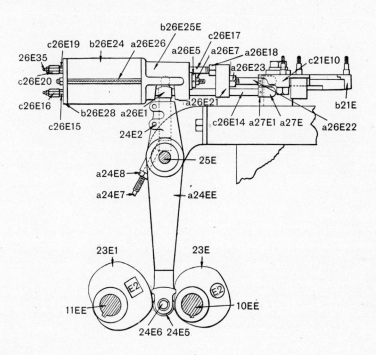

FIG. 1

Cams 23E and 23E1, cam lever a24EE, and jaw tongs spring box xc26E, for operating jaw tongs bell cranks b21E and c21E10.

Plate IV—JAW TONGS MECHANISM

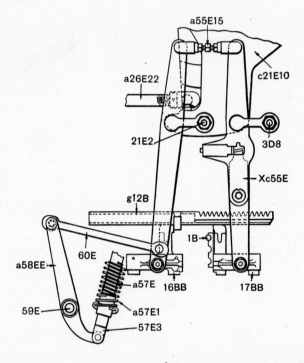

FIG. 2

Pin jaws 16BB and 17BB, operated by the pin jaw tongs xc55E, for bringing the head of the matrix jaw stop rack g12B to a position in line with the elevated air pin. The pin jaw 17BB is arrested by an elevated air pin (in the drawing shown at 1B), and the opposing pin jaw 16BB then advances to the pin jaw 17BB, carrying the matrix jaw stop rack to the position indicated by the elevated air pin. The pin jaw tongs springs a57E and a57E1 hold the rear pin jaw 16BB back until the front pin jaw 17BB is arrested by an elevated air pin.

Plate IV continued—Jaw Tongs Mechanism

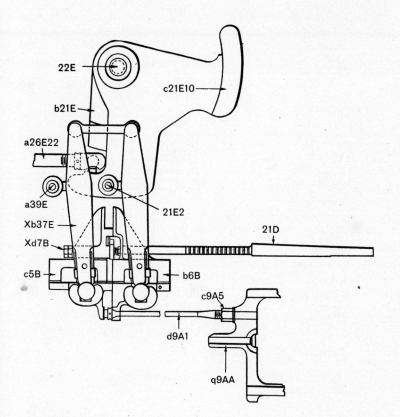

FIG. 3

Shows the matrix jaw tongs xb37E closed. In closing they carry the sliding frame q9AA by means of the draw rod d9A1 to a position corresponding with the position to which the matrix jaw stop rack g12B has been brought by the pin jaws 16BB and 17BB. The normal wedge 21D is also carried to a position corresponding with that of the matrix jaw stop rack.

Plate IV continued—Jaw Tongs Mechanism

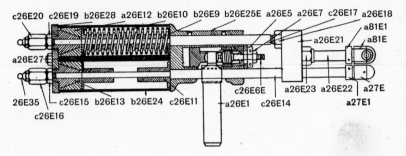

FIG. 4

Section through the spring box which operates the jaw tongs bell cranks b21E and c21E10. (The springs are not shown in the lower spring box.) The spring rod nuts c26E19 and c26E15 should be taken firmly up to the spring brake cone b26E13 and then locked. If the spring rod nuts c26E19 and c26E15 are not taken up to the ends of the spring brake cones the spring rods c26E17 and c26E14 will be loose lengthwise; if the nuts are screwed too far after reaching the ends of the cones the springs will be compressed; in each case the throw of the spring box bell crank will not be completely effective. Rear end of spring rods are drilled for the injection of grease to lubricate the wooden spring brakes a26E12 by means of grease gun 42CT1.

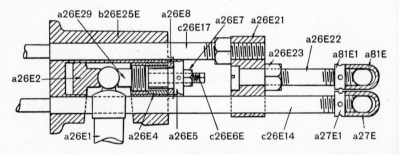

FIG. 5

Section through jaw tongs spring box tube cap b26E25E and crosshead a26E21. This mechanism is constructed so that the upper and lower bell cranks c21E10 and b21E may be adjusted independently. The lower spring rod c26E14 is not adjustable; therefore to adjust the upper jaw tongs bell crank c21E10 the spring box itself must be moved. The adjustment of the lower jaw tongs bell crank b21E is made by moving the ball socket a26E2 and the ball plug c26E6E (these two pieces are screwed together) to the right or left (as desired) in relation to the tube cap b26E25E. This is done by loosening the ball plug nut a26E7, and rotating the ball socket plug button a26E5 (a tongue on this enters a slot in the ball socket plug a26E4 and thus acts as a screwdriver). The ball socket a26E2 is prevented from rotating by the guide pin a26E3, which engages in a slot in the ball socket. Before testing the adjustment after altering the position of the ball plug, the ball plug nut a26E7 must be firmly tightened. After the ball socket and ball socket plug have been carefully adjusted upon the ball extension a26E1, care should be taken to see that the plug is not moved when loosening or tightening the ball plug nut a26E7; therefore when moving the ball plug nut always have a spanner upon the end of the ball plug c26E6E. After adjusting the lower spring box bell crank the upper bell crank must be adjusted. The adjustment of the upper jaw tongs bell crank c21E10 is made by screwing the upper spring rod c26E17 further into or further out of the crosshead a26E21.

Plate IV continued—Jaw Tongs Mechanism

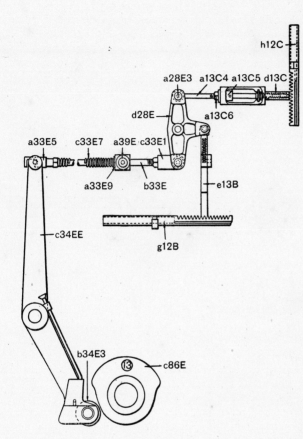

FIG. 1

Matrix jaws stop racks. After being positioned by the matrix jaws the stop racks are held firmly by the locking bars e13B and d13C until the matrix-case has been located and brought to rest. The stop racks are then released and carried by the pin jaws to the next position dictated by the perforations in the paper ribbon. The rear locking bar is adjusted by screwing the connecting rod a13C4 in or out as desired so that both locking bars seat in the base of the teeth of the stop racks simultaneously. The locking bar operating rod is then adjusted so that the locking bars withdraw clear of the teeth of the stop racks by $\frac{1}{32}''$ when the locking bar cam c86E is at the position of its highest throw (250°). After adjusting the rear locking bar d13C see that the point of the bar enters parallel between the teeth of the stop rack, as the bar is apt to be partly turned when tightening the lock nut a13C6.

Plate V—STOP RACKS AND LOCKING BARS

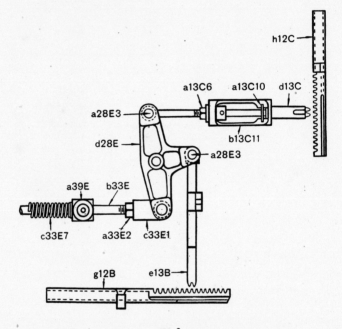

FIG. 2

Shows the locking bars e13B and d13C withdrawn from the stop racks, leaving the latter free to be moved to the next position as dictated by the perforations in the paper ribbon. When fully back the ends of the locking bars should clear the stop racks by $\frac{1}{32}''$.

Plate V continued—Stop Racks and Locking Bars

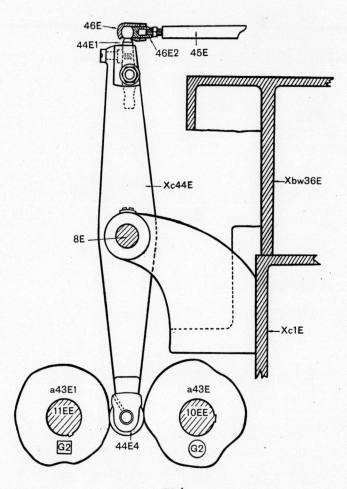

FIG. 1

Mould blade cams a43E and a43E1, cam lever xc44E, and mould blade connecting rod 45E.

Plate VI—MOULD BLADE OPERATING MECHANISM

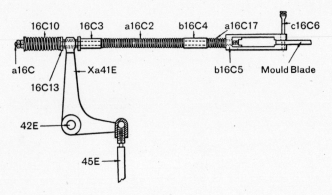

FIG. 2

Mould blade operating rod a16c and bell crank xa41e for working same. The forward (type ejecting) movement of the mould blade is checked by the blade striking its stop on the back of mould; excess forward motion of the bell crank is absorbed by the ejecting spring a16c2. The backward (type sizing) movement of the mould blade is checked by the blade pressing the mould blade abutment against the normal wedge, and the normal wedge against the space transfer wedge along the upper half of its surface or the type transfer wedge on the lower half of its surface (see Plate III, Figs. 1 and 3); excess backward motion of the bell crank is absorbed by the mould blade operating rod sizing spring 16c10.

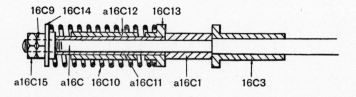

FIG. 3

Section showing assembly of parts at end of mould blade operating rod a16c.

Plate VI continued—Mould Blade Operating Mechanism

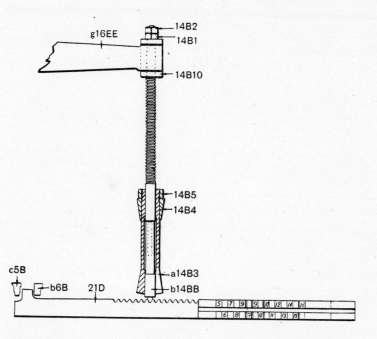

FIG. 4

As the matrix jaws c5B and b6B advance towards the head of the matrix jaws stop rack g12B they engage a projection on the normal wedge and carry the wedge to a position corresponding to that of the stop rack. As the stop rack can be carried to any one of 15 positions (according to the air pin blown up) so can the normal wedge be carried to any one of these 15 positions. Immediately after the matrix jaws have met and the normal wedge has therefore been correctly positioned, a locking pin b14BB descends and enters between two teeth of the normal wedge, fixing it in that position. The mould blade is pulled open to the distance decided by the position of the normal wedge. The graduations on the normal wedge represent different unit values of the fount being cast; these unit values may be varied as desired. The progression of units of the 15 positions is usually 5, 6, 7, 8, 9, 9, 10, 10, 11, 12, 13, 14, 15, 18. Immediately the normal wedge is locked in position by the locking pin b14BB the stop rack is released, and as the type is being cast the stop rack is brought to the next desired position by the action of the pin jaws 16BB and 17BB closing upon the air pin next to be blown up. When the centring pin lever g16EE is at its highest position the lower end of the normal wedge locking pin b14BB should be $\frac{1}{16}$" above the teeth of the normal wedge 21D. This is obtained by adjusting the nut 14B1.

· Plate VI continued—Mould Blade Operating Mechanism

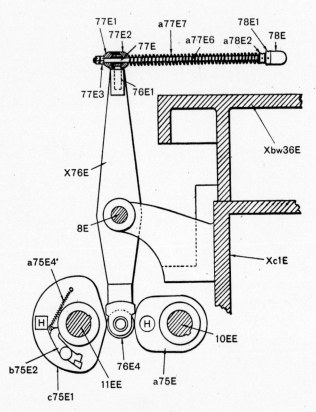

FIG. 1

Type pusher cams a75E and c75E1. Should the type become fixed in the type channel, or should any other obstruction overcome the pressure of the type pusher connecting rod springs a77E6 and a77E7 the type pusher cam lever ball extension 76E1 will pass along the connecting rod 77E and compress the springs without causing damage. The latch b75E2 on the cam c75E1 prevents the machine being moved in a backward direction when the driving belt is on the loose pulley.

Plate VII—TYPE PUSHER

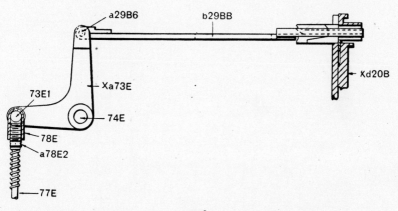

FIG. 2

Type pusher b29BB. This is adjusted by the connecting rod 77E so that when the pusher is at its extreme forward position the type will have passed beyond the type channel latches a50F2 and a51F3 by about $\frac{1}{2}''$, thus preventing the type from falling back as the type pusher recedes.

Plate VII continued—Type Pusher

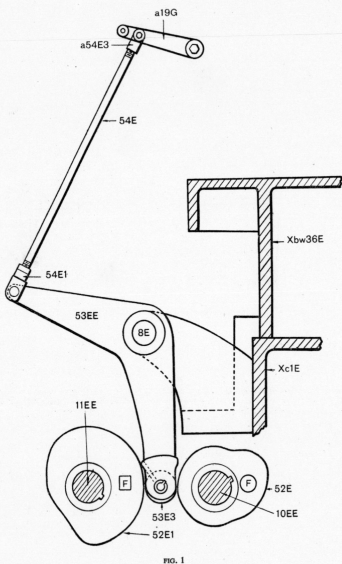

FIG. 1
Paper feed cams 52ᴇ and 52ᴇ1

Plate VIII—AIR TOWER

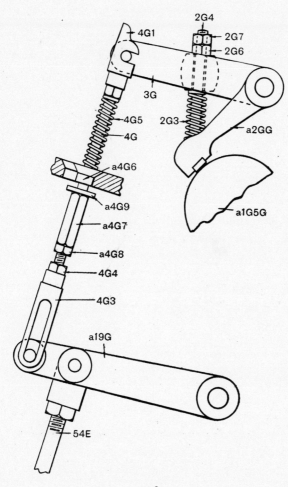

FIG. 2

Shows end of down stroke of air tower operating rod 54E, in which position the paper is clamped to the crossgirt a1G5G. For instructions concerning the adjustment of the paper feed mechanism see page 49.

Plate VIII continued—Air Tower

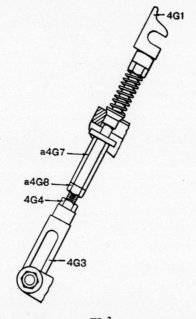

FIG. 3

Air bar clamping lever connecting rod **4G**. For adjustments see page 49.

For adjustments see page 49.

Plate VIII continued—Air Tower

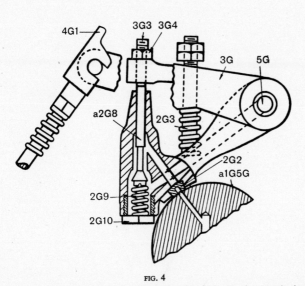

FIG. 4

Section through air bar clamping lever 3G. Shows air valve a2G8 opened to permit air to enter the groove in the leather packing 2G2, and thence through the perforations in the paper ribbon to the air pins.

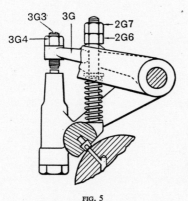

FIG. 5

Shows air bar clamping lever screw 3G3 clear of air bar valve a2G8.

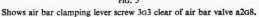

Plate VIII continued—Air Tower

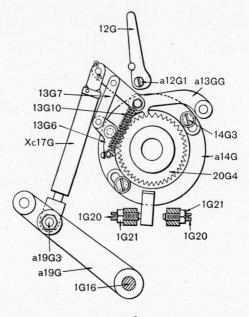

FIG. 6

Shows paper feed pawl a13GG ready to start feeding paper ribbon forward. The correct adjustment of the left-hand stop screw 1G20 causes the feed pawl 13G6 to stop midway between two teeth of the pin wheel ratchet 20G4.

Plate VIII continued—Air Tower

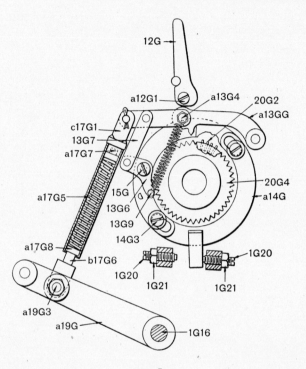

FIG. 7

Shows paper feed pawl a13GG at end of paper feed stroke, the paper feed pawl ring a14G being stopped by the right-hand stop screw 1G20. The correct adjustment of this stop screw causes the pin wheel ratchet to stop in such a position that the tooth on the upper portion of the paper feed pawl a13GG points centrally between two teeth on the pin wheel ratchet 20G4, and the perforations in the paper ribbon will align with the holes in the crossgirt a1G5G (assuming the keyboard has been correctly adjusted so that the type perforations are in line with the guide perforations on the sides of the paper ribbon).

Plate VIII continued—Air Tower

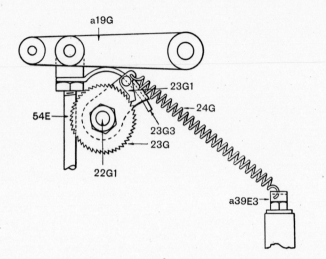

FIG. 8

Air tower lever a19G at end of its upper stroke, having raised the winding spool driving ratchet pawl 23G1. As soon as the air tower lever a19G commences to descend the winding spool operating spring 24G pulls the driving ratchet pawl 23G1, and thus rotates the winding spool driving ratchet 23G until the paper ribbon becomes taut upon the winding spool x21G. The lower end of the spring 24G is attached to the matrix jaw tongs stud arm a39E3.

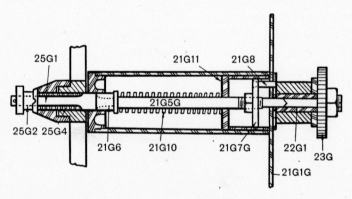

FIG. 9

Section through paper ribbon winding spool x21G. Each time the air tower lever a19G descends the driving ratchet 23G rotates. If the winding spool spring box plunger button 25G2 is engaged (as shown in the drawing) the pressure of the plunger spring 25G4 overcomes the pressure of the winding spool shaft spring 21G10, and causes the winding spool shaft driving disc pin 21G8 to enter a hole in the flange of winding spool driving shaft 22G1. Therefore as the driving ratchet 23G rotates it carries with the winding spool x21G. When the spring box plunger button 25G2 is held back the shaft spring 21G10 causes the winding spool shaft driving disc pin 21G8 to be withdrawn from the flange of winding spool driving shaft 22G1, leaving the winding spool free.

Plate VIII continued—Air Tower

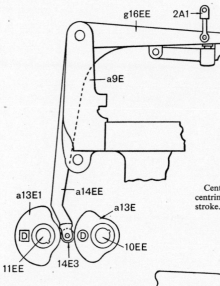

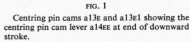

FIG. 1

Centring pin cams a13E and a13E1 showing the centring pin cam lever a14EE at end of downward stroke.

FIG. 2

Shows a matrix clamped to the mould by the centring pin g5A, the point of which has entered the coned hole in the upper end of the matrix. The centring pin may be so adjusted that the character will be cast upon the type body to its correct alignment both bodywise and setwise. The centring pin must slide freely in its bearing but there must be no side shake; if the centring pin is too loose or too tight in its bearing it may be adjusted on its upper end by the bushing adjusting sleeve a6A6, and on its lower end by the nut a6A22. The centring pin carries the spring abutment for operating the selecting lever cam lever operating arm a16E29.

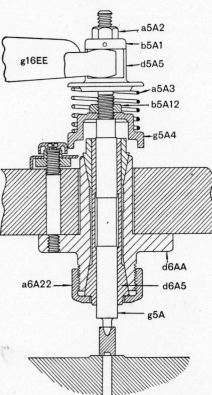

Plate IX—BRIDGE

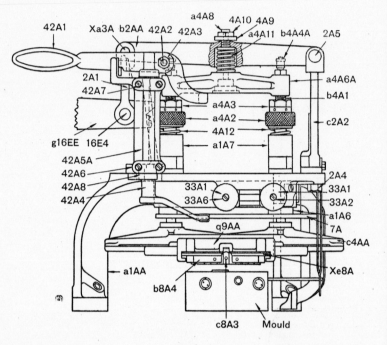

FIG. 3

Shows bridge details and mould. The matrix-case xe8A slides in the sliding frame q9AA, and the sliding frame moves along the carrying frame c4AA at right angles to the direction of movement of the matrix-case in the sliding frame. After the matrix-case has been drawn to the required position over the mould, the centring pin lever g16EE commences to descend, taking with it the bridge lever b2AA, the guide rod cross beam stud spring a4A11 pressing upon the cross beam a4a6A, and overcoming the resistance of the two carrying frame raising springs 4a12. The centring pin enters cone hole of selected matrix during the descent of the matrix-case. Just as the matrix reaches the mould the carrying frame c4AA is arrested by the guide rod stop nuts a4A2 coming in contact with the upper ends of the bridge bushings a1A6; this prevents the matrices from being forced against the mould, which would in time damage them. The centring pin then clamps the matrix to the mould, and a casting is made from it. The return stroke of the centring pin lever withdraws the matrix from the mould, and the matrix-case is then drawn to the next position required. The matrix-case is removed after placing the end of the cross beam lifting lever 42A1 under the cross beam a4A6A, and then pressing the opposite end of the lever down until the matrix-case is clear of the cross slide g5CC.

Plate IX continued.—Bridge

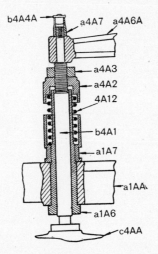

b4A4A   a4A7   a4A6A

a4A3

a4A2

4A12

b4A1

a1A7

a1AA

a1A6

c4AA

FIG. 4

Section through the bridge bushings a1A6 and the carrying frame guide rod stop nuts a4A2. The matrices are suspended in the matrix-case upon wires, which are slightly smaller in diameter than the holes in the matrix bodies. This provides for a slight vertical looseness of the matrices. The stop nuts a4A2 are adjusted upon the carrying frame guide rods b4A1 so that when the nuts reach the bridge bushings a1A6 the matrices will not press upon the mould; in other words, the force of the descent is borne by the bridge bushings and not by the mould. The centring pin then clamps the matrix firmly upon the mould ready for the casting to be made. Upon the return stroke of the centring pin lever the bridge lever b2AA presses against the guide rod cross beam stud adjusting nut 4A9, causing the cross beam a4A6A to be lifted, thus raising the carrying frame c4AA by means of the guide rods b4A1. When the centring pin lever is disconnected by removing the bridge lever link pin xa3A the carrying frame raising springs 4A12 prevent the matrix-case from falling loosely upon the mould, as this would very quickly damage the matrices.

Plate IX continued—Bridge

S

FIG. 5

Plan of matrix-case xe8ᴀ sliding frame q9ᴀᴀ and cross slide g5cc. The end of the matrix-case engages the cross slide, and is thus carried by the draw rod b5c1 to a position corresponding with any elevated air pin on the rear air pin block j3c. The sliding frame q9ᴀᴀ is carried by means of the draw rod d9ᴀ1 to a position corresponding with any elevated air pin on the front air pin block d3ʙʙ; the sliding frame thus moves the matrix-case in a direction at right angles to the movement of the cross slide g5cc. As there are 15 different stopping positions on the front pin block and 17 on the rear block, it follows that the matrix-case may be located in 255 different positions, each position presenting a matrix to the mould.

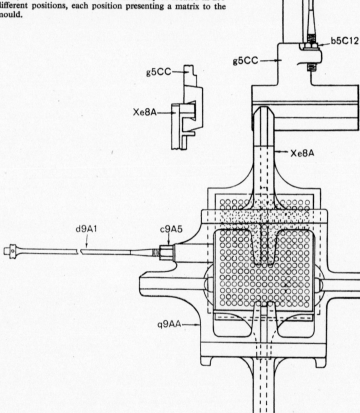

Plate IX continued—Bridge

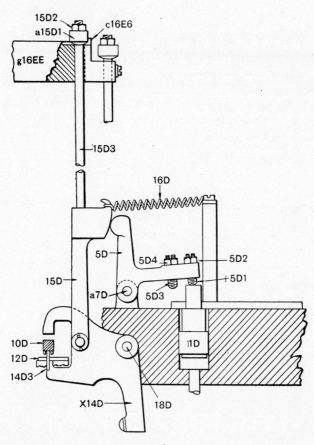

FIG. 1

Mechanism for raising justification wedges into the path of matrix jaws c5B, b6B. The operation of this mechanism also puts in action the mechanism for carrying the composed line of type to the galley, and causes the pump to be thrown out of action during the two revolutions of the machine occupied in placing the justification wedges in position for justifying the line next to be cast. When the air pin 1D is blown up, the bell crank 5D pushes the justification wedge lever arm rod 15D3 into a slot in the centring pin lever g16EE. As the latter rises the justification wedge lever x14D is lifted, and this lifts the justification wedge 10D, a projection on which is placed in the path of the matrix jaws c5B, b6B, and the wedge is carried to one of the 15 air pin positions on the B pin block. As the centring pin lever descends the rod 15D3 is pulled clear of the slot in the centring pin lever by the action of the spring 16D, and the justification wedge drops to the required position on the justification wedge centring tooth 12D. This action is repeated, as there are two justification wedges, and this procedure thus occupies two revolutions of the machine.

Plate X—JUSTIFICATION WEDGE LIFTING MECHANISM AND GALLEY STARTING MECHANISM

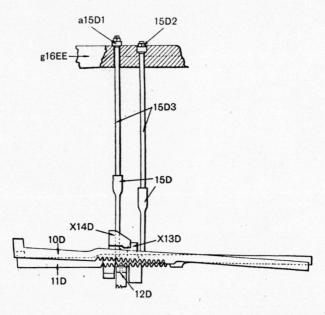

FIG. 2

Shows a justification wedge 10D lifted, so that it may be carried to its required position by the matrix jaws c5B and b6B. The companion justification wedge 11D is shown seated upon the justification wedge centring tooth 12D.

Plate X continued—Justification Wedge Lifting Mechanism and Galley Starting Mechanism

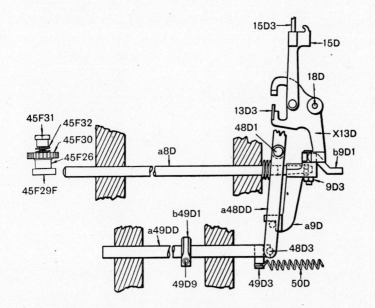

FIG. 3

This drawing shows the additional action of the justification wedge levers x13D and x14D when they are brought into action for lifting the justification wedges. The extension of the justification wedge levers presses against one end of the galley trip rod arm rock lever b9D1, and pushes forward the galley trip rod a8D. This presses against the galley trip lever distance cam 45F29F, and thereby causes the galley trip lever d45FF to move clear of the galley cam driving pawl 14F1F, which then engages the revolving galley camshaft ratchet 15F2, and the galley cam b14FF is thus rotated, causing the line of type to be taken to and placed in the galley. Fixed to the galley trip rod a8D is an extension called the galley trip rod arm a9D. As the galley trip rod is pushed forward this extension presses against the pump trip operating lever a48DD, and this moves forward the pump trip tube a49DD, causing the pump trip tube collar b49D1 to be placed in the path of the pump rocker arm trip latch a33H1, which thereby becomes disconnected from the pump operating lever 34H, and no casting takes place. The pump trip tube is returned to its normal position by the spring 50D.

Plate X continued—Justification Wedge Lifting Mechanism and Galley Starting Mechanism

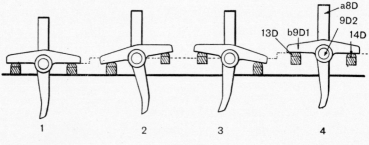

FIG. 4

This drawing shows the action of the justification wedge levers 13D and 14D upon the galley trip rod a8D, and how it is possible to cause the galley cam to remain untripped unless both justification wedge levers 13D and 14D are operated simultaneously. In what is called "single" justification the galley cam is tripped when only one justification wedge lever is operated; in "double" justification both justification wedge levers must be operated *simultaneously* to trip the galley cam. Diagram 1 shows the galley trip rod arm rock lever b9D1 at rest in its normal position. Diagram 2 shows one justification wedge lever in operation. Diagram 3 shows the other justification wedge lever in operation. Diagram 4 shows both justification wedge levers in operation simultaneously. It will be observed that when only one justification wedge lever is in operation the other end of the rock lever b9D1 swings against the justification wedge lever which is not in operation, and the galley trip rod a8D is pushed forward a certain distance. When both justification wedge levers are operated simultaneously the galley trip rod goes forward twice as far as when only one justification wedge lever is in operation. By altering the position of the trip lever distance cam adjuster from SJ to DJ, so that the galley cam will only trip when two justification wedge levers are in operation simultaneously, the line of type may contain many justified columns, as the galley can then only be tripped when the last column is completed, and where there are two justification perforations in the paper strip.

Plate X continued—Justification Wedge Lifting Mechanism and Galley Starting Mechanism

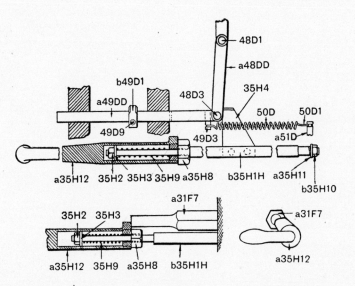

FIG. 5

Pump hand trip. When the pump trip handle a35H12 is pulled towards the attendant, pressure is put upon the handle spring 35H9, and this pulls the pump trip rod b35H1H. Attached to the pump trip rod is a plate 35H4, the upper end of which is bent over so as to engage the pump trip operating lever a48DD. Therefore when the handle a35H12 is pulled, the pump trip operating lever a48DD pushes the pump trip tube a49DD, and the pump trip tube collar b49D1 is placed in the path of the pump rocker arm latch a33H1, which thereby becomes disconnected from the pump operating lever 34H, and no casting takes place. The handle a35H12 may be held permanently forward by giving it a quarter turn so that it will rest against the main galley stand stud a31F7 (as shown in the lower portion of the drawing).

Plate X continued—Justification Wedge Lifting Mechanism and Galley Starting Mechanism

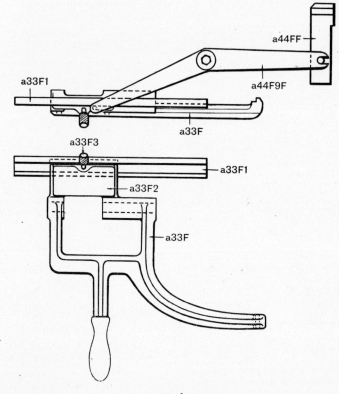

FIG. 1

Mechanism for stopping the machine automatically when lines are cast too long or too short. When the operating lever a32F (for starting the machine) is pulled so that the driving belt comes on the fixed pulley, the operating lever is held in position by the operating lever latch a33F. Attached to the latch is a bar a33F1, against which rests one end of the stop slide lever a44F9F. The other end of this lever engages the stop slide a44FF. If a line is too long the end type or types will press against the stop slide a44FF as the line is pushed into the galley. This releases the latch a33F from the operating lever a32F, and the pressure of the belt shifter ring rod spring 6E2 causes the belt to be brought over the loose pulley, thus stopping the machine. If the line is too short the line support xh29F or xh30F (according to which is in use) will press against the stop slide a44FF as the line is pushed into the galley, and this releases the latch a33F in the same manner as when the line is too long.

Plate XI—LINE SHIFTING AND GALLEY MECHANISM

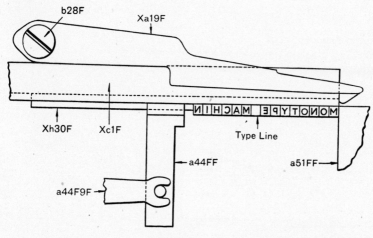

FIG. 2

Shows a short line being advanced towards the galley. In this case the line support xh29F or xh30F (according to which is in use) will press against the stop slide a44FF and thus release the latch a33F, thereby causing the machine to stop.

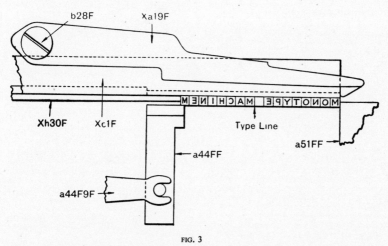

FIG. 3

Shows a long line being advanced towards the galley. In this case the extra type (the letter M) will press against the stop slide a44FF and thus release the latch a33F, thereby causing the machine to stop.

Plate XI continued—Line Shifting and Galley Mechanism

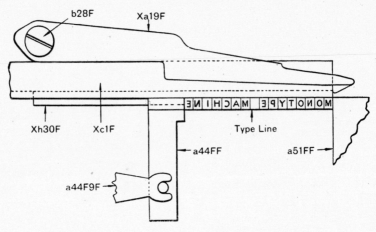

FIG. 4

Shows a line of correct length being advanced towards the galley. In this case neither the type nor the line support xh30F will press against the stop slide a44FF, and the machine will proceed to cast without interruption.

FIG. 5

Section through galley cam b14FF, galley cam sleeve 14F8, and the galley camshaft worm wheel 15F3. The worm shaft worm 80E6 is constantly revolving, taking with it the worm wheel 15F3. The worm wheel is fixed to the galley camshaft 15FF, at the upper end of which is also fixed the galley camshaft ratchet 15F2. The galley cam shaft 15FF revolves in the bearing of the galley cam sleeve 14F8, and normally the galley cam remains at rest. The line hook operating slide lever cam roller 25F1 runs in the upper cam groove of the galley cam b14FF; the rule lever cam roller 40F1 runs on a cam projection on the lower surface of the galley cam; the column pusher lever 5F is operated by a cam projection around the lower circumference of the galley cam.

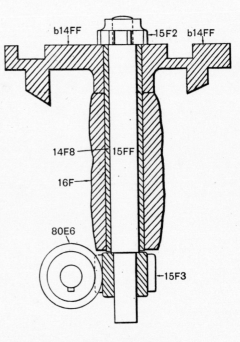

Plate XI continued—Line Shifting and Galley Mechanism

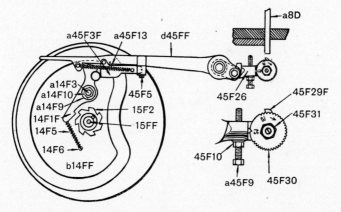

FIG. 6

Shows the galley cam driving pawl 14F1F held clear of the galley camshaft ratchet 15F2 by being held between the projection on the end of trip lever d45FF and the trip lever latch a45F3F. When the galley trip rod a8D is pushed forward it presses against the galley trip lever distance cam 45F29F, and thereby causes the galley trip lever d45FF to release the galley cam driving pawl 14F1F, which then engages the revolving galley camshaft ratchet 15F2, and the galley cam is thus rotated, moving with it the line hook operating slide lever 25FF, which pulls the line of type to a position directly in front of the galley. As the galley cam continues to rotate the rule lever xa40F lifts the rule e39FF clear of the line of type, and then the column pusher lever pressing against the column pusher spring box x8F causes the column pusher xc1F to push the line towards the galley. The rule e39FF then partly descends, to prevent the type falling backward; the column pusher recedes, the rule descends to its normal position, and the line hook operating slide lever 25FF carries the line hook xa19F to its normal position. The galley cam driving pawl 14F1F is then pulled clear of the galley camshaft ratchet 15F2 (as shown), and the galley cam continues to revolve without operating any of the mechanism. When the trip lever distance cam adjuster is set at DJ (as shown in the drawing), the trip lever d45FF will be released when the galley trip rod a8D is operated by a double justification perforation in the paper ribbon; when the trip lever distance cam adjuster is set at SJ, the trip lever will be released when the galley trip rod is operated by a single justification perforation in the paper ribbon.

Plate XI continued—Line Shifting and Galley Mechanism

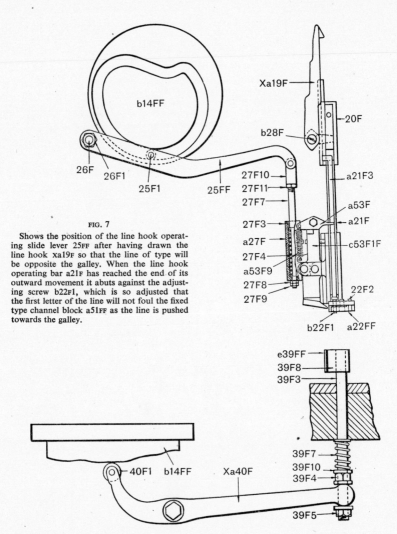

FIG. 7

Shows the position of the line hook operating slide lever 25FF after having drawn the line hook xa19F so that the line of type will be opposite the galley. When the line hook operating bar a21F has reached the end of its outward movement it abuts against the adjusting screw b22F1, which is so adjusted that the first letter of the line will not foul the fixed type channel block a51FF as the line is pushed towards the galley.

FIG. 8

Shows rule lever xa40F after lifting the rule e39FF clear of the line of type so that the line may be pushed into the galley. After the line has been pushed into the galley the rule partly descends and then pauses whilst the column pusher recedes. During this pause the lower edge of the rule should be about ¹⁄₃₂″ from the upper surface of the column pusher xc1F. This adjustment is made by loosening the lock nut 39F5, moving the rule lifting rod adjusting nut 39F4 up or down as desired and then tightening the lock nut. Note the order of the washers, nuts and spring.

Plate XI continued—Line Shifting and Galley Mechanism

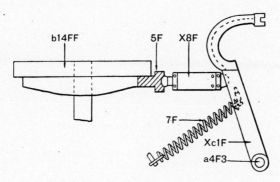

FIG. 9

The column pusher xc1F pushes the line of type into the galley.

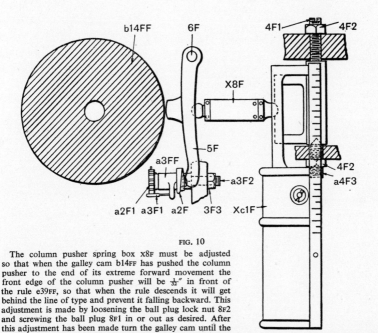

FIG. 10

The column pusher spring box x8F must be adjusted so that when the galley cam b14FF has pushed the column pusher to the end of its extreme forward movement the front edge of the column pusher will be $\frac{1}{32}''$ in front of the rule e39FF, so that when the rule descends it will get behind the line of type and prevent it falling backward. This adjustment is made by loosening the ball plug lock nut 8F2 and screwing the ball plug 8F1 in or out as desired. After this adjustment has been made turn the galley cam until the column pusher has completely receded, and then adjust the column pusher adjusting cam stand a3FF by moving the two stud nuts 3F3 so that when a 12-point type is between the type channel blocks xa50F and xa51F the front edge of the column pusher is ·008″ behind the front edge of the adjustable type channel block xa50F. When testing this adjustment the column pusher adjusting cam disc a2F1 should be turned so that the spring a3F1 comes at number 12 on the disc.

Plate XI continued—Line Shifting and Galley Mechanism

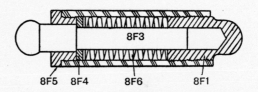

Section through the column pusher spring box x8F. The plug 8F1 is adjusted so that the correct forward movement is obtained on the column pusher xc1F.

Plate XI continued—Line Shifting and Galley Mechanism

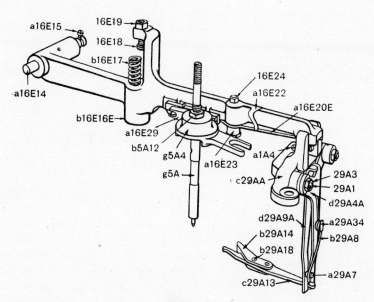

FIG. 1

Low quad mechanism. Attached to the centring pin lever g16EE is the low quad actuating lever b16E16E. This is adjusted vertically by the screw 16E18, and the right-hand end is guided in the fulcrum bracket c29AA. Attached to the actuating lever b16E16E is a selecting lever a16E20E, which is normally kept to one side by the spring a16E22. Upon the centring pin spring (lower) abutment g5A4 is a forked extension which engages with the selecting lever cam lever operating arm a16E29 attached to selecting lever cam lever a16E26 and pivoted on actuating lever. When a character matrix is presented to the mould the centring pin lever takes the centring pin and the low quad actuating lever b16E16E down together, and the end of the selecting lever a16E20E presses on the fulcrum bracket character lever d29A4A; this pressure is transferred to the equalizing gear mould blade lever c29A13 which in turn presses the upper mould blade back against the lower mould blade; the upper mould blade is consequently opened to the same measurement as the lower blade. Space matrices have no coned holes for the centring pin to enter. Therefore, when a space matrix is presented to the mould immediately the centring pin reaches the matrix its progress is arrested, but the actuating lever b16E16E continues its downward movement. In doing this the left-hand end of the selecting lever a16E20E is pushed back by the selecting lever cam lever, the forked extension on centring pin abutment (lower) restricting the downward movement of the selecting lever operating lever, and this brings the right-hand end of the selecting lever over the fulcrum bracket space lever d29A9A. As the actuating lever continues its course pressure is put upon the equalizing gear mould blade lever c29A13, and this in turn presses the upper mould blade *forward* (*i.e.*, in a direction opposite to the movement of the lower blade); therefore, whilst the upper blade closes the upper part of the mould aperture the lower mould blade is sized up in the usual manner. In other words, the upper mould blade becomes interposed between the matrix and the incoming metal, and the type body is cast short in length. The surplus motion on the centring pin lever is absorbed by the actuating lever spring b16E17. The equalizing gear mould blade lever c29A13 is so constructed that the pressure upon the lower mould blade is exactly the same when the upper blade is pushed back as when it is pushed forward.

Plate XII—LOW QUAD MECHANISM

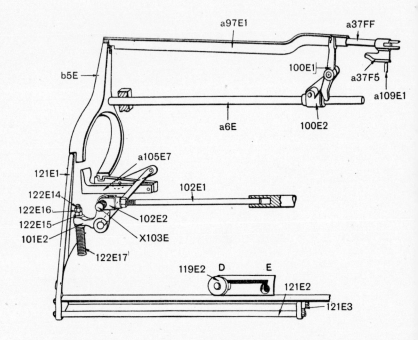

FIG. 1

Belt shifter operating bar and clutch control operating rod. The object of this mechanism is to prevent any change being made in the speed of the machine whilst the driving belt is over the fixed pulley. When the operating lever a32F is placed in operating position the belt shifter operating bar a97E1 is moved to the left, carrying with it the cam a37F5 and the belt shifter ring b5E. The former pushes down the interlocking lever operating rod a109E1, and a step on the latter is placed in front of the end of the sliding gear safety lever 121E1. When the machine is being driven it is impossible to move the sliding gear shifter yoke handle 119E2, as the safety lever is held by the belt shifter ring b5E.

Plate XIII—DISPLAY TYPE ATTACHMENT

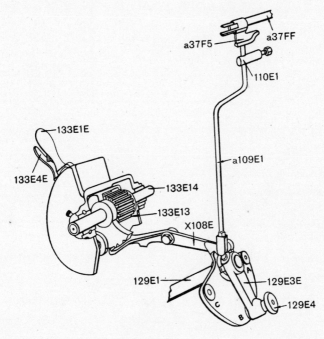

FIG. 2

Interlocking lever mechanism. When the operating lever a32F is placed in operating position the cam a37F5 pushes down the interlocking lever operating rod a109E1, and this causes the interlocking lever x108E to engage a slot in the speed bracket quadrant shaft lever 129E3E, preventing the handle from being moved. The other end of the interlocking lever x108E engages a slot in the end of the tumbler 133E1E preventing the tumbler from being moved.

Plate XIII continued—Display Type Attachment

T

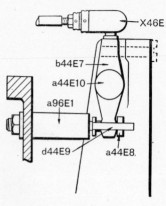

FIG. 3

Mould blade cam lever compound lever. When the screw a44E8 connects the compound lever b44E7 to the abutment a96E1 greater movement is given to the mould blade connecting rod 45E. The compound lever b44E7 is connected as shown above for casting type over 19 points up to 36 points in set. For casting type below 14 points in set the screw a44E8 must be connected to the upper end of the compound lever (as shown by the dotted line); the distance piece must have two levels on its operating side. The lower end of the compound lever b44E7 then operates against the low level of d44E9 when casting type from 14 to 19 points in set, and against the high level of d44E9 when casting type above 19 points in set. This is effected by loosening the screw a44E8 and turning the distance piece d44E9 90°.

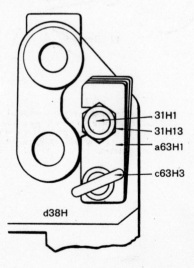

FIG. 4

Pump body spring rod stop plates a63H1. For particulars of the use of these plates see page 167

Plate XIII continued—Display Type Attachment

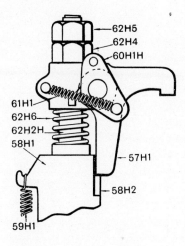

FIG. 5

Latch 57H1 and latch abutment plate 58H2 attached to pump mechanism, so that when required (as when casting display type) the piston may be caused to make a sudden down stroke. The drawing shows the latch engaged. To disengage the latch, the latch pin plate 60H1H must be moved upwards.

FIG. 6

Centring pin spring auxiliary spring. This auxiliary spring is placed between the centring pin spring abutments g5A4 and d5A5 when casting large display type, so that the pressure of the molten metal against a large area of the matrix surface will not force the matrix from its seating on the mould.

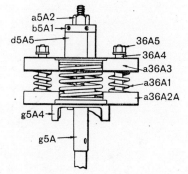

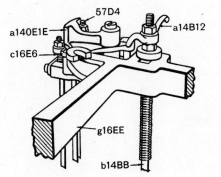

FIG. 7

Centring pin lever gag block. When it is desired to cast display type the gag block a140E1E must be removed from the normal wedge locking pin b14BB, to cause the normal wedge to maintain a fixed position. The engagement of the gag block with the transfer wedge shifter lever arm rod 57D4, as shown in the drawing, causes the space transfer wedge to remain in operation.

Plate XIII continued—Display Type Attachment

T*

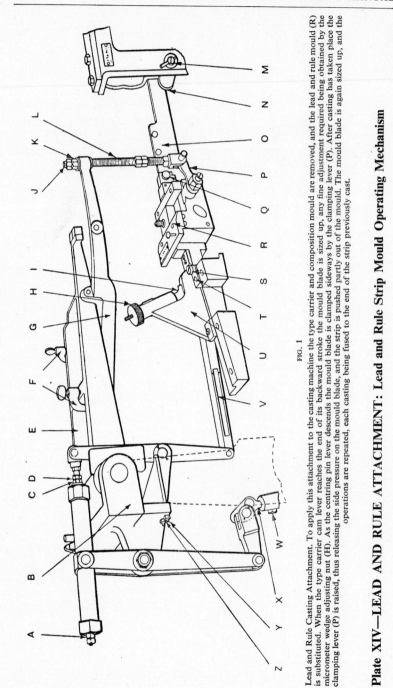

FIG. 1

Lead and Rule Casting Attachment. To apply this attachment to the casting machine the type carrier and composition mould are removed, and the lead and rule mould (R) is substituted. When the type carrier cam lever reaches the end of its backward stroke the mould blade is sized up, any fine adjustment required being obtained by the micrometer wedge adjusting nut (H). As the centring pin lever descends the mould blade is clamped sideways by the clamping lever (P). After casting has taken place the clamping lever (P) is raised, thus releasing the side pressure on the mould blade, and the strip is pushed partly out of the mould. The mould blade is again sized up, and the operations are repeated, each casting being fused to the end of the strip previously cast.

Plate XIV—LEAD AND RULE ATTACHMENT: Lead and Rule Strip Mould Operating Mechanism

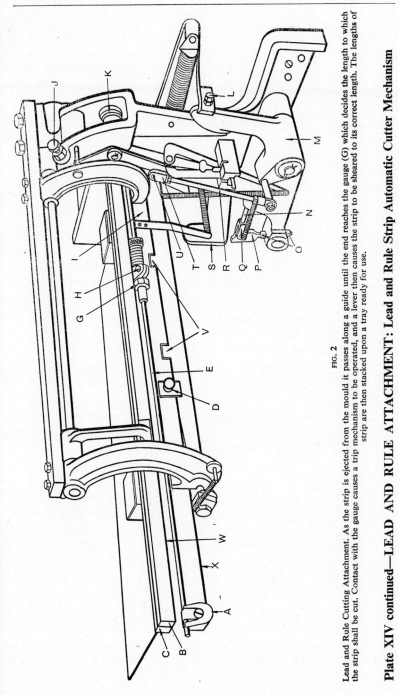

FIG. 2

Lead and Rule Cutting Attachment. As the strip is ejected from the mould it passes along a guide until the end reaches the gauge (G) which decides the length to which the strip shall be cut. Contact with the gauge causes a trip mechanism to be operated, and a lever then causes the strip to be sheared to its correct length. The lengths of strip are then stacked upon a tray ready for use.

Plate XIV continued—LEAD AND RULE ATTACHMENT: Lead and Rule Strip Automatic Cutter Mechanism

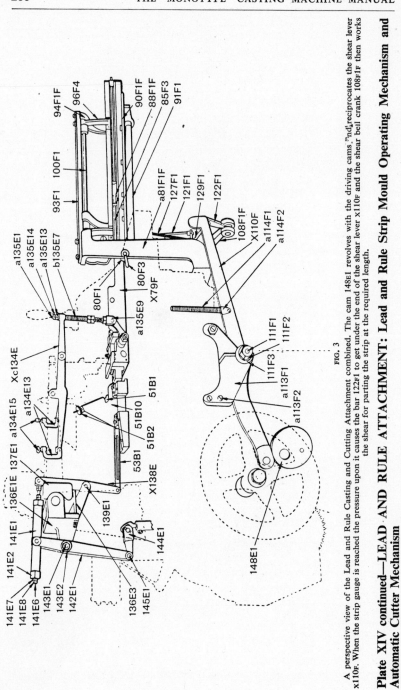

FIG. 3

A perspective view of the Lead and Rule Casting and Cutting Attachment combined. The cam 148E1 revolves with the driving cams and reciprocates the shear lever x110F. When the strip gauge is reached the pressure upon it causes the bar 122F1 to get under the end of the shear lever x110F and the shear bell crank 108F1F then works the shear for parting the strip at the required length.

Plate XIV continued—LEAD AND RULE ATTACHMENT: Lead and Rule Strip Mould Operating Mechanism and Automatic Cutter Mechanism

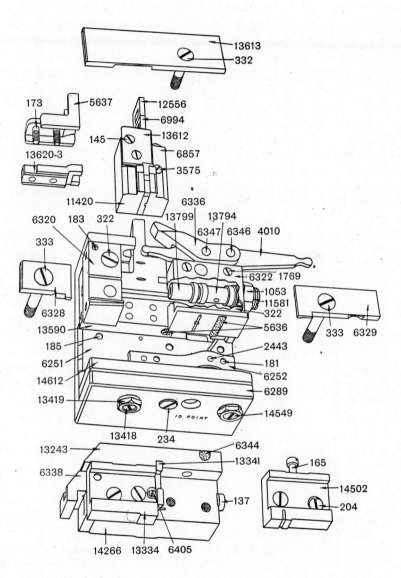

13613
332
173   5637
13620-3
145
11420
6320 183 322
333
6328
13590
185
6251
14612
13419
13243
6338
14266 13334 6405
13418 234
12556
6994
13612
6857
3575
6336
13799 13794
6347 6346 4010
6322 1769
1053
11581
322
5636
2443
181
6252
6289
14549
13418 234
10 POINT
6344
13341
165
14502
204
137
333 6329

Plate XV—COMPOSITION MOULD, Series 22,000

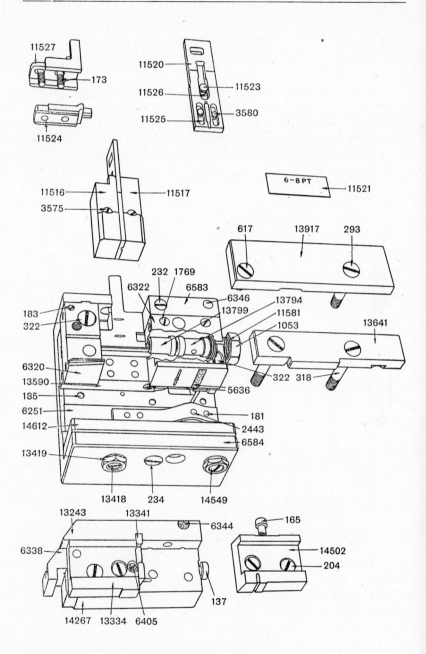

Plate XVI—QUAD AND SPACE MOULD

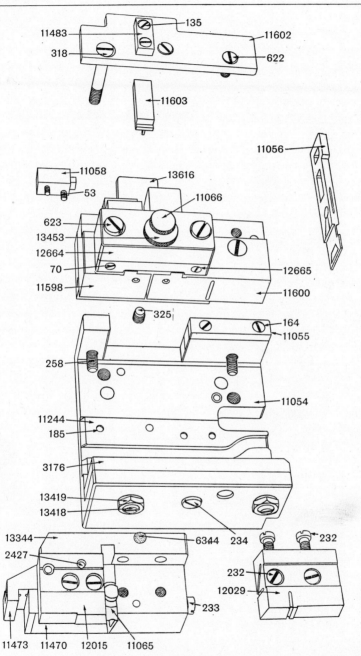

11483 — 135 — 11602
318 — 622
— 11603

11056

11058
53 — 13616
11066
623
13453
12664
70
11598 — 12665
— 11600
325
164
11055
258
11054
11244
185
3176
13419
13418
13344 — 6344   234 — 232
2427 — 232
12029
233
11473   11470   12015   11065

Plate XVII—SHORT LEAD AND RULE MOULD

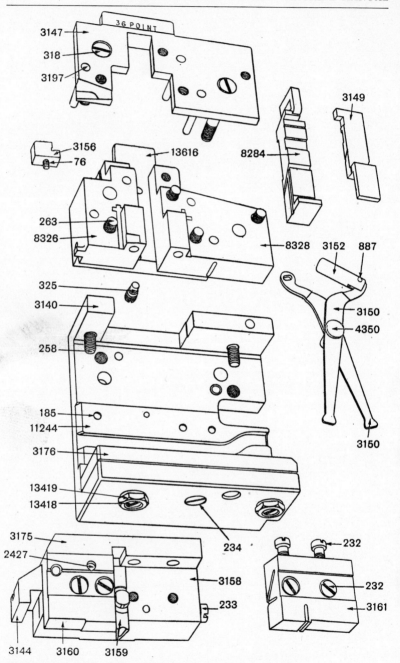

Plate XVIII—DISPLAY TYPE MOULD 14-36 point

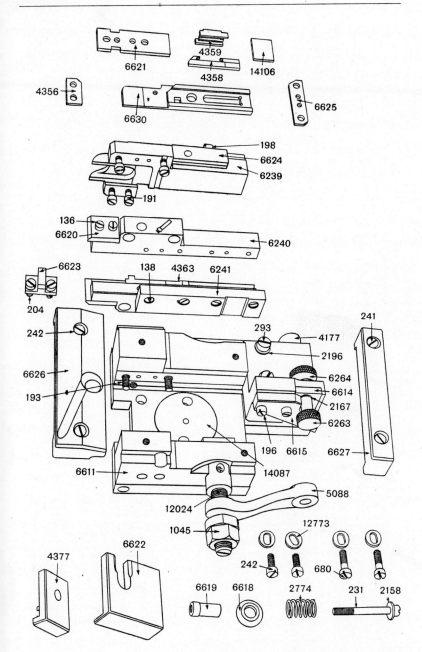

Plate XIX—LEAD AND RULE MOULD

MONTHLY HEIGHT CHECK OF MONOTYPE MOULDS

MOULD NO.	SIZE	HEIGHT											
		JAN.	FEB.	MAR.	APR.	MAY	JUNE	JULY	AUG.	SEPT.	OCT.	NOV.	DEC.

INDEX

U